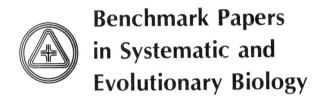

Benchmark Papers in Systematic and Evolutionary Biology

Series Editor: Howell V. Daly
University of California, Berkeley

PUBLISHED VOLUMES

MULTIVARIATE STATISTICAL METHODS: Among-Groups Covariation
William R. Atchley and Edwin H. Bryant
MULTIVARIATE STATISTICAL METHODS: Within-Groups Covariation
Edwin H. Bryant and William R. Atchley
CONCEPTS OF SPECIES
C. N. Slobodchikoff

VOLUMES IN PREPARATION

NUMERICAL TAXONOMY
M. W. Moss
POLLINATION
Robbin W. Thorp and Grady Webster

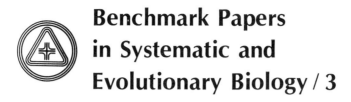

Benchmark Papers
in Systematic and
Evolutionary Biology / 3

A BENCHMARK® Books Series

CONCEPTS OF SPECIES

Edited by

C. N. SLOBODCHIKOFF
Northern Arizona University

Dowden, Hutchinson
& Ross, Inc.

STROUDSBURG, PENNSYLVANIA

Copyright © 1976 by **Dowden, Hutchinson & Ross, Inc.**
Benchmark Papers in Systematic and Evolutionary Biology, Volume 3
ISBN: 0–87933–224–7

78 77 76   2 3 4 5
Manufactured in the United States of America.

Library of Congress Cataloging in Publication Data

Main entry under title:

Concepts of species.

(Benchmark papers in systematic and evolutionary
biology ; v. 3)
    Bibliography: p.
    Includes indexes.
    1. Species--Addresses, essays, lectures.
I. Slobodchikoff, C. N.
QH83.C616 1976   574'.01'2   76-17090
ISBN 0-87933-224-7

Exclusive Distributor: **Halsted Press**
A Division of John Wiley & Sons, Inc.
ISBN: 0-470-15134-X

ACKNOWLEDGMENTS AND PERMISSIONS

ACKNOWLEDGMENTS

AMERICAN ASSOCIATION FOR THE ADVANCEMENT OF SCIENCE—*The Species Problem*
    Species Concepts and Definitions
    The Species Problem with Fossil Animals

AMERICAN PHILOSOPHICAL SOCIETY—*Proceedings of the American Philosophical Society*
    Species Before Darwin

CALIFORNIA BOTANICAL SOCIETY, INC.—*Madroño*
    Reality, Existence, and Classification: A Discussion of the Species Problem

SOCIETY OF SYSTEMATIC ZOOLOGY—*Systematic Zoology*
    An Operational Approach to Species Classification

PERMISSIONS

The following papers have been reprinted with the permission of the authors and copyright holders.

ACADEMIC PRESS, INC.—*Survey of Biological Progress*
    Animal Taxonomy and the New Systematics

ACADEMIC PRESS INC. (LONDON) LTD.
    Biological Journal of the Linnean Society
    The Biological Meaning of Species
    Proceedings of the Linnean Society of London
    The Development of Pre-Linnean Taxonomy

AMERICAN ASSOCIATION FOR THE ADVANCEMENT OF SCIENCE—*Science*
    Differentiation of Populations

CAMBRIDGE UNIVERSITY PRESS
    The British Journal for the Philosophy of Science
    The Effect of Essentialism on Taxonomy—Two Thousand Years of Stasis (I, II)
    Symposia of the Society for General Microbiology
    The Microbial Species—a Macromyth?

COLUMBIA UNIVERSITY PRESS—*Plant Speciation*
    The Biological Species
    The Evolutionary Species

Acknowledgments and Permissions

DR. R. A. CROWSON and ALDINE PUBLISHING COMPANY—*Classification and Biology*
The Species in Biological Systematics

THE ENTOMOLOGICAL SOCIETY OF ISRAEL—*Israel Journal of Entomology*
Uniparental, Sibling and Semi-species in Relation to Taxonomy and Biological Control

INTERNATIONAL ASSOCIATION FOR PLANT TAXONOMY—*Regnum Vegitabile*
The "Species Aggregate" in Theory and Practice

INTERNATIONAL BIOLOGICAL PROGRAMME—*Genetic Resources in Plants—Their Exploration and Conservation*
Taxonomy and the Biological Species Concept in Cultivated Plants

STICHTING INTERNATIONAL BUREAU FOR PLANT TAXONOMY AND NOMENCLATURE—*Taxon*
The Biological Species Concept and Its Evolutionary Structure
Comments on the Search for a "Perfect System"

UNIVERSITY OF CHICAGO—*The American Naturalist*
The Biological Species Concept: A Critical Evaluation
Taxonomy, Language and Reality

SERIES EDITOR'S PREFACE

The volumes of the Benchmark Series in Systematic and Evolutionary Biology make accessible to students and scientists alike a broad selection of topics from these interrelated fields. While other series are primarily ecological, genetic, or behavioral, this series concerns the classification of organisms, techniques useful in systematics, and those processes or aspects of biological relationships that are essentially evolutionary in nature. Within the past decade or two, entirely new areas of research have emerged as techniques were developed and used and concepts altered by discoveries. Many new ideas have sprung from a joining of systematic and evolutionary biology with other disciplines: biogeography and the geological drift of continents; molecular evolution and immunological cross-reactions; genetics of natural populations and the biochemical electrophoresis of proteins; evolutionary strategies and mathematical models. In these examples and others, we are witnessing the convergence of investigations on the central questions of evolution by scientists of disparate backgrounds. It is not an easy task for the undergraduate or researcher to acquire information drawn from so many sources. This Benchmark series is planned not only to provide reproductions of selected original papers but to assist in interpreting and indexing current interdisciplinary contributions.

Some volumes will be mainly historical, because systematists retain a strong interest in the early attempts to cope with the classification of organisms and the understanding of their lineages. The development of the theory of evolution and of biological nomenclature are among the retrospective topics planned for the series. Facsimile reproductions and translations will make classic papers readily available, some for the first time.

This, the third volume of the series, is devoted to concepts of species. C. N. Slobodchikoff's investigations of the perplexing patterns of variation in parasitic wasps, the effects of selection on parthenogenetic wasps, and, most recently, the ecology of tenebrionid beetles, have stimulated him in his own research to reexamine the nature of species and their recognition by taxonomists.

In this Benchmark are selections from the large and varied literature. Here you will find papers dealing with historical development,
questions of reality, applications to various organisms, and alternative
viewpoints. The nature of species will continue to spark debate. The
editor has provided a collection of articles that permit us to understand
the present issues and to judge our future progress.

HOWELL V. DALY

PREFACE

The selections in this book were chosen primarily because they represent a point of view or illustrate the historical and philosophical development of species concepts. Since papers on species are quite numerous, many good papers had to be excluded because of space limitations. In making selections, I had two objectives in mind. One objective was to bring together enough material about the historical background, the philosophical bases, and the present views on species to permit critical evaluation of present species concepts within the framework of current biological theory. The other objective was to choose papers that could be used by students of systematics and evolutionary biology to expand their understanding of the problems posed by the species question.

In gathering material for this book, I was aided by a number of people. Particular thanks go to E. Colbert, D. L. Hull, and E. Mayr for providing background material on several aspects of species problems. Special thanks go to my wife, Anne, for her patience and willingness to help in the preparation of the book.

C. N. SLOBODCHIKOFF

CONTENTS

Contents

CONTENTS BY AUTHOR

INTRODUCTION

The selections in this book all deal with various concepts of species in biology. They also deal with what biologists commonly think of as species definition. *Concept* is a rather nebulous term that refers to an idea, or a theoretical structure; *definition* is usually a more concrete term that refers to a set or properties. Hull (1974) points out that, throughout history, philosophers have insisted that class names (such as species) "must be defined in terms of properties that are severally necessary and jointly sufficient for membership in the class; that is, each of the properties taken separately is necessary for membership and the whole set taken together is sufficient." According to this usage, a group of organisms may be called a species if, and only if, all the organisms in that group possess a common set or properties. As Hull (1974) points out, this usage is not well suited for defining species within an evolutionary framework. In practice, most biologists use *species concept* to refer to a theoretical construct of the role and limits of the species in biological theory, and *species definition* to refer to a rule that assigns groups of organisms to a species class.

Two major species concepts are currently in use; although several others have been proposed, they have not been widely accepted. The major ones are the typological species concept and the biological species concept.

The *typological species concept* has its roots in Aristotelian essences. According to Aristotle, each species (or Form) has an essence, an intrinsic nature that makes it what it is. This intrinsic nature is universal for the species and is possessed by all the individuals that make up the species. The essence may be derived by intuition—from observing a number of individuals and abstracting that which is universal

1

in them. Individuals, in turn, have two sets or properties, essential ones and accidental ones. *Essential properties* are the defining characteristics of a given species; *accidental properties* are characteristics that vary from one individual to another. Accidental properties are not related to the nature, or essence, of a species.

Since each species has an essence, the essence may be characterized by describing a set of universal properties for each species. Thus we have the process of species description, in which a taxonomist attempts to characterize a given species by describing its general (universal or essential) properties. Since morphological properties are the most convenient to describe for most organisms, morphology has been, and is, commonly used for species descriptions. On the assumption (at least in the early stages of typological thought) that species do not change and that essences are immutable, a type specimen is designated for comparison purposes with the description, to demonstrate the essential properties of a given species. Since change and time are not taken into account, the concept is a static one.

The typological procedures of description and type designation are encouraged by the International Codes of Botanical and Zoological Nomenclature, which require descriptions and type specimens for a name to be considered valid in biological nomenclature. Although most systematists deprecate the typological concept, several positive points must be mentioned. One is that typological procedure, description, and type specimens provide pragmatic starting points for all subsequent studies of species. A species name provides a convenient method of communicating information about a group of organisms. Any procedure that separates organisms into discrete groups and assigns names is useful to that extent. Descriptions and types provide reference points for standardizing the communication of information about discrete groups. Even if typological species do not necessarily reflect actual species in nature, they are useful as first approximations on which subsequent studies and refinements can be based. Another positive point is that the great majority of the species names currently recognized and the discrete groups to which these names refer were established and recognized by means of typological procedures. Although a number of taxonomists claim that they use the biological species concept in recognizing species, in practice most species are recognized on a morphological basis. Most taxonomists consider a group of organisms to be a species if all the organisms in the group are more similar morphologically to each other than they are to organisms in other groups. The justification for saying that the biological species concept is applied in this procedure are the assumptions that (1) reproductive isolation parallels morphological divergence, and (2) the presence of morphological "gaps" in sets of characters implies that groups of organisms separated by such gaps are reproductively isolated.

An outgrowth of the typological–morphological procedure is the *phenetic species concept.* In this context, phenetic is used to refer to the numerical and computer techniques summarized by Sokal and Sneath (1963) and Sneath and Sokal (1973). As in the case of the typological–morphological species concept, the phenetic species concept is based mostly on morphological characters, but the relationships between characters and between organisms are analyzed by computer algorithms to produce some meaningful groupings of organisms. This concept has been applied for the purpose of identifying discrete groups of organisms, and makes no claim to infer evolutionary relationships. One phenetic species definition is provided by Sneath and Sokal (1973): "We may regard as a species (a) the smallest (most homogeneous) cluster that can be recognized upon some given criterion as being distinct from other clusters, or (b) a phenetic group of a given diversity somewhat below the subgenus category, whether or not it contains distinct subclusters." A more operational definition is given by Michener (1970): "A species is a group of organisms not itself divisible by phenetic gaps resulting from concordant differences in character states (except for morphs such as those resulting from sex, caste, or age differences), but separated by such phenetic gaps from other such groups." The latter definition, it must be noted, is applicable also to the morphological procedure of species recognition in the typological species concept.

The other major concept currently in use is the *biological species concept,* which is based on reproductive isolation between groups of organisms. One modern definition of biological species is that of Mayr (Paper 15): "Species are groups of interbreeding natural populations that are reproductively isolated from other such groups." Reproduction as a species attribute is an old concept. In the seventeenth century, John Ray wrote about plant species breeding true from seeds. Lamarck wrote in 1803 that ". . . we called every collection of like individuals, or of those almost entirely alike, species; and we observed that the reproduction of these individuals preserves the species and propagates it by successively continuing to reproduce like individuals." Similarly, De Candolle, in 1813, had a reproductive criterion for species: ". . . the collection of all individuals who resemble each other more than they resemble others; who are able by interfertility to produce fertile individuals, and who reproduce themselves by breeding in such a way that it is possible by analogy to suppose that they all derive originally from a single individual." De Candolle's discussion of species even incorporates an evolutionary element.

In its more general sense, that of genetic continuity, the reproductive criterion is applied for typological and phenetic species. Without a criterion of genetic continuity, it would be impossible to group, for example, insect larvae and adults, or the two sexes of sexually dimor-

3

phic birds, into the same species. However, in the modern formulation of the biological species concept, reproductive isolation, rather than anything else, is the key feature. Proponents of the biological species concept state that reproductive isolation is a key to the process of speciation, and therefore the biological species reflects the actual organization of organisms in nature.

As a concept, the biological species has certain disadvantages. First, it is not applicable to organisms that reproduce asexually, since no interbreeding criterion can be applied to such organisms. Second, like the typological and phenetic concepts, it is static, not taking into account changes through time. Complicating the matter even more is the partial reproductive isolation exhibited by some species. As a special case of genetic continuity, the biological species has a certain utility in dealing with organisms that reproduce sexually. Similarly, the typological and phenetic concepts, while easier to apply and of more practical utility, have the drawback of being inconsistent with evolutionary and biological theory. However, although the biological species concept attempts to reflect evolutionary processes, its drawbacks lie in this very area.

The problems associated with the typological and biological species concepts point out the difficulties of establishing a universal species concept that would apply to all organisms. To be universal, a species concept would have to satisfy the following conditions: (1) be dynamic; (2) allow organisms to be sorted into discrete groups, i.e., be operational or have an operational component; (3) account for morphological, behavioral, ecological, physiological, and genetic similarities among populations included within a species; (4) account for morphological, behavioral, ecological, physiological, and genetic differences among populations included within a species; (5) account for differences between population groups of different species; (6) apply to all forms of genetic continuity and types of reproduction; (7) be consistent with the theoretical framework of evolution.

I would like to suggest that some of the difficulties of species concepts could be eliminated if the species is considered as a unit of selection. Ehrlich and Raven (Paper 17) have presented an array of evidence suggesting that stabilizing selection maintains species even though most populations are reproductively isolated. Other evidence (e.g., Thoday and Gibson, 1970) suggests that selection can produce reproductive isolation within an interbreeding population.

A *selection species concept* would hold that a species is a system of genetically similar individuals and populations maintained as a cohesive unit by a set of selection pressures that balance the disruptive forces imposed by environmental factors, mutation, or genetic recombination. This system maintains a steady state through time as long as all forces are equally balanced. An imbalance in environmental and/or genetic forces acting on a population changes the selection pressures on that population, resulting in morphological, behavioral, ecological, physiological, and genetic divergence from the cohesive species unit. Depending on the rate of change in selection pressures, reproductive isolation between diverging bisexual populations may proceed gradually or rapidly until the ability to interbreed is lost. However, a change in selection pressures, induced by shifts in environmental or genetic forces before the ability to interbreed is lost, may restore full reproductive compatibility.

Since selection pressures have to be estimated from such factors as predation rates and differential survival, an operational definition for the selection species concept would have to involve approximations through some iterative process. Taken as a system, the species can have its morphological, behavioral, ecological, physiological, and genetic characteristics (states) evaluated at a given time (time zero). This can serve as an initial approximation of a species unit. For purposes of identification, such an initial approximation, even at a gross level, would be fully adequate. For purposes of reducing the error of the first approximation, successive evaluations at subsequent times would produce refined estimates of the balance of disruptive and stabilizing forces, and the cohesiveness of a given species unit.

Part I

HISTORICAL AND PHILOSOPHICAL ORIGINS OF SPECIES CONCEPTS

Editor's Comments
on Papers 1 Through 4

The papers in this section serve as an introduction to the historical and philosophical bases of our present ideas about species. Hopwood (Paper 1) briefly discusses some of the historical foundations of classification. Our present classification system has many conceptual elements that are derived from Aristotle's *scala naturae*, scale of nature. As Hopwood points out, the *scala naturae* ranked organisms according to characters. At any point on the scale, all the organisms ranked below that point shared a particular character, whereas groups of organisms ranked above that point did not. The "phylogenetic scale" used by biologists to place "primitive" and "advanced" groups probably has its roots in the *scala naturae*.

Zirkle (Paper 2) discusses some of the historical uses and concepts of species prior to Darwin. In reading Zirkle's paper, it is important to note that the changeability of species discussed there could have two explanations. One is that until fairly recently, species were quite broadly defined. What are now considered separate species were often considered varieties or different expressions of the same species. Thus, when Zirkle reports that Theophrastos (368–284 B.C.) described how

8

a water snake changed into a marsh viper when the marshes dried up, this does not necessarily mean that Theophrastos considered the water snake to have changed species. He could have considered both water snakes and vipers to be expressions of the "snake" species. Even some of Linneaus's species in 1745 often included what we now think of as species groups or whole genera (Lindroth, 1957). Another explanation is that even if individuals changed their species and produced hybrid offspring, this was considered to be part of the accidental variation (see the Introduction) associated with individuals. In no case did the essence of the species change. Thus, in the above example, even if an individual water snake changed into a viper, the essence of the water snake species did not change, nor did the essence of the viper species. Species were fixed and static from the standpoint of their essences, although individuals were believed to be free to change from one species to another.

The historical development of different species concepts is discussed by Mayr (Paper 3). Mayr points out that Linneaus did much to establish and further the idea of the constancy (or fixity) of species. The concept of species constancy, or the doctrine that individual organisms within a species do not change their form in a seemingly random pattern, provided a great stimulus for taxonomy. If all the individuals in a species had a constant form, they could then be described and catalogued in a consistent fashion. With that idea, some order was established from chaos. The idea of species constancy can be traced back to Linneaus's *Philosophia Botanic* (1751). According to Ramsbottom (1938), Linneaus recognized in his notes and writings that species were variable and that varieties could change their form. However, in his writings Linneaus adhered to the concept that varieties and individuals stayed within their own species, even if the individuals were influenced by environmental factors and assumed a somewhat different form. In this respect, the constancy of species expressed in the *Philosophia Botanica* seems to have represented a simplification of Linneaus's actual ideas and observations.

Some of the historical, philosophical, and immediate implications of essentialism, and the influence of essentialism on species concepts, are discussed by Hull (Papers 4A and 4B). Hull also explores some of the conditions and criteria necessary for a species definition. In a 1974 Addendum to his paper, he mentions some of the changes in both the conceptual framework of taxonomy and in his ideas since 1965.

1

Reprinted from *Proc. Linn. Soc. Lond.*, **170**, 230–234 (1957–1958)

THE DEVELOPMENT OF PRE-LINNAEAN TAXONOMY

By A. Tindell Hopwood

The urge to classify is a fundamental human instinct ; like the predisposition to sin, it accompanies us into the world at birth and stays with us to the end. A child in its nursery sorting beads according to their colours, is doing essentially the same thing as the marine biologist sorting plankton in the laboratory. Moreover, their activities do not differ in principle from that of John Henry Newman when, seated before the fire in his old age, he burned the greater part of the accumulated correspondence of a lifetime.

That these three examples could be multiplied indefinitely suggests that a large part of human effort depends on the classification of objects. If this be so, there ought to be some general principle underlying what is, as we well know, a semi-automatic action. Now the child's beads are either red or not red ; the biologist's organisms are either zoaea larvae or something else ; and Cardinal Newman's letters were either worth keeping or they were not. In short, we are here dealing with examples of Excluded Middle, that any given object is either A or not-A.

This method of forming groups is sufficient for most ordinary purposes. To distinguish a horse from a cow, a sheep from a pig, or a cat from a dog is all that the majority of people require. Since any sane person knows what a horse, or a cat, or a dog looks like none of the groups needs definition : the distinctions are made by virtue of our experience of life. Everyday classification, then, is mainly dependent on two factors, our general knowledge and the law of Excluded Middle, and because biological classification is but a special case of a general rule there can be no doubt that in its beginnings the same two principles were employed.

Now any attempt to discover the course of a trend of mental activity that has its root very far back in human history speedily encounters two main obstacles, namely the scarcity of documents and the extreme difficulty of interpreting them. Both obstacles are present in full measure when we consider the foundations on which European science was built.

It is generally agreed, and for my present purpose is demonstrably true, that the study of science in Europe began with the Greeks, who were heirs to the thought and method of Assyria, Chaldaea and Egypt. There is also general agreement that the study of living organisms developed from the practice of the art and mystery of medicine.

Of Assyro-Chaldaean medicine we know very little, but the few documents that exist suggest that it was largely based on magical formulae directed to the expulsion of the evil spirits that possessed the patient, although some simples and minerals were also used with beer or fat as excipients.

Much the same is true of Egyptian medicine, but the Edwin Smith papyrus, which dates from about 1800 B.C., is evidence that side by side with the magic there existed a scientific tradition based on careful observation and, to some extent, on experiments. Moreover, internal evidence indicates that this scientific tradition went back to the early part of the third millenium B.C. None-the-less, there is no trace of any interest in a biological classification, neither is there anything that might be described as a nascent biology ; a result that is entirely in keeping with the severely practical, unspeculative nature of Egyptian thought.

The Greeks, whatever their origin, were far otherwise ; from the very first they sought the ultimate causes of things. Thales of Miletus, the founder of the Ionian school, is an obscure figure in history who lived during the last third of the seventh century B.C. and the first half of the sixth. He seems to have left no writings of his own and what little is known about him depends entirely on the testimony of others. None-the-less, his successors looked up to him as the founder of Greek science ; as Aristotle wrote, ' he was the first to seek the material cause of all things ' (*Metaphys.*, *A*, 3). This is more than a bald statement of fact ; it implies that, as the first to seek a general principle underlying his observations, Thales was the first to use the method of induction.

The next landmark in biological history is also of Ionian origin, namely the Hippocratic corpus. It was written at diverse times by diverse hands in diverse places, but, though the whole is imbued with a spirit of observation and experiment, it does not make a specific contribution to the development of the theory of classification. For that one must look to Plato.

Plato, an amateur of mathematics, had very little interest in living things. Aristotle wrote, ' From his earliest years Plato was familiar with the Heraclitean doctrine of Cratylus, that all sensible things are in a constant state of flux and that we can have no knowledge of them. To the end of his life Plato remained loyal to those tenets— '; and, in the introduction to the *Timaeus*, Plato himself said, ' We must, then, in my judgment, first make this distinction : what is that which is always real and has no becoming, and what is that which is always becoming and is never real ? That which is apprehensible by thought with a rational account is the thing that is always unchangeably real ; whereas that which is the object of belief together with unreasoning sensation is the thing that becomes and passes away, but never has real being.'

Plato was not very interested in the thing that has no proper being. None-the-less, he made a contribution of the highest order to the theory of classification, for, in the *Sophistes* and the *Politicus*, he laid down the rules of dichotomy— sometimes called ' logical division '—and showed how by summing the differentiae one arrives at the definition of the species. He also showed how the definition of the species may vary according to the differentiae selected at each step in the dichotomy. He did not apply the method to biology, but used it in the two dialogues just mentioned to characterize both the sophist and the statesman.

Aristotle discussed and criticized the method in at least four of his major works, namely, the *Analytica Priora*, *Analytica Posteriora*, *De Partibus* and *Metaphysica*. Of these, the third is that most closely concerned with the history of Taxonomy.

The direction of the argument is made clear from the outset and, as the following quotations from the *De Partibus* show, Aristotle was upholding the claims of a natural classification, as he understood it, in contrast to the artificial systems to which dichotomies inevitably lead.

' Some writers propose to reach the definitions of the ultimate forms of animal life by bipartite division. But this method is often difficult and often impracticable.'

' Again it is not permissible to break up a natural group, Birds for instance, by putting its members under different bifurcations, as is done in the published dichotomies, where some birds are ranked with animals of the water and others placed in a different class.'

' If such natural groups are not to be broken up, the method of Dichotomy cannot be employed, for it necessarily involves much breaking up and dislocation.'

' The method then that we must adopt is to attempt to recognise the natural groups—each of which groups combines a multitude of differentiae, and is not defined by a single one as in dichotomy."

It so happens that almost all Aristotle's writings on Zoology have survived, making it possible to judge how far he was able to observe the principles laid down in his criticisms of Plato. First of all, however, we must consider the arrangement of his works and the nature of the evidence on which his conclusions were based : we must also keep in mind that for Aristotle, as for the Greeks in general, the universe was something in orderly motion, possessing 'psyche' or soul, and in some sense a living whole.

So far as the arrangement is concerned, the logical treatises precede those on natural history, and the latter those on metaphysics, ethics and the arts. Secondly, of the biological treatises, those dealing with the soul and the manifestations of the psyche precede the *Historia Animalium*, whereas those dealing with the functions of animals, their parts, their movements, the manner of their generation and so forth, follow it. This succession is neither accidental, nor is it wholly dependent on the whims of later editors. There is plenty of internal evidence to show that, broadly speaking, it reflects the order in which the books were written., So, for example, the *De Partibus* refers to the *Historia*, and the *De Generatione* to the *De Sensu*, clearly indicating the order of writing. A further consideration is that the treatises were written for use in the Lyceum ; one might almost call them Aristotle's lecture notes, and the order suggests very strongly that he regarded his system of logic as the foundation on which all else rested.

As for the nature of the evidence on which his conclusions were based it was of two kinds, namely ; what he knew from his own observations, and what he had learned by report. In neither instance do we possess the whole, for at least one important work, that on anatomy, has been lost. None-the-less, there is seldom much difficulty in distinguishing between the two types of evidence, neither can there be any doubt that when he had to rely on the reports of others he examined them critically before he accepted them. All this evidence, astounding in its quantity and variety, is dealt with in an orderly manner, yet nowhere is his system of classification formally set out. On the other hand, there is so much internal evidence that to recover at least the broad outlines is by no means impossible.

Overriding all else is the great division into those animals that have red blood and those that are bloodless, a division that corresponds almost exactly to our vertebrates and invertebrates. The former are then divided into the vivipara and the ovipara. The vivipara comprise our mammals, including the cetacea and man, and the latter the remainder of the vertebrates from birds to fish. The ovipara are then divided into those with perfect eggs (birds, reptiles and amphibia) and those with imperfect eggs (ovoviviparous reptiles and fish, as well as fish in general) ; a division which it is tempting to compare with our views on cleidoic and non-cleidoic eggs.

Continuing in this way and using a different character at each successive step, Aristotle constructed a *scala naturae* which was remarkably accurate considering the period in which he lived. It depended on the theory of subordination of characters, which determines that a given character is universal to those subordinate to it, but is itself particular to a higher category. For example, a species is universal to its sub-species and particular in respect of its genus.

This *scala naturae* has often been regarded as an early form of evolutionary arrangement, but this is a mistaken view. As I tried to show some years ago, a universe of Euclidean space with time as a discrete entity does not allow of an evolutionary process. Every event is precisely situated in space and time and no transition between them is possible. That the Greeks were aware of this is shown by the famous paradoxes of Zeno the Eleatic, who posed the problems of the arrow in flight, and of Achilles and the tortoise.

An even more potent factor existed in Aristotle's own thought. The point has been discussed at length by Abel Rey and by Léon Robin to whose works reference should be made. Here there is only room for the barest outline.

The world was not created ; it has existed from all time in the harmony of its real qualitative relationships, which are real only because they are permanent (cf. Plato, *supra*). Even the changes that take place follow an eternal plan. Everything is based on the philosophy of the concept, and concepts cannot change because they are eternal.

After Aristotle there was a gradual decline. It began in the Hellenistic schools of Alexandria and culminated in the early Middle Ages. By then Aristotle was almost unknown in the West and even Plato was better known from the neo-Platonists of Alexandria than from his own writings. The rediscovery of Aristotle began about the middle of the twelfth century and by the beginning of the thirteenth century had become so dangerous in the eyes of the theologians that his works were formally proscribed by the University of Paris in 1210, 1215 and 1231. On the other hand, the University of Toulouse gave specific permission for their use in 1229 and, in 1245, was condemned by the Pope for its temerity. Taking this background into account, together with the influence of Plato, or at least of neo-Platonism, on the prevailing Augustinianism, it is not surprising that the scientists, among whom Robert Grosseteste, Bishop of Lincoln and Chancellor of Oxford University, is a well-known figure, devoted their time to physics rather than to biology. None-the-less, it was during this period that the importance of direct observation and experiment began to be recognized once again.

Of the few mediaeval biologists, Albertus Magnus (1206–1280) was the most important, because he was the first Christian to look to reason instead of faith for an explanation of natural phenomena. He turned to Aristotle for his physics and biology. His zoological observations are worthy of note ; for example, he was the first to describe the vocal sacs of frogs, but his services to taxonomy were small. Neither did his successors, whose work in Ornithology has been so admirably summarized by Stresemann do very much during the next three centuries to develop taxonomic science.

In so far as he required a system the great Conrad Gesner (1516–1565) leaned heavily on Aristotle, but his species were set out alphabetically in the mediaeval manner. Walter Charleton (1619–1707), physician to Charles II, followed the example of Aldrovandus and others in dividing the birds according to their habits : his main groups being thus arranged

1. Land dwelling species
   (*a*) Flesh-eaters
   (*b*) Insect-eaters
   (*c*) Grain-eaters
   (*d*) Berry-eaters

2. Water-birds
   (*a*) Palmipedes
   (*b*) Fissipedes
       (i) Fish-eaters
       (ii) Insect-eaters
       (iii) Plant-eaters.

This was practically the last attempt to classify organisms according to Aristotle's principles : it was published in 1668.

Eight years later, Willughby's posthumous work *Ornithologia Libri Tres* was published by his close friend and literary executor John Ray (1627–1705) to be followed in 1693 by Ray's own *Synopsis Methodica Animalium Quadrupedium*. Ray is generally regarded as the author of the method of classification adopted in both these works, a method that was revolutionary in that it entirely disregarded Aristotle's principles and went back to the dichotomies of Plato, on occasion becoming trichotomous when that was more suited to the author's purpose.

Ray, one must admit, was a genius who displayed consummate skill in choosing his differentiae. Because of this his arrangement was as accurate as it

13

well could be considering the period when it was drawn up. It held its own for nearly a century, being used by some workers in preference to the Linnaean method. There were some whose preference was backed by reason, but there were others, and Pennant was among them, who objected to the Linnaean arrangement because man was therein associated with the monkeys. When Bishop Samuel Wilberforce protested against Darwin's views on human evolution, he was not being original, he was merely bringing Pennant up to date, and, dare it be said, had Huxley known that he might not have been so rude !

2

Reprinted from *Proc. Am. Philos. Soc.*, **103**(5), 636–644 (1959)

SPECIES BEFORE DARWIN

CONWAY ZIRKLE

Professor of Botany, University of Pennsylvania

(*Commemoration of the Centennial of the Publication of* The Origin of Species *by Charles Darwin, Annual Meeting of the American Philosophical Society, April, 1959*)

IN ANY association test given to a literate person, the name of Charles Darwin would almost certainly elicit the word "evolution." A biologist might go further and reply "evolution by means of natural selection." And, in this, the nineteen hundred and fifty-ninth year of man's salvation and the hundredth since the publication of Darwin's great work, almost any scholar might reply, *"The Origin of Species."* Darwin showed by the title that he chose for his book that the validity of his theory of evolution depended upon the mutability or non-mutability of the units that the systematists have labeled "species." He knew that, if he could prove that species evolved, he would prove also that no logical limit could be set to the process and that genera, families, and orders must also evolve. But evolution on the sub-species level did not imply necessarily that the whole organic world had reached its present state through the process of evolution, i.e. through a natural and continuous proliferation of new and original forms.

At the time of Darwin, the crucial point in any general theory of evolution was the stability or instability of species. To the biologists of 1859, changes in such subordinate units as races and varieties seemed unimportant. Varieties, they thought, could be altered by even trivial changes in the environment but this mutability showed only that life itself was labile and that living forms could adapt themselves to routine contingencies. The universally held belief in the inheritance of acquired characters made it easy for the biologists to look upon these varietal adaptations as heritable and to admit that evolution did occur on the sub-species level. But most of them continued to believe that the species themselves owed their origin to special and individual acts of creation. There was, in fact, no logical contradiction between a belief in a limited system of evolution and a belief in special creation. The very theologians who thought that all human beings were descended from Adam, had to believe in a partial evolution, that is, in human evolution on the racial level, for they had only to look at the different races of men to see that they differed from one another and that the differences were inherited.

Thus the evolutionists at the time of Darwin had only to show that the mutability that was so obvious on the varietal level extended beyond varieties. Darwin's young friend, Alfred Russell Wallace, who developed the concept of natural selection independently, showed this by the title he chose for his paper—the paper that he presented jointly with Darwin at the famous meeting of the Linnaean Society. It was entitled, "On the tendency of varieties to depart indefinitely from the original type." In the Darwin-Wallace view, species were merely varieties that had been altered so greatly that they had passed the point of no return. To most of their contemporaries, however, this view was truly revolutionary, for the whole taxonomic framework of the mid-nineteenth century was based on the assumed stability of species.

The biologists, however, had not always believed that species were stable. Indeed, the idea that species had to remain exactly as they had been created was relatively new. It had been accepted for only a little over a hundred years when Darwin and the other evolutionists rejected it. A century earlier most biologists had believed that, if one species saw fit to change into another, it could do so, but that such changes were not really important. Anyone who happened to observe a mutating species, however, might be interested enough to describe what he saw, but no one, seemingly, felt it necessary to pursue the matter further. The biologists of the time just accepted at face value the many published accounts of degenerating species, but this degeneration—this generating away from the normal—gave them no inkling whatever of evolution.

The theory of evolution pre-supposes of course that species are mutable, but mutability in itself ot imply evolution. Species must be able ly to change but to change in an orderly r and with reasonable systematic limits, before they can be organized into an evolutionary sequence. A scientific theory of evolution, however, requires more than a mere description of an orderly procession of changing species. It needs a rational explanation. If the biologists could not identify the forces that make living things evolve, the theory of evolution would be little more than an intriguing mystique. Unfortunately, to most laymen this is just what evolution is. Evolution could never have attained its present status in the scientific world if the biologists had not discovered what caused it.

Finding a logical explanation of evolution turned out to be no real problem. In fact, two perfectly good explanations were immanent in biological hypotheses that had been stated as early as the fourth century before Christ but, as it happened, those who accepted these hypotheses did not know all that their acceptance implied. It was not until the nineteenth century that these hidden explanations of evolution emerged. Evolution, we know today, would have to occur (1) if acquired characters were inherited and if they accumulated indefinitely, and (2) if individuals varied spontaneously in their hereditary traits and if nature preserved some of the variants and destroyed others.

The first real use of the inheritance of acquired characters to explain evolution dates only from around the beginning of the nineteenth century. At this time, Erasmus Darwin (1794) and the Chevalier de Lamarck (1802) assumed that the results of this kind of inheritance were cumulative, and that the accumulation had no assignable limits. This nineteenth-century application of what is really an ancient doctrine has now become so prominent that the doctrine's earlier and more general meaning is practically forgotten. Today the "inheritance of acquired characters" is synonymous with Lamarckism and, to most biologists, Lamarckism is just a pre-Darwinian theory of evolution.

Belief in the inheritance of acquired characters antedates any records we have of a belief in organic evolution by about two thousand years. We can actually trace it back as far as the Bronze Age myth of Phaëton. When Phaëton, the half-human son of Apollo, drove the chariot of the sun across the sky, the horses ran away and drew the chariot so close to the land of the Ethiopians that it scorched the inhabitants black—a skin character that we know to be heritable, because today the Ethiopians are still black. Centuries later the Grecian scientists accepted this type of inheritance as axiomatic. Hippocrates used it to explain how the Scythians got their long narrow heads, and Aristotle told how a letter branded on the arm of a slave, reappeared on the arm of his son and later on but somewhat blurred on the arm of his grandson. Pliny, Plutarch, Suetonius, Galen, and Justinus all endorsed the belief, which, with such reputable sponsors, naturally persisted until modern times. I have recorded elsewhere (Zirkle, 1946) some hundred instances of its acceptance during the Middle Ages and Renaissance, and also some fourteen instances of its being endorsed by contemporaries of Lamarck. Here we can expend no more time in tracing its history.

We should, however, record the modern deterioration of the doctrine. We know, today, that it has no validity whatever; it is only an archaic error, one that has been discarded by all honest scientists. But a hundred years ago, the biologist found it to be a valuable ancillary explanation of evolution—an explanation that formed a valuable supplement to the theory of natural selection.

The other ancient doctrine that was used to explain evolution has just been mentioned—it is natural selection. To the biologists of today, natural selection is *the* cause of evolution. Mutations may produce new characters; the chance loss of genes in small isolated populations may cause such groups to differ from one another; but these are only subordinate factors. Natural selection is always at work—it is the court of last appeal—and natural selection alone determines which novelties persist and which are destroyed.

At first, Darwin thought that natural selection offered a sufficient explanation of evolution, and it was not until later that he found it necessary to adopt the inheritance of acquired characters as an auxiliary factor. As we know, it is to Darwin that we owe the proof that evolution is the inevitable consequence of nature's selecting certain types and destroying others, but Darwin was not the first to discover the evolutionary implications of this partiality. Lamarck almost got the idea, but he saw natural selection as through a glass darkly. In 1813, however, William Charles Wells described natural selection accurately and used it to show how the different human races had come into being. In 1831 Patrick Matthews actually explained the origin of species by means of natural selection and, in 1858, Klippart showed how nature could displace one variety or species of wheat by another. In this year also, Alfred Russell Wallace showed how natural selection could transform varieties into species.

The classical philosophers who described natural selection, however, did not use it to account for evolution. Empedocles used it to explain the existence of adaptation by showing how it eliminated all individuals who were unadapted. Epicuros followed where Empedocles led, and Lucretius showed in detail how the elimination of the unfit insured that all who lived were fit. Aristotle, however, rejected natural selection explicitly and accepted in its stead a teleological explanation of adaptation and Aristotle dominated the intellectual world for over two thousand years. Thus, even though natural selection has been recognized, since classical antiquity, it was recognized only as a remote possibility. It languished as an unwanted and somewhat sinful alternative to an almost universally accepted teleology. We know today that, in the biological world, natural selection can account for the existence of what would be highly improbable on a basis of chance. In ancient and medieval times, however, the very existence of the improbable suggested the activity of some supernatural agency. But natural selection kept cropping up. In the second century of our era, Maximus of Tyre found it a useful means for explaining adaptation as did Denis Diderot in the eighteenth. But natural selection was not used to explain evolution until the nineteenth century.

While the teleologists could ignore natural selection, they could not keep it from invalidating a number of their arguments. Once it was admitted that nature played favorites and selected certain fortunate individuals, it was easy to show that the incidents previously cited to prove the existence of design were not chance samples of unselected events, hence it followed that those arguments to support teleology that were based on probability theory were completely irrelevant. Even the teleologists themselves were not true samples of unselected organisms. The mere fact that they were alive showed that they were fit. Indeed, no group of unadapted philosophers could ever contemplate their own unadaptation or argue learnedly as to why it was that they were extinct.

While the concepts of the inheritance of acquired characters and natural selection both existed from classical antiquity, a well-developed and scientific theory of evolution had to await the nineteenth century. At first glance, this late advent of evolution might seem to call for an explanation, especially when we consider that the original concept of species bears a very close resemblance to the one that we accept today. Although this resemblance may be superficial, it is very real. The ancients believed that no species were really constant, but that they all mutated whenever the occasion arose. Species were seemingly just unstable and ephemeral units, erratic and unpredictable. But the ancients had no real idea of organic evolution. The assumed behavior of species was too chaotic to give any rational clue as to their origin.

If we are to follow the devious trail of the species concept at this late date we shall have to traverse some strange country and explore some odd fantasies and superstitions. We can begin our journey most conveniently perhaps by examining the origin of the word.

Obviously we cannot determine what a word means by tracing its etymology, but the origin of a word does shed light upon what it meant when it started on its career. The first scholars who used the word "species" wrote in Latin and, when they switched to their vernaculars, they carried the Latin word with them. Thus, the word "species" in our modern languages is only a bit of naturalized Latin. "Species" comes from "specere" meaning to look at, to behold. The species of an object then are merely its appearances, not its inward essence. Thus the word used to label the concept introduced an uncertainty principle into the concept itself because, from the very earliest times, appearances proverbially have been deceitful.

The word "species" also was used within the framework of the dualistic philosophy that dominated both classical and Christian thinking. In this setting, the appearances of an object—its species—seemed superficial, and appearances were contrasted routinely with some inner reality—with some inner Platonic ideal. Thus, if species turned out to be ephemeral, if they changed erratically into other species, it really meant very little. It was only to be expected. Naturally, in such a setting all species took on some of the qualities of the specious. That a beautiful body could contain an ugly soul was a possibility that no one doubted, and consequently the fair outward appearance of an animal or a man or, in the intellectual field, of a doctrine might be very misleading and even dangerous. The word "species" had such connotations that, in one of its subordinate meanings, it was synonymous with a phantom or an illusion, a species could be a specter or an apparition.

The species of a human being then were his appearances, they were the attributes of his material body, not those of his immortal soul. In an age when the material was scorned and the spiritual revered, a man's species were naturally subordinate to his inner spiritual being, although supposedly his body and his soul were intermingled and each could, to some degree, influence the expression of the other. The material, while it could limit the spiritual, could not really contaminate it, as St. Thomas Aquinas concluded when he discussed a case of inherited feeble-mindedness. The problem that confronted St. Thomas was: Is the soul of a child "traduced" from the souls of its parents? He decided that it was not. He recognized that such diseases as gout could be inherited and that mental deficiency actually was inherited as when idiots begot idiots, but this did not mean that the soul of the idiot child was derived from the soul of its idiot parents. It only meant that the material vehicle of the soul's expression was defective and that only the defective vehicle was hereditary. (Sentences, Bk. II, Quart. 81, Art. I). The material species of the idiot were like those of its parents, but its soul was its own.

We cannot, in any reasonable time, cover all the medieval usages of the word "species." Two more examples, however, will help us explore the milieu in which the biological term developed and which contributed to its biological meaning. The first is from theology. In the miracle of the Host, when the bread and wine become the flesh and blood of Christ, the species of the bread and wine remain unchanged—chemically they are still bread and wine—only their inner essence becomes flesh and blood. Here in theology the word "species" means the same as the word "accidents."

The second example comes from a widespread superstition, but a superstition that the scholars, philosophers, and scientists accepted routinely, i.e., the belief in the werewolf. This creature, a man by day but a wolf after dark (no modern interpretation please), changed only its species. Its inner reality remained the same; it remained a sinful human soul. Lest this final example seem too far-fetched for a serious paper presented to a learned audience, let me call attention to the fact that the history of science cannot be separated entirely from the history of superstition. Indeed, Lynn Thorndyke calls his great work *The History of Magic and Experimental Science.*

We should now be in a position to understand how erratic and variable biological species were thought to be during the period that preceded the beginnings of our post-Renaissance science. In tracing the history of these pre-Darwin concepts we can begin conveniently with the contributions of Aristotle and Theophrastos. Neither of these—the father of zoology and the father of botany—ever conceived of stable and unchanging species. Indeed, Theophrastos devoted almost an entire book (*Enquiry into Plants,* Bk II) to describing how plants changed their species. He stated categorically that plants changed their species when they were transplanted to a different country, and that the change was caused by their growing in a different soil and living in a different climate. He also noted the difference between cultivated plants and their wild relatives, and he assigned this difference to prolonged and skillful cultivation.

He was especially impressed by the fact that many plants did not breed true from seed, and he noted particularly that no cultivated fruit trees ever bred true. Only by vegetative reproduction—by cuttings and by grafting—could superior varieties of fruit be kept from degenerating. This practice—this reproduction of fruit trees vegetatively—is extremely old; it antedates history. The farmers, as well as the philosophers, knew that whenever fruit trees reproduced by seeds, as they did in nature, they routinely produced new varieties. Thus it seemed only reasonable to infer that species were variable in nature and that they were altered as the time, place, and circumstances demanded.

It would be needlessly repetitive to quote all of the records we have of grafted trees producing seedlings which differed from the parental types, and of the inferences the philosophers drew from this rather common occurrence. One instance, however, is worth citing. Seven hundred years after Theophrastos, St. Augustine used the olive tree to clarify a theological problem. He stated correctly that the seedlings descended from the cultivated olive developed into wild olives. This, he argued, showed how nature worked and how it happened that baptized Christians could beget only degenerate sinners, and how it was that the children of even holy parents had to be baptized before they could escape from their original nature, and develop into cultivated olives. The virtues obtained through even the most effective baptism lasted apparently only one generation. Moral imperfection, however, was normal for the human stock. It was acquired character, inherited from the sin of Adam.

Theophrastos described how one species of mint changed into another, how wheat changed into darnel, and how one kind of fruit changed spontaneously into another. He even gave specific instructions for changing one-seeded wheat and rice wheat into the more valuable wheat that was in general cultivation. Other classical writers followed his lead. Nicolaus of Damascus, for example, repeated much of what Theophrastos had written, and the poet Virgil told in his *Georgics* how wheat and barley mutated into wild oats. Theophrastos did not confine himself to the plant kingdom but stated that animals mutated more than plants did because, in their migrations from place to place, they experienced many environmental changes while plants grew anchored in one spot. He described, for example, how the water snake changed into a viper when the marshes dried up.

Aristotle did not list as many species changes as Theophrastos did, but he never considered species to be permanent or unalterable units. He believed in spontaneous generation and stated specifically that many kinds of fish, eels, and insects were produced equivocally. Some species, he thought, could not come into being any other way, but others, once they had been generated, could continue their line just like those that had originated univocally. He believed in the most promiscuous hybridization and that hybridization produced new species. He stated that "Lybia is always bringing forth something new [because in that country] animals of different species unite, since owing to the fact that there is very little water, they all meet together at the few places where springs are to be found, and so animals of different species unite." Aristotle insisted that these hybrids were fertile and that the mule only was sterile. Pliny and other writers naturally followed where Aristotle led, and we have many accounts of what animal hybridizations produced. The camel apparently got around and was, by nature, experimental. When it crossed with a panther it produced the giraffe, when it mated with the wild boar it produced the

two-humped camel, while, according to Oppian, when the camel crossed with the sparrow it produced the ostrich. The origin of the many varieties of dogs was due, supposedly, to the fact that the bitches were broad-minded and their owners took advantage of this fact. The different breeds were descended from crosses of dogs with tigers, lions, wolves, foxes, and goats. The latter mixture produced the wild boar.

We need not pursue these classical writings further. The coming of Christianity did not bring stability to the concept of species. Today, St. Augustine is actually cited as an evolutionist. He thought that all the species need not have been created in actuality during the six days of creation but that they were merely created potentially and that they could have come into actual being much later. Eight hundred years after St. Augustine, St. Thomas Aquinas discussed the subject in detail and admitted that ". . . new species of animals are produced by putrefaction, by the power which the stars and elements received at the beginning. Again, animals of new kinds arise occasionally from the connection of individuals belonging to different species . . ." (*Summa.* Pt. I; quaest. 73: art. 1: ad. 3).

The Arabs, during the period when they dominated the intellectual life of the Mediterranean World, also considered species to be far from stable. Indeed, some of them claimed to be able to produce new species of plants from graft hybrids but this, like most of their other notions, they took from the classical scholars. For example, their predecessors, Florentinus (*ca.* A.D. 220), Diophanes (*ca.* A.D. 350), and Palladius (*ca.* A.D. 375) (*cit.* Bassos) reported that the orange was a new species and was created by grafting the lemon on the pomegranate (Zirkle, 1951). Ibn Wahshya told how kumquats could be made by grafting oranges on olives, and Abt-al-Latif (1162–1231) described the banana as originating from a seed of the date palm that had been inserted into the corm of the colocasia (*cit.* Zirkle, 1935). Thus, diverse species of plants united and made new species and, in this way, we secured many new and valuable fruits which the earlier Greeks and Romans did not have.

In Medieval and Renaissance Europe, species still seemed to be somewhat ephemeral and a little evasive. The records, however, are far too voluminous to quote, but we may mention the *Opus Ruralium Commodorum* of Peter of Crescentius written in 1305. Peter devoted three

19

chapters to the cultivated plants that shifted their species erratically.

We will skip the fifteenth century completely and mention only briefly a few of the descriptions of species alterations that belong to the sixteenth. Polydorus Vergil told, in 1531, how good cultivation produced superior varieties and how neglect caused species to degenerate. In 1559, Levinus Lemnius included in his book on the miracles of nature a four thousand word chapter entitled *Herbas Mutationibus* and here he told how varieties and species changed spontaneously and how they could be altered artificially. In 1584, Julius Caesar Scaliger, perhaps the greatest scholar of the century, published a commentary on the work of Theophrastos in six books and in 1556 one in two books on *De Plantis*, falsely ascribed to Aristotle. He treated the instability of species in detail. In 1570, Conrad Heresbach, who wrote on agriculture, described the best techniques for changing the color of carnations. In 1576, the herbalist, Charles de l'Ecluse, told how tulips continually broke from their type and changed both their kinds and their colors. In 1599, Martin Del Rio discussed the question as to how the small grains changed into each other.

We will have to dismiss the seventeenth century rather cavalierly and merely list the names and dates of a few of those who described the degeneration and mutation of species. Francis Bacon (1626), Alphonso Carranza (1629), Thomas Johnson (1633), Giovanni Baptista Ferrario (1633), Johannes Benedictus Sinibaldus (1642), Robert Sharrock (1660), Honorati Fabri (1600), Antonius Le Grand (1672), Sir Matthew Hale (1677), Emanuel Koenig (1680), and John Ray (1686). The number of citations such as these could be increased indefinitely. These are merely the ones that I ran across when I was searching the literature for something else.

Today, it is easy for serious scientists to ignore the records of species instability written by our sixteenth- and seventeenth-century precursors. It is true that these intellectual ancestors of ours were frequently careless, generally credulous and, at times, even superstitious. But they observed accurately and they reported correctly that organic units were basically unstable and that animals and plants did not always breed true. They called all such instances "degeneration," i.e., generating away from the normal. From our vantage point in the twentieth century, we can describe

this degeneration in scientific terms and we can now explain most of what our predecessors saw. First, we know that they observed bud sports and even propagated varieties that arose from somatic mutation. Second, they saw the effect of xenia but, of course, did not know what caused it. This is not remarkable, because xenia, or the influence of foreign pollen on tissues outside of the embryo proper, was not explained until 1899 (Nawaschin). Third, they noted the results of cross-pollination but, again, they did not recognize the fact of pollen contamination and, of course, they knew nothing of what it could do to their seeds. Finally, they observed the effects of Mendelian segregation but—and this need not surprise us—they knew nothing of Mendelism. A few of their descriptions of degeneration, however, will show how their accurate observations led to a general misunderstanding. They will also show how their observations helped to preserve the belief in the instability of species.

The effects of xenia are sometimes spectacular, especially in Indian corn (*Zea mays*). Here, when different color varieties are grown near one another the wind cross pollinates them, and grains of many different colors will appear on the same ear. This mixture of colors was described some fifty times in the seventeenth century, but our first record of it is a little earlier. It appears in the *Krauterbuch* of Tabernaemontanus, first published in 1588. Here the author printed rhapsodic descriptions of these ears of many colors, and he gave detailed instructions for coloring the outline drawings that he printed in the text. But the reason for these beautiful ears evaded him. To him, plant sports meant only that the Deity was in a sportive mood. He began his accounts as follows:

And one sees an especially great and wonderful mystery in these spikes, the Lord God, through the medium of nature, which must serve everyone, disports himself and performs wonders in his works and so notably in the case of this plant that we must rightly be amazed and should learn to know the One True Eternal God even from his creatures alone.

The results, as we have stated, were botanically spectacular. The botanists were duly impressed, and God, apparently, was pleased with his work.

Horticultural varieties, heterozygous for many Mendelian factors will not breed true, and this kind of behavior resulted in a mystery that could be very annoying. It completely frustrated Master James Garret, a friend of the John Gerard who published *The Herball, or General History of Plants* in 1597. Master Garret raised tulips and he wanted his tulips to breed true from seed. Gerard recorded his friend's frustration:

Notwithstanding my loving friend Master *James Garret,* a curious searcher of Simples, and learned Apothicarie in London, hath undertaken to find out if it were possible, the infinite sorts by diligent sowing of their seeds, and by planting those of his own propagation, and by others received from his friends beyond the seas, for the space of twentie years, not being yet able to attaine to the end of his travaile, for that each new yeare bringeth forth new plants of sundrie colours not before seene; all which to describe particularlie, were to roule *Sisphus* stone, or number the sandes.

The contamination of valuable garden plants by the pollen of their wild relatives could be both an annoyance and an expense, as is shown by an unfortunate incident in the life of Richard Baal, an incident that was recorded in 1680 by Robert Morison in his *Plantarum Historiae.* At this time it was the custom of English gardeners to buy their cabbage seeds from Holland. They believed that seeds raised in England would degenerate. But Richard Baal was a skeptic. He raised some fine garden cabbages from seeds that he had imported and he collected and sold the seed from his cabbages. The seed, however, produced only the wild and useless *Brassica longifolia aperta,* the wild maritime cabbage. Baal's customers sued him for damages and he had to refund the money he received for the seed and also compensate them for wasting their time and their ground. This episode was also reported by John Ray in 1686 and by Johann Wahlbom, a student of Linnaeus, in 1746. At this later date, sex in plants was well understood, and Baal's troubles were correctly assigned to the vagabond pollen of the wild English cabbage.

During the eighteenth century our modern concept of species slowly took shape, but a majority of the biologists continued to believe that species were only ephemeral forms. The growing taxonomic knowledge, however, showed that species were stable, at least in the time scale that was available to the investigators. A sharp distinction was beginning to be made between varieties and species and, as the century passed, only the former continued to be looked upon as unreliable. Species supposedly retained their characteristics but some indirect evidence indicated that the retention was not absolute. The great Comte de

Buffon had shed most of the earlier and more naive views of species and to him species were real units (to Buffon, species were what we now call Genera or even Families), but their numbers, resemblances to each other, and their interaction in hybrids led him to believe that what we may call "Linnaean" species were not completely stable but were altered very slowly as the years passed. He was, in fact, a precursor of Darwin. The idea of the complete fixity of species was beginning to take shape in other quarters, however, and it had become the accepted belief of the theologians. The theologians now held that species remained just as God had made them in the six days of creation—they remained just as God wanted them to be.

Buffon's voluminous *Histoire Naturelle* was published over a period of fifty-five years (1749–1804), and in this opus he occasionally let his evolutionary views shine through. The theologians in the Sorbonne found these ideas objectionable. They took a firm stand and Buffon soon learned of his errors. Buffon was always tactful and he conformed cheerfully whenever it was necessary. He always deferred to the "sublime truths of theology" and admitted that his science was subordinate and he would not offend the theologians again until after he had published two or three more volumes. He retained many valuable perquisites and arranged his life carefully so that he could live comfortably and continue to write.

In the middle of the eighteenth century, Linnaeus revolutionized taxonomy. The knowledge of species and their breeding properties became much more exact. Species *were* found to be stable and, when they changed, they changed very slowly, and over an immense period of time. Linnaeus found that species did breed true but he also discovered that mutation did occur and he listed a number of major mutations. He described what he found in accurate detail and this led to some confusion. Indeed one historian of botany, Edward Lee Greene, devoted a chapter to Linnaeus as an evolutionist, and he quotes Linnaeus to show that he was both for and against evolution. Some historians have missed the complications that faced Linnaeus and have assumed that Linnaeus really believed in evolution and that his anti-evolutionary statements were due to theological pressure. Some have even assumed that his relations to the Swedish Lutherans were the same as Buffon's were to the French

s. This may be true, but it seems more
that Linnaeus was only an honest scien-
.....u was doing the best he could when he was
confronted with a very complex problem.

At the beginning of the nineteenth century,
belief in the fixity of species prevailed in both the
religious and scientific worlds. The causes of this
were many. The belief might have been inevitable—a natural consequence of a phase through
which our growing science had to pass—but it
was aided by a couple of historical accidents, by
the personal talents and characteristics of certain
men who expressed themselves definitely on the
subject of special creation and evolution. We
need mention but two of these, Baron Georges
Cuvier and the Chevalier de Lamarck.

Cuvier was a careful, accurate, and active
scientist who soon acquired great prestige among
his colleagues. He was a firm believer in special
creation and he explained the fossil record by
assuming that the earth had experienced a number of catastrophes. Lamarck on the other hand
was an evolutionist but, while he was undoubtedly
a great man, he was so utterly humorless that he
was forever making himself ludicrous. He could
not endorse a doctrine without injuring it—without making it appear dubious. Belief in the
inheritance of acquired characters had been accepted almost universally for over twenty-five
hundred years; it was an ancient and honorable
doctrine, but it was endangered and almost destroyed by Lamarck's endorsement. Lamarck's
talents for making himself ridiculous have been
described elsewhere so they need not be depicted
here (Zirkle, 1946). Here we may state merely
that the biologists of the first half of the nineteenth century did not want to accept his ideas
nor did they want to be associated with him in
any way. Certainly no sane biologist wanted to
be known as a Lamarckian.

It was not until Darwin showed his fellow
scientists that they could be evolutionists without
being Lamarckians that evolution was welcomed.
By the middle of the nineteenth century the evidence for evolution was overwhelming but the
biologists did not want to be called Lamarckians
and laughed at. When Darwin wrote, evolution
was not so much in the air as it was underground.
But when Darwin made evolution respectable
intellectually, its triumph was assured. For evolution to be accepted it needed only a rational explanation.

One fact in the history of the species concept

should be emphasized. The earlier belief that
species were ephemeral and mutable did not pro-
mote a belief in evolution. A scientific theory of
evolution became possible only after the stability
of species had been established. Evolution demands that species change but it demands that
they change in an orderly fashion.

Following the publication of Darwin's *Origin
of Species,* the prevalent view of species became
post-Darwinian, and this is the view that we hold
today.

REFERENCES

ABT-AL-LATIF. 1810. Relation de l'Egypt etc. (tr. by de Sacy). Paris.
ARISTOTLE. 1910. Generation of animals (tr. by Arthur Platt). Oxford, Oxford Univ. Press.
BACON, FRANCIS. 1626. Silva silvarum. London.
BASSOS, CASSIANOS. 1704. Geoponicorum sive de re rustica. Cantabrigiae.
BUFFON, GEORGES LOUIS LECLERC DE. 1749–1804. His- toire Naturelle. Paris.
CARRANZA, ALPHONSO. 1629. Tractatus . . . de partu naturali et legitimos. Geneva.
CUVIER, GEORGES. n.d. Le Regne animal. Paris.
DARWIN, CHARLES. 1859. The origin of species. London.
DARWIN, ERASMUS. 1794. Zoonomia: or the laws of organic life. London.
DEL RIO, MARTINUS ANTONIUS. 1599. Disquistiones magicae. Louvain.
EMPEDOCLES. 1908. Fragments. Tr. into English verse by W. E. Leonard. Chicago, Open Court Publish- ing Co.
FABRI, HONORATI. 1677. 1st. ed. 1660. Tractatus Duo etc. Nirembergae.
FERRARIO, GIOVANNI BATTISTE. 1633. Florum Cultura. Rome.
GALEN. 1821–1833. Opera omnia. Leipzig.
GERARD, JOHN. 1597. The herball or general history of plants. London.
GREENE, EDWARD LEE. 1912. Carolus Linnaeus. Phila- delphia, Christopher Sower.
HALE, SIR MATTHEW. 1677. The primitive origination of mankind. London.
HERESBACH, CONRAD. 1586. 1st ed. 1570. Foure bookes of husbandry (tr. by Barnebe Googe). London.
HIPPOCRATES. 1886. The genuine works of Hippo- crates (tr. by Francis Adams). New York.
JOHNSON, THOMAS. 1633. Gerard's herball or general historie of plants. 2nd ed. Edited by Thomas Johnson. London.
JUSTINUS. 1746. The history of the world. London.
KLIPPART, J. H. 1858. Origin, growth, diseases, varie- ties, etc., of the wheat plant. Ohio. *Annual Report Board of Agriculture* **12**: 568–816.
KOENIG, EMANUEL. 1680. Regnum vegetabile etc. Basel.
———. 1708. Regnum vegetabile. 1st ed. 1680. Basileae.
LAMARCK, J. B. P. A. DE MONET DE. 1802. Recherche sur l'organisation des corps vivants. Paris.
l' ECLUSE, CHARLES DE. 1576. Rariorum aliquot stirpum per Hispanias observatarum. Antwerp.

LE GRAND, ANTONIUS. 1672. Instituio philosophias secundum principia Renati Descartes. London.

LEMNIUS, LEVINUS. 1559. Occulta naturae miracula. Antwerp.

LINNAEUS, CAROLUS. 1779. Systema plantarum. Francofurti a/M.

LUCRETIUS. 1916. De natura rerum (tr. by Leonard). London, E. P. Dutton.

MATTHEWS, PATRICK. 1831. Naval timber and aboriculture. London.

MAXIMUS of TYRE. 1804. The dissertations of Maximus of Tyre (tr. by Thomas Taylor). London.

MORISON, ROBERT. 1680. Plantarum historiae universalis Oxoniensis. Oxford.

NAWASCHIN, S. 1899. Neuen Beobachtungen über Befruchtung usw. *Botanische Centralblatt* **77**: 62.

OPPIAN. 1918. Halieutica (tr. by Mair). London, Heinemann.

PALLADIUS. 1898. Palladi veri illustris opus agriculturae (ed. J. C. Schmitt). Leipzig.

PETER OF CRESCENTIUS. 1486. Opus Ruralium Commodorum. Argentinae.

PLINY. 1602. The historie of the world (tr. by Philemon Holland). London.

PLUTARCH. 1909. Concerning such whom God is slow to punish (tr. by John Philips). Boston and New York, Little.

RAY, JOHN. 1686. Historia plantarum. London.

ST. AUGUSTIN. 1886–1888. Marriage and concupiscence (tr. by Peter Holmes). New York.

ST. THOMAS AQUINAS. 1911–1917. Opera omnia. London, Washbourne.

SCALIGER, JULIUS CAESAR. 1556. In libros duos, qui inscribunter de plantis. Aristotole autore. Lutetia.

——. 1584. Animadversiones in historias Theophrasti. Lugdimi.

SHARROCK, ROBERT. 1660. The history of the propagation and improvement of vegetables. London.

SINIBALDUS, JOHANNES BENEDICTUS. 1642. Geneanthropeiae, sive de hominis generatione. Rome.

SUETONIUS. 1899. History of twelve Caesars (tr. by Philemond Holland). London.

TABERNAEMONTANUS, JACOBUS THEODORUS. 1588. Neuw Krauterbuch. Basel.

THEOPHRASTOS. 1916. Enquiry into plants (tr. by Sir Arthur Hort). London, Heinemann.

THORNDYKE, LYNN. 1923–1958. History of magic and experimental science. New York, Macmillan, Columbia Univ. Press.

VERGIL, POLYDORUS. 1531. 1651. Historiae Anglicae. Leyden.

VIRGIL. 1744. Georgics (tr. by Martyn). London.

WAHLBOM, JOHANN GUSTAV. 1749. Sponsalia plantarum. *Amoen. Acad.* **1**: 61–109.

WALLACE, A. W. 1858. On the tendency of varieties to depart indefinitely from the original type. *Jour. Linnaean Society (Zool.)* **3**: 45.

WELLS, WM. CHAS. 1818. Two essays upon double and single vision, etc. London.

ZIRKLE, CONWAY. 1935. The beginnings of plant hybridization. Philadelphia, Univ. of Penna. Press.

——. 1946. The early history of the idea of the inheritance of acquired characters and of pangenesis. *Trans. Amer. Philos. Soc.* **35**: 91–151.

——. 1951. The knowledge of heredity before 1900. In: Genetics in the 20th Century (ed. by L. C. Dunn). New York, Macmillan.

Reprinted from *The Species Problem*, E. Mayr (ed.), Am. Assoc. Adv. Sci. Publ. 50, 1957, pp. 1-22

SPECIES CONCEPTS AND DEFINITIONS

ERNST MAYR: MUSEUM OF COMPARATIVE ZOOLOGY, HARVARD COLLEGE, CAMBRIDGE, MASSACHUSETTS

The importance of one fact of nature is being recognized to an ever increasing extent: that the living world is comprised of more or less distinct entities which we call species. Why are species so important? Not just because they exist in huge numbers, and because each species, when properly studied, turns out to be different from every other, morphologically and in many other respects. Species are important because they represent an important level of integration in living nature. This recognition is fundamental to pure biology, no less than to all subdivisions of applied biology. An inventory of the species of animals and plants of the world is the base line of further research in biology. Whether he realizes it or not, every biologist—even he who works on the molecular level—works with species or parts of species and his findings may be influenced decisively by the choice of a particular species. The communication of his results will depend on the correct identification of the species involved, and thus, on its taxonomy.

Yet, when I was first approached by the Chairman of the Division of Zoology of the American Association for the Advancement of Science to organize a symposium on the species problem I was, to put it mildly, hesitant. Much discussion of this subject in recent years suggested that there was perhaps no need for such a symposium. Ensuing correspondence, however, convinced me otherwise, and certain publications showed clearly that further thinking on this subject is welcome, if not necessary. The species problem continues to be one of the most disputed subjects in biology, in spite of the intense preoccupation with it during the past two hundred years. The recent publications by Spurway, Burma, and Arkell attest this. This symposium can be considered a success if it throws light on some of the disputed questions or even if it does nothing more than lead to a more precise phrasing of the basic points of disagreement.

One way of laying a foundation for such an investigation is to recall some of its history. Who was the first to realize that there is a species problem and what was his proposed solution? What were the subsequent developments? Time does not permit a thorough coverage of the field, but even a glance at the high lights is revealing. If we open a history of biology, the two names mentioned most prominently under the heading of "Species" will be Linnaeus and Darwin. Linnaeus will be cited as the champion of two characteristics of the species, their constancy and their sharp delimitation (their "objectivity"). One of the minor tragedies in the history of biology has been the assumption during the hundred and fifty years after Linnaeus that constancy and clear definition of species are strictly correlated and that one must make a choice of either believing in evolution (the "inconstancy" of species) and then having to deny the existence of species except as purely subjective, arbitrary figments of the imagination, or, as most early naturalists have done, believing in the sharp delimitation of species but thinking that this necessitated denying evolution. We shall leave the conflict at this point and merely anticipate the finding made more than a hundred years after Linnaeus that there is no conflict between the fact of evolution and the fact of the clear delimitation of species in a local fauna or flora.

The insistence of Linnaeus on the reality, objectivity, and constancy of species is of great importance in the history of biology for three reasons. First, it meant the end of the belief in spontaneous generation as far as higher organisms are concerned, a belief which at that time was still widespread. Lord Bacon and nearly all leading writers of the pre-Linnaean period, except Ray, believed in the transmutation of species and the Linnaean conception "of the reality and fixity of species perhaps marks a necessary stage in the progress of scientific inquiry." (See Poulton, 1903, pp. lxxxiv-lxxxvii for further references on the subject). "Until about 1750 almost no one believed that species were

25

stable. Linnaeus had to show that species were not erratic and ephemeral units before organic evolution as we know it could have any meaning." (Conway Zirkle in litt.) The idea that the seed of one plant could occasionally produce an individual of another species was so widespread that it died only slowly. We all know that it raised its ugly head once more during the past ten years. In spite of Redi's and Spallanzani's experiments spontaneous generation was still used in 1851 by the philosopher Schopenhauer as an explanation for the origin of higher categories. Linnaeus thus did for the higher organisms what Pasteur did one hundred years later for the lower.

A second reason why his emphasis was important is that it took the species out of the speculations of the philosophers who approached the species problem in the spirit of metaphysics and stated, for instance, that "only individuals exist. The species of a naturalist is nothing but an illusion" (Robinet, 1768). We shall return later to the point why species are more than merely an aggregate of individuals.

A third reason why the insistence on the sharp delimitation of species in the writings of Linnaeus is of historical importance is that it strengthened the viewpoint of the local naturalist and established the basis for an observational and experimental study of species in local faunas and floras, of which Darwin took full advantage.

Linnaeus was too experienced a botanist to be blind to the evidence of evolutionary change. Greene (1912) gathered numerous citations from his writings which clearly document Linnaeus' belief in the common descent of certain species, and Ramsbottom (1938) and Sirks (1952) have traced how Linnaeus expressed himself more and more freely on the subject, as his prestige grew. Paradoxically, Linnaeus did more, perhaps, to lay a solid foundation for subsequent evolutionary studies by emphasizing the constancy and objectivity of species than if he, like Darwin, had emphasized the opposite.

Darwin looked at the species from a viewpoint almost directly opposite to that of Linnaeus. As a traveler naturalist and particularly because of his studies of domesticated plants and animals he was impressed by the fluidity of the species border and the subjectivity of their delimitation. The views of both Linnaeus and Darwin underwent a change during the life of each. With Linnaeus the statements on the constancy of species became less and less dogmatic through the years. In Darwin, as the idea of evolution became firmly fixed in his mind, so grew his conviction that this should make it impossible to delimit species. He finally regarded species as something purely arbitrary and subjective. "I look at the term species as one arbitrarily given for the sake of convenience to a set of individuals closely resembling each other, and that it does not essentially differ from the term variety which is given to less distinct and more fluctuating forms. . . . The amount of difference is one very important criterion in settling whether two forms should be ranked as species or variety." And finally he came to the conclusion that "In determining whether a form should be ranked as a species or a variety, the opinion of naturalists having sound judgment and wide experience seems the only guide to follow" (Darwin, 1859). Having thus eliminated the species as a concrete unit of nature, Darwin had also neatly eliminated the problem of the multiplication of species. This explains why he made no effort in his classical work to solve the problem of speciation.

The seventy-five years following the publication of the *Origin of Species* (1859) saw biologists rather clearly divided into two camps, which we might call, in a somewhat oversimplified manner, the followers of Darwin and those of Linnaeus. The followers of Darwin, which included the plant breeders, geneticists, and other experimental biologists minimized the "reality" or objectivity of species and considered individuals to be the essential units of evolution. Characteristic for this frame of mind is a symposium held in the early Mendelian days, which endorsed unanimously the supremacy of the individual and the nonexistence of species. Statements made at this symposium (Bessey, 1908) include the following: "Nature produces individuals and nothing more. . . . Species have no actual existence in nature. They are mental concepts and nothing more. . . . Species have been invented in order that we may refer to great numbers of individuals collectively."

Taxonomists, one of the speakers claimed, did not merely name the species found in nature but actually "made" them. "In making a species the guiding principle must be that it shall be recognizable from its diagnosis." A leftover from this period is the statement of a recent author: "Distinct species must be separable on the basis of ordinary preserved material."

It is a curious paradox in the history of biology that the rediscovery of the Mendelian laws resulted in an even more unrealistic species concept among the experimentalists than had existed previously. They either let species saltate merrily from one to another, as did Bateson and DeVries, defining species merely as morphologically different individuals, or they denied the existence of species altogether except as intergrading populations. Whether these early Mendelians considered species as continuous or discontinuous units, they all agreed in their arbitrariness and artificiality. There is an astonishing absence of any effort in this school to study species in nature, to study natural populations.

A study of natural populations had become the prevailing preoccupation in an entirely independent conceptual stream, that of the naturalists, which ultimately traces back to Linnaeus. The viewpoint of the naturalist was particularly well expressed by Jordan (1905), who stated "The units of which the fauna of a region is composed are separated from each other by gaps which, at a given place, are not bridged by anything. This is a fact which can be checked by any observer. Indeed, the activity of a local naturalist begins with the searching out of these units which with Linnaeus we call species." (For a more detailed discussion see Mayr, 1955.) Although this was the prevailing viewpoint among taxonomists, it was completely ignored by the general biologists by whom, as a result of Darwin's theory, "Species were mostly regarded merely as arbitrary divisions of the continuous and ever changing series of individuals found in nature . . . of course, active taxonomists did not overlook the existence of sharply and distinctly delimited species in nature— but as the existence of those distinct units disagreed with the prevailing theories, it was mentioned as little as possible" (Du Rietz, 1930). The two streams of thought are still recognizable today even though most geneticists, under the leadership of Dobzhansky, Huxley, Ford, and others, have swung into Jordan's camp. The principal opponents of the concept of objectively delimitable species are today found among philosophers and paleontologists. Publications maintaining this viewpoint are those of Gregg (1950), Burma (1949, 1954), Yapp (1951), and Arkell (1956). These are only the most recent titles in a vast literature, some of which is cited in the bibliography.

The point which is perhaps most impressive when one studies these voluminous publications is the amount of disagreement that has existed and still exists. The number of possible antitheses that have been established in this field may be characterized by such alternate views, to mention only a few, as follows:

Subjective *versus* objective;
Scientific *versus* purely practical;
Degree of difference *versus* degree of distinctness;
Consisting of individuals *versus* consisting of populations;
Only one kind of species *versus* many kinds of species;
To be defined morphologically *versus* to be defined biologically.

To give a well-documented history of the stated controversies would fill a book. As interesting as this chapter in the history of human thought is, the detailed presentation of the gropings and errors of former generations would add little to the task before us. Let us concentrate therefore on the gradual emergence of the ideas which we, today, consider as central and essential. Three aspects are stressed in most modern discussions of species, that (1) they are based on distinctness rather than on difference and are therefore to be defined biologically rather than morphologically, (2) they consist of populations, rather than of unconnected individuals, a point particularly important for the solution of the problem of speciation, (3) they are more succinctly defined by isolation from non-conspecific populations than by the relation of conspecific individuals to each other. The crucial species criterion is thus not the fertility of individuals, but rather

29

the reproductive isolation of populations. Let us try to trace the emergence of these and related concepts.

It is not surprising that species were considered merely "categories of thought" by many writers in periods so strongly dominated by idealistic philosophy as were the eighteenth and nineteenth centuries. Thoughts as that expressed in the above quoted statement of Robinet were echoed by Agassiz, Mivart, and particularly among those paleontologists who considered their task merely the classification of "objects" (= fossil specimens). In opposition to this, an increasingly strong school developed which considered species as "definable," "objective," "real." Linnaeus was, of course, the original standard bearer of this school to which also belonged Cuvier, De Candolle, and many taxonomists in the first half of the nineteenth century. They supported their case sometimes by purely morphological arguments such as Godron (1853) who stated: "c'est un fait incontestable que toutes les espèces animales et végétables se séparent les unes des autres par de caractères absolues et tranchées." Others used a more biological argument, as I will discuss below.

What is unexpected for this pre-Darwinian period, however, is the frequency with which "common descent" is included in species definitions. When such an emphatically anti-evolutionary author as v. Baer (1828) defines the species as "the sum of the individuals that are united by common descent," it becomes evident that he does not refer to evolution. What is really meant is more apparent from Ray's species definition (1686) or a statement by the Swedish botanist Oeder (1764) that it characterizes species "dass sie aus ihres gleichen entsprungen seien und wieder ihres gleichen erzeugen." Expressions like "community of origin" or "individus descendants des parents communs" (Cuvier) are frequent in the literature. These are actually attempts at reconciling a typological species concept (with its stress of constancy) with the observed morphological variation. Constancy was a property of species taken very seriously not only by Linnaeus and his followers but curiously enough also by Lamarck and by Darwin himself: "The power of remaining constant for a good long period I look at as the essence of a species" (letter to Hooker, Oct. 22, 1864). Such constancy in time was the strongest argument in favor of a morphological species concept, but it could be proved only by the comparison of individuals of different generations. Different morphological "types" that are no more different than mother and daughter or father and son can safely be considered as conspecific. They are "of the same blood." It is obvious that this early stress of descent was essentially the consequence of a morphological species concept. Yet this consideration of descent eventually led to a genetic species definition.

Virtually all early species definitions regarded species only as aggregates of individuals, unconnected except by descent, as is evident not only from the writings of Robinet, Buffon, and Lamarck, but also of much more recent authors (e.g., Britton, 1908; Bessey, 1908). The realization that these individuals are held together by a supraindividualistic bond, that they form populations, came only slowly. Illiger (1800) spoke of species as a community of individuals which produce fertile offspring. Brauer (1885) spoke of the "natural tie of blood relationship" through which the "individuals of a species are held together," and which "is not a creation of the human mind . . . if species were not objective, it would be incomprehensible that even the most similar species mix only exceptionally and the more distant species never." Plate (1914) was apparently the first to state explicitly the nature of this bond: "The members of a species are tied together by the fact that *they recognize each other as belonging together* and reproduce only with each other. The systematic category of the species is therefore entirely independent of the existence of Man." Finally, in the language of current population genetics this community becomes the "co-adapted gene pool," again stressing the integration of the members of the population rather than the aggregation of individuals (a viewpoint which is of course valid only for sexually reproducing organisms).

The growth of thinking in terms of populations went hand in hand with a growing realization that species were less a matter of difference than of distinctness. "Species" in its earlier typological version meant merely "kind of." This, as far as inanimate objects are concerned, is measured in terms of difference. But one cannot apply this same standard to "kinds of" organisms, because there are various biological "kinds." Males and females may be two very different "kinds" of animals. Jack may be a very different "kind" of a person from Bill, yet neither "kind" is a species. Realization of the special aspects of biological variation has led to a restriction in the application of the term species to a very particular "kind," namely the kind that would interbreed with each other. The first three authors found * by me who state this clearly are Voigt (1817), "Man nennt Spezies . . . was sich fruchtbar mit einander gattet, fortpflanzt"; Oken (1830), "Was sich scharet und paaret, soll zu einer Art gerechnet werden"; and Gloger (1833), "What under natural conditions regularly pairs, always belongs to one species." (He stated that by stressing "regularly" he wanted to eliminate the complications due to occasional hybridization.) Gloger later (1856) gave a different, but similar definition: "A species is what belongs together either by descent or for the sake of reproduction." It is interesting how completely all these definitions omit any reference to morphological criteria. They are obviously inapplicable to asexually reproducing organisms.

This is an exceedingly short outline of some of the trends in the development of a modern species concept. More extensive treatments can be found in the publications of Geoffroy St. Hilaire (1859), Besnard (1864), de Quatrefages (1892), Bachmann (1905), Plate (1914), Uhlmann (1923), Du Rietz (1930), Kuhn (1948), and other authors cited in the bibliography. Several conclusions are self-evident. One is that biological or so-called modern species criteria were already used by authors who published more than one hundred years ago, long before Darwin. Another is that a steady clarification is evident, yet that there is still much uncertainty and widespread divergence of opinion on many aspects of the species problem. It is rather surprising that not more agreement has been reached during the past two

* Still earlier statements can no doubt be found in the extensive literature, particularly on hybridization.

hundred years in which these questions have been tossed back and forth. This certainly cannot be due to lack of trying, for an immense amount of time and thought has been devoted to the subject during this period. One has a feeling that there is a hidden reason for so much disagreement. One has the impression that the students of species are like the three blind men who described the elephant respectively as a rope, a column, or a giant snake when touching its tail, its legs, and its trunk.

Perhaps the disagreement is due to the fact that there is more than one kind of species and that we need a different definition for each of these species. Many attempts have been made during the last hundred years to distinguish these several kinds of species, among the most recent being those of Valentine (1949) and Cain (1953). Camp and Gillis (1943) recognized no less than twelve different kinds of species. Yet, a given species in nature might fit into several of their categories, and in view of this overlap no one has adopted either this elaborate classification or any of the simpler schemes proposed before or afterwards.

Species Concepts

An entirely different approach to the species problem stresses the kaleidoscopic nature of any species and attempts to determine how many different aspects a species has. Depending on the choice of criteria, it leads to a variety of "species concepts" or "species definitions." At one time I listed five species concepts, which I called the practical, morphological, genetic, sterility, and biological (Mayr, 1942). Meglitsch (1954) distinguishes three concepts, the phenotypic, genetic, and phylogenetic, a somewhat more natural arrangement. Two facts emerge from these and other classifications. One is that there is more than one species concept and that it is futile to search for *the* species concept. The second is that there are at least two levels of concepts. Such terms as "practical," "sterility," "genetic" signify concrete aspects of species which lead to what one might call "applied" species concepts. They specify criteria which can be applied readily to determine the status of discontinuities found in nature. Yet they are secondary, derived concepts, based on underlying philosophical concepts, which might also be called primary or theoretical concepts. I believe that the analysis of the species problem would be considerably advanced, if we could penetrate through such empirical terms as phenotypic, morphological, genetic, phylogenetic, or biological, to the underlying philosophical concepts. A deep, and perhaps widening gulf has existed in recent decades between philosophy and empirical biology. It seems that the species problem is a topic where productive collaboration between the two fields is possible.

An analysis of published species concepts and species definitions indicates that all of them are based on three theoretical concepts, neither more nor less. An understanding of these three philosophical concepts is a prerequisite for all attempts at a practical species definition. And all species criteria or species definitions used by the taxonomist in his practical work trace back ultimately to these basic concepts.

The Typological Species Concept. This is the simplest and most widely held species concept. Here it merely means "kind of." There are languages, as for instance German, where the term for "kind" (*Art*) is also used for "species." A species in this concept is "a different thing." This concept is very useful in many branches of science and it is still used by the mineralogist who speaks of "species of minerals" (Niggli, 1949) or the physicist who speaks of "nuclear species." This simple concept of everyday life was incorporated in a more sophisticated manner in the philosophy of Plato. Here, however, the word *eidos* (*species,* in its Latin translation) acquired a double meaning that survives in the two modern words "species" and "idea" both of which are derived from it. According to Plato's thinking objects are merely manifestations, "shadows," of the eidos. By transfer, the individuals of a species, being merely shadows of the same type, do not stand in any special relation to each other, as far as a typologist is concerned. Naturalists of the "idealistic" school endeavor to penetrate through all the modifications and variations of a species in order to find the "typical" or "essential" attributes. Typological thinking finds it easy to reconcile the observed variability of the individuals of a species with the dogma of the constancy of species because the variability does not affect the essence of the eidos, which is absolute and constant. Since the eidos is an abstraction derived from individual sense impressions, and a product of the human mind, according to this school, its members feel justified in regarding a species "a figment of the imagination," an idea. Variation, under this concept, is merely an imperfect manifestation of the idea implicit in each species. If the degree of variation is too great to be ascribed to the imperfections of our sense organs, more than one eidos must be involved. Thus species status is determined by degrees of morphological difference. The two aspects of the typological species concept, subjectivity and definition by degree of difference, therefore depend on each other and are logical correlates.

The application of the typological species concept to practical taxonomy results in the morphologically defined species, "degree of morphological difference" is the criterion of species status. Species are defined on the basis of their observable morphological differences. This concept has been carried to the extreme where mathematical formulas were proposed (Ginsburg, 1938) that would permit an unequivocal answer to the question whether or not a population is a different species.

Most systematists found this typological-morphological concept inadequate and have rejected it. Its defenders, however, claim that all taxonomists, when classifying the diversity of nature into species, follow the typological method and distinguish "archetypes." At first sight there seems an element of truth in this assertion. When assigning specimens either to one species or to another, the taxonomist bases his decision on a mental image of these species that is the result of past experience with the stated species. The utilization of morphological criteria is valuable and productive in the taxonomic practice. To assume, however, that this validates the typological species concept overlooks a number of important considerations. To begin with, the mental construct of the "type" is subject to continuous revision under the impact of new information. If it is found that two archetypes represent nothing more than two "kinds" within a biological species, they are merged into a single one. It was pointed out above that males and females are often exceedingly different "kinds" of animals. Even more different are in many animals the larval stages, or in plants sporophyte and gametophyte, or in polymorph populations the various genotypes. A strictly morphological-typological concept is inadequate to cope with such intraspecific variation. It is equally incapable of coping with another difficulty, namely an absence of visible morphological differences between natural populations which are nevertheless distinct and reproductively isolated, and therefore to be considered species. The frequent occurrence of such "cryptic species" or "sibling species" in nature has been substantiated by various genetic, physiological, or ecological methods. They form another decisive argument against defining species on a primarily morphological basis. Any attempt in these two situations to define species "by degree of difference" is doomed to failure. Degree of difference can be specified only by a purely arbitrary decision.

More profound than these two essentially practical considerations is the fact that the typological species concept treats species merely as random aggregates of individuals which have the "essential properties" of the "type" of the species and "agree with the diagnosis." This static concept ignores the fact that species are not merely classes of objects but are composed of natural populations which are integrated by an internal organization and that this organization (based on genetic, ethological, and ecological properties) gives the populations a structure which goes far beyond that of mere aggregates of individuals. Even a house is more than a mere aggregate of bricks or a forest an aggregate of trees. In a species an even greater supraindividualistic cohesion and organization is produced by a number of factors. Species are a reproductive community. The individuals of a species of higher animals recognize each other as potential mates and seek each other for the purpose of reproduction. A multitude of devices insures intraspecific reproduction in all organisms. The species is an ecological unit which, regardless of the individuals of which it is composed, interacts as a unit with other species in the same environment. The species, finally, is a genetic unit consisting of a large, intercommunicating gene pool whereas each individual is only a temporary vessel holding a small portion of this gene pool for a short period of time. These three properties make the species transcend a purely typological interpretation or the concept of a "class of objects."

The very fact that a species is a gene pool, with numerous devices facilitating genic intercommunication within and genic separation from without, is responsible for the morphological distinctness of species as a byproduct of their biological uniqueness. The empirical observation that a certain amount of morphological difference between two populations is normally correlated with a given amount of genetic difference is undoubtedly correct. Yet, it must be kept in mind at all times that the biological distinctness is primary and the morphological difference secondary. As long as this is clearly understood, it is legitimate and indeed very helpful to utilize morphological criteria. This caution has been exercised, consciously or unconsciously, by nearly all proponents of the morphological species concept. As pointed out by Simpson (1951) and Meglitsch (1954), they invariably abandon the morphological concept when it comes in conflict with biological data. This was true for Linnaeus himself and for his followers to the present day.

The typological species concept has a certain amount of operational usefulness when applied to inanimate objects. Ignoring the population structure of species, however, and incapable of coping with the facts of biological variation, it has proved singularly inadequate as a conceptual basis in taxonomy. Much of the criticism directed against the taxonomic method was provoked by the application of the typological concept by taxonomists themselves or by other biologists who mistakenly considered it the basis of taxonomy.

The Second Species Concept. This is sometimes called the nondimensional species concept and has no generally accepted designation. The essence of this concept is the relationship of two coexisting natural populations in a nondimensional system, that is, at a single locality at the same time (sympatric and synchronous). This is the species concept of the local naturalist. It was introduced into the biological literature by the English naturalist John Ray and confirmed by the Swedish naturalist Linnaeus. It is based not on difference but on distinction, and this distinction in turn is characterized by a definite mutual relationship, namely that of reproductive isolation. The word "species" is here best defined in combination with the word "different." The relationship of two "different species" can be objectively defined as reproductive isolation. We have, thus, an objective yardstick for this species concept, something that is absent in all others. Philosophers have objected to the use of the terms "objective" or "real" for species, and it may be more neutral to use the terms arbitrary or nonarbitrary (Simpson, 1951). Presence or absence of interbreeding of two populations in a nondimensional system is a completely nonarbitrary criterion. Since the nondimensional species concept is based on a relationship, the word species is here equivalent to words like, let us say, the word brother, which also has a meaning only with respect to a second phenomenon. An individual is a brother only with respect to someone else. Being a brother is not an inherent property as hardness is a property of a stone. Describing a presence or absence relationship makes this species concept nonarbitrary.

This species concept seems so self-evident to every naturalist that it is only rarely put in words. That the species is more than an aggregate of individuals, held together by a biological bond, has long been realized, as was pointed out in the historical survey above. The interbreeding within the species is more conspicuous, and it was thus more often emphasized than is the reproductive isolation against other species. Eimer, as early as 1889 (p. 16) defined species as "groups of individuals which are so modified that successful interbreeding [with other groups] is no longer possible." The first author, however, who stated the nondimensional species concept in its full extent and implication was Jordan (1905).

In spite of its theoretical superiority, the nondimensional species has a number of serious drawbacks (which will be discussed later), particularly its limitation to sexually reproducing species and to such without the dimensions of space and time.

Yet, as a basic, nonarbitrary yardstick, this is the species concept on which we have to fall back whenever we encounter a borderline situation.

The Third Species Concept. This is a concept of an entirely different kind, it is the concept of the polytypic or multidimensional species. In contradistinction to the other two concepts, of which one is based on a degree of difference, the second one on the completeness of a discontinuity, this concept is a collective one. It considers species as groups of populations, namely such groups as interbreed with each other, actually or potentially. Thus this species concept is a concept of the same sort as the higher categories, genus, family, or order. Like all collective categories it faces the difficulty, if not impossibility, of clear demarcation against other similar groupings. What this species gains in actuality by the extension of the nondimensional situations in space and time, it loses in objectivity. As unfortunate as this is, it is inevitable since the natural populations, encountered by the biologist, are distributed in space and time and cannot be divorced from these dimensions. Thus, this species concept likewise has its good and its bad points.

Species Definitions

All our reasoning in discussions of "the species" can be traced back to the stated three primary concepts. As concepts, of course, they cannot be observed directly, and we refer to certain observed phenomena in nature as "species," because they conform in their attributes to one of these concepts or to a mixture of several concepts. From these primary concepts, just discussed, we come thus to secondary concepts, based on particular aspects of species. We have already mentioned the so-called morphological species concept, which, in most cases, is merely an applied typological concept, using morphological criteria. The case of the so-called genetic species concept shows that all three of the basic concepts can be expressed, on this level, in genetic terms. Some geneticists, for instance, subscribed to the typological concept and defined species by the degree of genetic difference as did Lotsy or DeVries; others stressed the genetic basis of the isolating mechanisms between species thereby endorsing the nondimensional species concept; still others finally emphasized the gene flow among interbreeding populations in a multidimensional system, thus adopting the multidimensional collective species concept. All three groups of geneticists thought they were dealing with a uniquely "genetic species concept," yet they were merely observing secondary manifestations of the primary concepts.

It is evident from the analysis of the morphological and genetic species concepts, that such derived concepts are attempts to deal directly with the discontinuities in nature. In the past, almost every taxonomist worked with his own personal yardstick based on a highly individual mixture of elements from the three basic concepts. As a consequence one taxonomist might call species every polymorph variant, a second one every morphologically different population, and a third one every geographically isolated population. Such lack of standards, which is still largely characteristic for the taxonomic literature, has been utterly confusing to taxonomists and other biologists alike. It has therefore been the endeavor of many specialists within recent decades to find a standard yardstick, on which there could be general agreement. A historical study of species definitions indicates clearly a trend toward acceptance of a synthetic species definition, often referred to as "biological species" definition. It is essentially based on the nondimensional ("reproductive gap") and the multidimensional ("gene flow") species concepts. Nearly all species definitions proposed within the last fifty years incorporate some elements of these two concepts. This is evident from the species definitions of Jordan (Mayr, 1955), Stresemann (1919), and Rensch (1929). Du Rietz (1930) called the species "a syngameon . . . separated from all others by . . . sexual isolation." Dobzhansky (1935) was apparently the first geneticist to define species in the terms customary among naturalists and taxonomists, namely interbreeding and reproductive isolation; other recent definitions are variants of the same theme. Mayr (1940) defined species as "groups of actually or potentially interbreeding natural populations which are reproductively iso-

40

lated from other such groups." Simpson (1943) gave the definition "a genetic species is a group of organisms so constituted and so situated in nature that a hereditary character of any one of these organisms may be transmitted to a descendent of any other," and Dobzhansky (1950) defined the species as "the largest and most inclusive . . . reproductive community of sexual and cross-fertilizing individuals which share in a common gene pool."

It might be useful to mention some qualifications which are often included in species definitions but needlessly so. Anything that is equally true for categories above and below species rank should be omitted, since there is no sense burdening a species definition with features which do not help discrimination between species and infraspecific populations.

1. Species characters are adaptive. This component of Wallace's (1889) species definition was correctly rejected by Jordan (1896). Adaptiveness is not diagnostic for species characters and not even necessarily true. Not every detail of the phenotype needs to be adaptive as long as the phenotype as a whole is adaptive and as long as the genotype itself is the result of selection.

2. Species are evolved and evolving. Again this is true for the entire organic world from the individual to the highest categories and adds nothing to the species definition.

3. Species differ genetically. This is only the morphological species concept expressed in genetic terms. It does not permit discriminating species from infraspecific populations or from individuals.

4. Species differ ecologically. This qualification is unnecessary and misleading for the same reasons as the genetic one. Ecological differences exist for all ecotypes within species and in general for all geographical isolates. Conspecific populations are sometimes more different ecologically than are good species.

A yardstick, such as the biological species concept, is not automatic. To apply it properly requires skill and experience. This is particularly true in the recognition of situations where it cannot be applied, for one reason or another, and where the worker has to fall back on the criterion of "degree of difference." It will be one of the tasks of this symposium to investigate to what extent the diversity of animal and plant life permits application of the standard yardstick of the biological species concept. When can it not be applied and for what reasons? What types of difficulties are there? And finally, are there perhaps other basic concepts in addition to the stated ones? By approaching the species problem with new questions and new material, perhaps this symposium can make a contribution to its solution.

REFERENCES

Arkell, W. J. 1956. The species concept in paleontology. *Systematics Assoc. Publ. No. 2*, pp. 97-99.

Bachmann, H. 1905. Der Speziesbegriff. *Verhandl. schweiz. naturforsch. Ges.*, 87, 161-208.

Baer, K. E. von. 1828. *Entwickelungs-Geschichte der Thiere*. Königsberg.

Besnard, A. F. 1864. Altes und Neues zur Lehre über die organische Art (Spezies). *Abhandl. zool. mineral. Ver. Regensburg*, 9, 1-72.

Bessey, C. E. 1908. The taxonomic aspect of the species question. *Am. Naturalist*, 42, 218-24.

Brauer, F. 1885. Systematisch-zoologische Studien. *Sitzber. Akad. Wiss. Wien*, 91 (Abt. 1), 237-413.

Britton, N. L. 1908. The taxonomic aspect of the species question. *Am. Naturalist*, 42, 225-42.

Burma, B. H. 1949a. The species concept: A semantic review. *Evolution*, 3, 369-70.

Burma, B. H. 1949b. The species concept: Postscriptum. *Evolution*, 3, 372-73.

Burma, B. H. 1954. Reality, existence, and classification: A discussion of the species problem. *Madroño*, 7, 193-209.

Cain, A. J. 1953. Geography, ecology and coexistence in relation to the biological definition of the species. *Evolution*, 7, 76-83.

Camp, W. H., and C. L. Gillis. 1943. The structure and origin of species. *Brittonia*, 4, 323-85.

Darwin, C. 1859. *On the Origin of the Species by Means of Natural Selection*. London.

Dobzhansky, T. 1935. A critique of the species concept in biology. *Phil. Sci.*, **2**, 344-55.

Dobzhansky, T. 1950. Mendelian populations and their evolution. *Am. Naturalist*, **84**, 401-18.

Doederlein, L. 1902. Über die Beziehungen nahe verwandter "Thierformen" zu einander. Z. *Morphol. Anthropol.*, **26**, 23-51.

Dougherty, E. C. 1955. Comparative evolution and the origin of sexuality. *Systematic Zool.*, **4**, 145-69.

Du Rietz, G. E. 1930. The fundamental units of botanical taxonomy. *Svensk. Bot. Tidsskr.*, **24**, 333-428.

Eimer, G. H. T. 1889. *Artbildung und Verwandtschaft bei Schmetterlingen.* Jena, Vol. II, p. 16.

Geoffroy Saint Hilaire, I. 1859. Histoire naturelle génerale des règnes organiques, **2**, 437, Paris.

Ginsburg, I. 1938. Arithmetical definition of the species, subspecies and race concept, with a proposal for a modified nomenclature. *Zoologica*, **23**, 253-86.

Gloger, C. L. 1833. *Das Abändern der Vögel durch Einfluss des Klimas.* Breslau.

Gloger, C. L. 1856. Ueber den Begriff von "Art" ("Species") und was in dieselbe hinein gehört. *J. Ornithol.*, **4**, 260-70.

Godron, D. A. 1853. *De l'espèce et des races dan les êtres organisés et specialment de l'unité de l'espèce humaine.* Paris, 2 vols.

Greene, E. L. 1912. Linnaeus as an evolutionist. In *Carolus Linnaeus,* pp. 73-91. C. Sower & Co., Philadelphia, Pa.

Gregg, J. R. 1950. Taxonomy, language and reality. *Am. Naturalist,* **84**, 419-35.

Huxley, J. 1942. *Evolution, the Modern Synthesis.* Allen and Unwin, London.

Illiger, J. C. W. 1800. *Versuch einer systematischen vollständigen Terminologie für das Thierreich und Pflanzenreich.* Helmstedt.

Jordan, K. 1896. On mechanical selection and other problems. *Novit. Zool.*, **3**, 426-525.

Jordan, K. 1905. Der Gegensatz zwischen geographischer und nichtgeographischer Variation. Z. *wiss. Zool.*, **83**, 151-210.

Kuhn, E. 1948. Der Artbegriff in der Paläontologie. *Eclogae Geolog. Helv.*, **41**, 389-421.

Lorkovicz, Z. 1953. Spezifische, semispezifische und rassische Differenzierung bei *Erebia tyndarus* Esp. *Rad. Acad. Yougoslave*, **294**, 315-58.

Mayr, E. 1940. Speciation phenomena in birds. *Am. Naturalist,* **74,** 249-78.

Mayr, E. 1942. *Systematics and the Origin of Species.* Columbia University Press, New York, N.Y.

Mayr, E. 1949. The species concept: Semantics versus semantics. *Evolution,* **3,** 371-72.

Mayr, E. 1951. Concepts of classification and nomenclature in higher organisms and microorganisms. *Ann. N.Y. Acad. Sci.,* **56,** 391-97.

Mayr, E. 1955. Karl Jordan's contribution to current concepts in systematics and evolution. *Trans. Roy. Entomol. Soc. London,* pp. 45-66.

Mayr, E. 1956. Geographical character gradients and climatic adaptation. *Evolution,* **10,** 105-8.

Mayr, E., and C. Rosen. 1956. Geographic variation and hybridization in populations of Bahama snails (*Cerion*). *Am. Museum Novit.,* **1806,** 1-48.

Mayr, E., E. G. Linsley, and R. L. Usinger. 1953. *Methods and Principles of Systematic Zoology.* McGraw-Hill Book Co., New York, N.Y.

Meglitsch, P. A. 1954. On the nature of the species. *Systematic Zool.,* **3,** 49-65.

Niggli, P. 1949. *Probleme der Naturwissenschaften* (Der Begriff der Art in der Mineralogie). Basel.

Plate, L. 1914. Prinzipien der Systematik mit besonderer Berücksichtigung des Systems der Tiere. In *Die Kultur der Gegenwart,* III (iv, 4), pp. 92-164.

Poulton, E. B. 1903. What is a species? *Proc. Entomol. Soc. London* for 1903, pp. lxxvii-cxvi.

Quatrefages, A. de. 1892. Darwin et les précurseurs français. Paris.

Ramsbottom, J. 1938. Linnaeus and the species concept. *Proc. Linnean Soc. London.* (150 session), pp. 192-219.

Ray, J. 1686. *Historia Plantarum,* p. 40.

Rensch, B. 1929. *Das Prinzip geographischer Rassenkreise und das Problem der Artbildung.* Bornträger Verl., Berlin.

Schopenhauer, A. 1851. *Parerga und Paralipomena: kleine philosophische Schriften.* Vol. 2, pp. 121-22. Berlin.

Simpson, G. G. 1943. Criteria for genera, species, and subspecies in zoology and paleozoology. *Ann. N.Y. Acad. Sci.,* **44,** 145-78.

Simpson, G. G. 1951. The species concept. *Evolution,* **5,** 285-98.

Sirks, M. J. 1952. Variability in the concept of species. *Acta Biotheoretica,* **10,** 11-22.

Spring, A. F. 1838. *Ueber die naturhistorischen Begriffe von Gattung, Art und Abart und über die Ursachen der Abartungen in den organischen Reichen.* Leipzig.

Spurway, H. 1955. The sub-human capacities for species recognition and their correlation with reproductive isolation. *Acta XI Congr. Intern. Orn.,* Basel, 1954, pp. 340-49.

Stresemann, E. 1919. Über die europäischen Baumläufer. *Verhandl. Orn. Ges. Bayern,* **14,** 39-74.

Sylvester-Bradley, P. C. 1956. The species concept in paleontology. Introduction. *Systematics Assoc. Publ. No. 2.*

Thomas, G. 1956. The species concept in paleontology. *Systematics Assoc. Publ. No. 2,* pp. 17-31.

Uhlmann, E. 1923. Entwicklungsgedanke und Artbegriff in ihrer geschichtlichen Entstehung und sachlichen Beziehung. *Jena. Z. Naturw.,* **59,** 1-114.

Valentine, D. H. 1949. The units of experimental taxonomy. *Acta Biotheoretica,* **9,** 75-88.

Voigt, F. S. 1817. *Grundzüge einer Naturgeschichte als Geschichte der Entstehung und weiterer Ausbildung der Naturkörper.* Frankfurt a.M.

Wallace, A. R. 1889. *Darwinism: An Exposition of the Theory of Natural Selection, with Some of Its Applications.* London.

Yapp, W. B. 1951. Definitions in biology. *Nature,* **167,** 160.

4A

Reprinted from *Br. J. Philos. Sci.,* **15**(60), 314–326 (1965)

THE EFFECT OF ESSENTIALISM ON TAXONOMY— TWO THOUSAND YEARS OF STASIS (I) *

David L. Hull

I *Introduction and Purpose*

A CONVENIENT year to designate as the beginning of the scientific revolution is 1543. In that year Nicholas Copernicus published *De Revolutionibus Orbium Coelestium* and Andreas Vesalius published *De Humani Corporis Fabrica.* In a little more than a hundred years classical physics reached its fruition in Newton's *Principia.* At first biology promised a similar development with the work of Leewenhoek, Schwammerdam, and Malpighi, but no theoretical achievements even vaguely comparable to those in physics were forthcoming. It wasn't until the nineteenth century with the work of Darwin and Lamarck on evolution, of Mendel on genetics, of Pasteur on micro-organisms, and of Schleiden and others on cell theory that biology came of age. In taxonomy the scientific revolution has been even slower in making itself felt. Although John Ray and Carolus Linnaeus made some advances in the methodology of taxonomy and in organising their taxa, they made no significant contributions to taxonomic theory as devised by Aristotle. As biology lagged behind physics in divesting itself of scholastic influence, taxonomy lagged far behind the other biological sciences. In fact, contrary to popular opinion, the process is still far from complete. And taxonomy only now is reaching a stage of maturity comparable to that of physics 300 years ago or to that of other biological sciences of fifty or a hundred years ago. Why is this?

Karl R. Popper's answer is that ' the development of thought since Aristotle could, I think, be summed up by saying that every discipline as long as it used the Aristotelian method of definition has remained arrested in a state of empty verbiage and barren scholasticism, and that the degree to which the various sciences have been able to make any progress depended on the degree to which they have been able to get

★ Received Feb. 1964

rid of this essentialist method '.[1]   In no other science is this statement as true as it is in taxonomy, for in no other science is definition as important as it is in taxonomy.   Correspondingly, in no other science has there been as much empty verbiage about the meaning of a word as there has been in taxonomy about the meaning of ' species '.   But Darwin supposedly put a stop to all that.   He himself said in commenting on such endless disputes, ' When the views advanced by me in this volume . . . are generally admitted, we can dimly foresee that there will be a considerable revolution in natural history.   Systematists will be able to pursue their labours as at present; but they will not be incessantly haunted by the shadowy doubt whether this or that form be a true species.   This, I feel sure and I speak after experience, will be of no slight relief '.[2]

Darwin's views on the evolution of species *have* been generally admitted; there *has* been a considerable revolution in natural history (phylogenetic taxonomy), but a spectre of essentialism continues to haunt the taxonomist.   Ernst Mayr says, for example, ' It is a curious paradox that so many taxonomists still adhere to a strictly static species concept, even though they admit freely the existence of evolution '.[3] And again, ' It is a curious paradox in the history of biology that the rediscovery of Mendelian laws resulted in an even more unrealistic species concept among the experimentalists than had existed previously '.[4] With the discovery of biology's two most important theories, one would think that something as basic as the unit of classification would have come into clearer perspective instead of becoming more blurred. In the first instance taxonomists admit that species evolve but find it impossible to define species names accordingly.[5]   In the second they admit that there is a genetic continuity among the members of a species

---

[1] Karl R. Popper, *The Open Society and Its Enemies*, Princeton, 1950, p. 206

[2] Charles Darwin, *The Origin of Species*, New York, 1859, p. 447

[3] Ernst Mayr, *Systematics and the Origin of Species*, New York, 1942, p. 103

[4] Ernst Mayr, ' Species concepts and definition', *The Species Problem*, Washington, 1957, p. 5

[5] Throughout this paper ' species names ' and ' taxa names ' will be used. These phrases are not presently used in taxonomy, but some terminological device must be made to mark the logically crucial distinction between defining the names of categories such as species, genus, and phylum and defining the names of taxa classed at these category levels such as *Bos bos*, Homo and Protozoa. A second distinction is also important—the distinction between defining a word and defining (or delineating) a group. The name of a particular taxon is defined in terms of certain properties. The membership of that taxon is thus delineated.

but deny species any reality.   Both have combined to contribute to the continuation of the species problem.

As A. J. Cain has pointed out,[1] the solution to Mayr's paradoxes can be found in a remnant of essentialism which has not been fully eliminated from taxonomy.   It is responsible for taxonomists retaining what is loosely called a static species concept, which in turn is responsible for species being divested of reality.   Of course, there are other reasons for taxonomists wanting to retain the trappings of Aristotelian definition, most probably the same reasons which led Aristotle to devise his system in the first place.   Presented with the welter of diverse forms to be classified, a taxonomist can greatly simplify his task if he pretends that certain properties are ' essential ' for definition.   But he would have to do just that—pretend—since the names of taxa cannot be defined in terms of essential characters without falsification on a scale which should have been evident even to the most uncritical investigator with only a limited knowledge of the organisms being classified.

The conflict between reality and theory was largely ignored by early taxonomists both because they did not understand the logic of Aristotelian definition very clearly and because even scientists have a way of not noticing what conflicts with their philosophical presuppositions. At any rate, the thesis of this paper is not that Aristotelian definition was responsible for taxonomists being unable to define taxa names appropriately (although this is certainly true).   The thesis of this

[1] A. J. Cain, ' Logic and memory in Linnaeus's system of taxonomy ', *Proceedings of the Linnaean Society London*, 1958, **169**, 149. In this article Cain makes the point that Aristotelian definition of species names had given rise to difficulties in the species concept. He does not go on to extend his analysis to ' species ' itself which is the purpose of this paper.

Also in this article Cain criticises the use of ' diagnostic ' properties by present day phylogeneticists, which he identifies with the practice of weighting some properties more heavily than others because of their varying phylogenetic significance. Thus, it is charged that the variable weighting of properties according to their phylogenetic significance is a development from Aristotelian logic. Cain, op. cit., pp. 150, 161-162. R. R. Sokal and P. H. A. Sneath reiterate the charge in their recent book. R. R. Sokal and P. H. A. Sneath, *Principles of Numerical Taxonomy*, San Francisco, 1963, pp. 8, 16, 34. Unfortunately for this thesis the variable weighting of different characters according to their presumed phylogenetic importance is in direct opposition to the Aristotelian theory of essences. According to Aristotle either a character is essential or it is not. One character cannot be more essential than another. If the variable weighting of properties as now practised by the phylogeneticists is a development from Aristotle, it is an illogical development. Perhaps this is what Cain intended.   This is not what Sokal and Sneath interpreted him to mean.

paper is that Aristotelian definition is responsible for taxonomists being unable to define ' species ' adequately. The actual distribution of properties among organisms has finally forced taxonomists to abandon Aristotelian definitions of taxa names. There is no comparable conflict to force taxonomists to abandon their attempts to define ' species ' in the Aristotelian manner. Nevertheless, it will be argued that Aristotelian definition is just as inappropriate for ' species ' as it is for the names of taxa.[1]

2 *Essentialism*

Karl Popper characterises essentialism as follows:

> I use the name *methodological essentialism* to characterize the view, held by Plato and many of his followers, that it is the task of pure knowledge or ' science ' to discover and to describe the true nature of things; i.e. their hidden reality or essence. It was Plato's peculiar belief that the essence of sensible things can be found in other and more real things— in their primogenitors or Forms. Many of the later methodological essentialists, for instance Aristotle, did not altogether follow him in determining this; but they all agreed with him in determining the task of pure knowledge as the discovery of the hidden nature or Form or essence of things. All these methodological essentialists also agreed with Plato in holding that these essences may be discovered and discerned with the help of intellectual intuition; that every essence has a name proper to it, the name after which the sensible things are called; and that it may be described in words. And a description of the essence of a thing they called a ' definition '.[2]

In taxonomy this philosophical position became known as typology. The three essentialistic tenets of typology are (1) the ontological assertion that Forms exist, (2) the methodological assertion that the task of taxonomy as a science is to discern the essences of species, and (3) the logical assertion concerning definition. These three separate tenets must be distinguished if we are to avoid making such statements as those that have been made accusing Darwin and Lamarck of being ' typologists '. They were typologists only in the sense that they retained part of the third element of essentialism—the logic of Aristotelian definition. ' According to essentialism (especially Aristotle's version of it) a definition is a restatement of the inherent essence or

---

[1] It is not being claimed here that the typical practising taxonomist is consciously aware of the logic of Aristotelian definition and has opted for it rather than for some other type of definition.

[2] Popper, 1950, p. 34

nature of a thing. At the same time, it states the meaning of a word—of the name that designates the essence'.[1] In Aristotle's view three things can be known about any entity—its essence, its definition, and its name. The name names the essence. The definition gives a complete and exhaustive description of the essence. Derivatively, the name is the name of the entity and the definition a description of it. 'Aristotle considers the term to be defined as a name of the essence of the thing, and the defining formula as the description of the essence. And he insists that the defining formula must give an exhaustive description of the essence or the essential properties of the thing in question'.[2]

Disregarding all the talk about essences, what Aristotle was advocating in modern terms is definition by properties connected conjunctively which are severally necessary and jointly sufficient.[3] For example, being a three-sided plane closed figure is necessary and sufficient for being a triangle. Such a mode of definition is eminently suited for defining eternal Forms. It is not very well suited for defining the names of evolving species or for 'species' itself, and yet it is exactly this mode of definition which has been assumed to be the only mode of definition permissible until recently. Evolutionary theory necessarily challenged the ontological assertion that species as Forms existed. Quite obviously it also challenged the methodological assertion. If there were no Forms, then the task of taxonomy could not be to discern them. But evolutionary theory had a third consequence for taxonomy, and it was *this* consequence which Darwin and his followers *did not see*. Aristotelian definition had to be abandoned both for species names and for 'species'. Typologists could ignore the actual untidy distribution of properties among living organisms and the variety of methods of reproduction used to perpetuate species. Evolutionists could not.

3 *Aristotelian Definition and Evolution*

From the beginning taxonomists have sought two things—a definition of 'species' which would result in real species and a unifying principle which would result in a natural classification. The fervour

---

[1] Karl R. Popper, *Conjectures and Refutations*, New York, 1962, 19

[2] Popper, 1950, p. 208

[3] The important distinction for this paper, however, is not between definite conjunctive and definite disjunctive definitions but between definite definitions of either kind and indefinitely long disjunctive definitions.

with which taxonomists searched for such a unifying principle is evident in the following quotation by Linnaeus. ' For a long time I have laboured to find it; I have discovered many things, but I have not been able to find it. I shall continue to search for it as long as I live '.[1] In evolutionary theory taxonomists at last had their unifying principle. A natural classification would be a classification which in some sense ' represented ' phylogeny.[2] From its very inception the enthusiasm with which some taxonomists welcomed the phylogenetic programme was equalled only by the vehemence with which others rejected it. It is obvious why typologists opposed phylogenetic taxonomy, but phylogenetic taxonomy also met with resistance from taxonomists who accepted evolutionary theory but who denied it any relevance to taxonomy. This latter group has come to be known as the classificationists. Their modern counterparts are the numerical or neo-Adansonian taxonomists. The explanation for the early classificationist stand can be found again in the third element of essentialism.[3] Although all early phylogeneticists and most classificationists abandoned the first two assertions of essentialism, neither abandoned Aristotelian definition.

Because of evolution taxonomists felt confronted by a dilemma. If they accepted evolutionary theory as the unifying principle of a natural classification, they had to abandon any hope of ever having real species. If they wished to retain real species, they had to give up any hope of ever having a natural classification. The rationale behind this dilemma can be seen in the following quotations from Lamarck, Lyell, and Darwin. Lamarck said, for example, ' The part of the work of naturalists which concerns the determination of what one calls " species " becomes day by day more defective, that is to say, more entangled and more confused, because it is executed in the almost universally admitted supposition that the productions of nature constitute species constantly distinguished by invariable characters, and whose existence is as ancient as that of nature itself '.[4] Lamarck's conclusion was then that since species couldn't be defined by an invarying list of

---

[1] Tindell Hopwood, ' Animal classification from the Greeks to Linnaeus ', *Lectures on the Development of Taxonomy*, London, 1950, p. 26

[2] David L. Hull, ' Consistency and Monophyly ', *Systematic Zoology*, 1960, **13**, 1-11

[3] Adanson was unique in several respects, two of which are that he abandoned all the tenets of essentialism before evolutionary theory and that evolution had no relevance for taxonomy but for the very simple reason that it hadn't been discovered yet.

[4] J.-B. Lamarck, *Discours D'Ouverture*, Paris, 1097, p. 110

characters, they couldn't be real. Lyell replied, 'If species are not real, the obvious consequences are alarming: unlimited change becomes not only possible but even necessary. Species will no longer have well-defined limits, classification becomes a purely arbitrary exercise, and any species may easily be transformed into another'.[1] Even Darwin said that once his or an analogous view was accepted, 'systematists will have only to decide (not that this will be easy) whether any form be sufficiently constant and distinct from other forms to be capable of definition; and if definable, whether the difference be sufficiently important to deserve a specific name. . . . In short, we shall have to treat species in the same manner as those naturalists treat genera, who admit that genera are merely artificial combinations made for convenience. This may not be a cheering prospect; but we shall at least be free from the vain search for the undiscovered and undiscoverable essence of the term species'.[2]

When the logic of the preceding argument is set out in full, it goes something like this. The only basis for a natural classification is evolutionary theory, but according to evolutionary theory, species developed gradually, changing one into another. If species evolved so gradually, they cannot be delimited by means of a single property or set of properties. If species can't be so delineated, then species names can't be defined in the classic manner. If species names can't be defined in the classic manner, then they can't be defined at all. If they can't be defined at all, then species can't be real. If species aren't real, then 'species' has no reference and classification is completely arbitrary.

Elements of this same argument can be found in the writings of modern taxonomists. For example, A. J. Cain says the following things: 'But when good series are available, forms that seem to be good species at any one time may become indefinable since they are successive stages in a single evolutionary line and intrograde smoothly with each other[3] . . . with the passage of time, they change continuously and are gradually transformed into two modern species, without any sudden discontinuity which could be used as a specific boundary. . . . [4] The limits of both subspecies and species within a genus are equally arbitrary, since there is no reason to make a break in a continuous

[1] William Coleman, 'Lyell and the "reality" of species', *Isis*, 1962, **53**, 326
[2] Darwin, 1859, p. 447
[3] A. J. Cain, *Animal Species and Their Evolution*, London, 1954, p. 107
[4] Cain, 1954, p. 111

series at any one point rather than at another '.[1]   Cain concludes that the problem is insoluble.[2]   Ernst Mayr concurs, saying, ' Even though the number of cases that cause real difficulties is very small, the fact remains that an objective delimitation of species in a multidimensional system is an impossibility '.[3]   And G. G. Simpson says, ' Certainly the lineage must be chopped into segments for the purposes of classification, and this must be done arbitrarily . . . , because there is no non-arbitrary way to subdivide a continuous line. . . . '[4]

Even though ' species ' has all the faults mentioned, A. J. Cain says that species as single phyletic lines are ' less artificial, subjective or arbitrary than any other rank '.[5]   Mayr says, ' The species is an important unit in evolution, in ecology, in the behavioral sciences, and in applied biology.[6]   . . . it has a very distinct biological significance. . . . '[7] And Simpson says, ' The point will be discussed later, but even here it is advisable just to mention that such arbitrary subdivision does not necessarily produce taxa that are either " unreal " or " unnatural ", as has sometimes been stated.   A simple but, at this point, sufficiently explanatory analogy is provided by a piece of string that shades continuously from, say, blue at one end to green at the other.   Cutting the string into two is an arbitrary act, but the resulting pieces are perfectly real sections of the string that existed as natural parts of the whole before they were severed '.[8]

Quite obviously taxonomists still believe there is a species problem and at the heart of it is the biologically uninteresting but the logically crucial notion of *definition*.

4 Taxa Names as Cluster Concepts

Mayr says that although there has been steady clarification of the issue, ' there is still much uncertainty and widespread divergence of opinion on many aspects of the species problem. It is rather surprising that not more agreement has been reached during the past two hundred years in which these questions have been tossed back and forth.   This certainly cannot be due to lack of trying, for an immense amount of time and thought has been devoted to the subject during this period.

---

[1] Cain, 1954, p. 113   [2] Cain, 1954, p. 114
[3] Ernst Mayr, ' Difficulties and importance of the biological species ', *The Species Problem*, Washington, 1957, p. 376
[4] G. G. Simpson, *Principles of Animal Taxonomy*, New York, 1961, p. 165
[5] Cain, 1954, p. 183   [6] Mayr, 1957, p. 385
[7] Mayr, 1957, p. 384   [8] Simpson, 1961, pp. 60–61

One has the feeling that there is a hidden reason for so much disagree-ment '.[1] One of the reasons why more agreement has not been reached is that the classificationists and phylogeneticists disagree over the purposes of taxonomy. One wants the unit of classification to be the unit of identification. The other wants it to be the unit of evolu-tion. But there is also a hidden reason for so much disagreement—the philosophical predisposition on the part of taxonomists of both schools for Aristotelian definition. An important clue that Aristotelian definition is at fault is the conclusion reached by Mayr and almost all other taxonomists who have attended to the species problem that ' perhaps the disagreement is due to the fact that there is more than one kind of species and that we need a different definition for each of these species '.[2]

The influence of Aristotelian definition on taxonomic thought can best be revealed by investigating the definition of a type of term for which taxonomists have already abandoned Aristotelian definition— the definition of taxa names. It is commonplace now to recognise what Adanson realised almost two hundred years ago that taxa names cannot be defined by sets of properties the members of which are severally necessary and jointly sufficient, for seldom is a property of any taxonomic value distributed both universally and exclusively among the members of a taxon. The properties which are used to define the names of taxa do not respect taxonomic boundaries. For example, depending on whether the hemichordates are included in the phylum Chordata or whether they are made a separate phylum, none of the properties used to define ' Chordata ' are both necessary and sufficient. If the hemichordates are included in Chordata, then a few of the properties are possessed exclusively by the chordates; e.g. noto-chord, dorsal hollow nerve cord, metameric musculature, internal skeleton of cartilage or bone, and a closed circulatory system. But then none of the properties are possessed universally. Possession of internal gill slits comes the closest to being universally distributed; however, some hemichordates do not have anything that faintly resembles gill slits. If on the other hand the hemichordates are not included in Chordata, then several defining properties become uni-versally possessed by the chordates; e.g. notochord, dorsal hollow nerve cord, and gill slits. But then several of the properties which were exclusively chordate cease to be possessed exclusively by them; e.g. dorsal hollow nerve cord. The only property that is both uni-versally and exclusively possessed by the chordates is the notochord,

[1] Mayr, 1957, p. 10   [2] Mayr, 1957, p. 10

although some vertebrates and urochordates possess one only in the embryo or larva. Even if only contemporary forms are taken into consideration, Aristotelian definition simply won't do.

Traditionally a word is considered to be explicitly defined if and only if a set of properties can be given such that each property is severally necessary and the entire set of necessary properties is jointly sufficient. For example, a bachelor is a male adult human being who has never married and a sibling is one of at least two children of the same parents. If 'A' is the word to be defined and a, b, c, and d are properties, then the logical structure of such a definition is 'A ^{DF} a.b.c.d' Words can also be defined disjunctively without violating the spirit of Aristotelian definition. For example, a sibling is a brother or a sister and an uncle is the brother of one's father or the brother of one's mother or the husband of one of one's aunts. The logical structure of such a definition is 'A ^{DF} a∨b∨c∨d.' In such a disjunctive definition each property is severally sufficient and the possession of at least one of the properties is necessary.[1]

However, neither of these types of definition is appropriate for defining the names of taxa and, hence, for delineating taxa. Whether from the viewpoint of phylogenetic or numerical taxonomy, taxa names can be defined only *by sets of statistically covarying properties arranged in indefinitely long disjunctive definitions.* The logical structure of such a definition is 'A ^{DF} a.b.c.d∨b.c.d.e∨a.c.d.f and so on'. Usually no one particular property or set of properties is necessary and any one of numerous sets is sufficient. An example from ordinary discourse of a word which can be defined only in such a manner is 'lemon'. A description of a lemon would contain such properties as coming from a particular type of tree, having a sour taste, an ovoid shape and so on. None of these properties is necessary since a fruit could lack any one of them and still be a lemon. Several different but overlapping sets of properties are accordingly each sufficient.[2]

In defining taxa names as cluster concepts, taxonomists have (whether they realise it or not) adopted a new and rather controversial philosophical position. They have abandoned the simple dichotomy

---

[1] Each disjunct may also be a conjunction of two or more properties without altering the logic of a definite disjunctive definition as long as each conjunction has a certain set of members.

[2] Michael J. Scriven, 'The Logic of Criteria', *The Journal of Philosophy*, 1959, **56**, p. 860

between analytic and synthetic connections in definition. The traditional view is that either a defining property is analytically connected to the word it defines or it is not. There is no middle ground. According to one version of the new position, ' Any property that is connected with another in such a way that it does not make sense to deny its application will be said to be analytically connected with it, as, e.g. brotherhood is connected with siblinghood. A property that does not meet this requirement, but which would have to occur in a thorough explanation of the meaning of the term nonetheless, will be said to be normically connected with it. Other connections will be called synthetic '.[1] With rare exception the properties that occur in the definitions of the names of taxa are normically connected. They are not analytically connected because an individual or a population could lack any one or few of the properties and still be a member of the taxon. Yet they are not merely synthetic because they are the *only* properties used in the definitions.

In terming certain properties 'normic', laws are implied. In phylogenetic taxonomy these laws are those of evolutionary and gene theories. Which properties are normic and how important each is for definition is determined by these theories. Advocates of traditional Aristotelian definition and the simple, clear-cut analytic-synthetic distinction on which it is based usually counter attempts to define words as cluster concepts by one of two moves. They claim that such words are ' used in a fuzzy way by the casual users, but that (*a*) usually these users can be persuaded on reflection to accept certain necessary and sufficient conditions as analytic and to reject other connections as synthetic, or (*b*) the fuzzy concept should be replaced by a more precise one, which can be defined in a traditional way '.[2]

Neither of these alternatives is viable in the case of taxa names. Taxonomists certainly do not use the names of taxa casually and could not accept certain necessary and sufficient conditions as analytic even if they wanted to, as the chordate example showed. Nor can they replace the taxa names they now have with more precise ones and still fulfil the purposes of phylogenetic taxonomy. For example, all and only the vertebrates, the cephalochordates and the urochordates possess a notochord at some time in their ontological development. No other property covaries with this property. Even so a taxon ' Notochordata ' could be formed by making the possession of a notochord both necessary and sufficient. On the other hand, the vertebrates, cephalo-

[1] Scriven, 1959, p. 861   [2] Scriven, 1959, p. 859

chordates, urochordates, enteropneusts and some pterobranchs (both of the hemichordates), and an extinct echinoderm possess gill slits at some time in their ontological development. No other property covaries with it. If the possession of gill slits was made both necessary and sufficient, a taxon 'Branchiata' could be defined traditionally. But the preceding definitions are *just* the type of definition of taxa names which modern taxonomists have striven to avoid.[1] Whether a classification is to be merely useful (the position of numerical taxonomy) or both useful and phylogenetically significant (the phylogenetic position), taxa names can be defined only by sets of statistically covarying properties.

All the examples of cluster concepts given thus far have a second peculiarity. After several members of the disjunction have been given, the definition is terminated with a phrase like 'and so on'. In the case of most taxa names, the reason for not listing all of the disjuncts is not that the list is too long or too well known to bother writing down but that it *cannot be completed*. The property of cluster concepts which bothers traditionalists most is that often the entire disjunction cannot be·stated. It is indefinitely long. Instead of being detrimental for the purposes of phylogenetic taxonomy, such indefiniteness is essential.

Morton Beckner says of defining the name of a taxon K that if we had an enumeration of the defining properties and if the number of properties sufficient for membership were determined once and for all, then ' we have provided ourselves with the means of defining K as a monotypic class. We can form all the distinct classes that are the Boolean product of k members of G (the set of defining properties), and then say that X is a member of K if and only if it is a member of the class which is the Boolean sum of these Boolean products. In short, K would be the disjunction of all conjunctions of k members of G. This function lays down a single condition which is both necessary and sufficient for membership in K'.[2] But in the case of phylogenetic taxonomy seldom can either of the two conditions which prefaced the quotation be realised until K and its neighbouring taxa [3] have ceased

[1] Cain, 1954, p. 18

[2] Morton Beckner, *The Biological Way of Thought*, New York, 1959, p. 24. Ludwig Wittgenstein was an early proponent of cluster concepts or 'family resemblances,' as he termed them. He also foresaw the possibility of Beckner's move and commented on it appropriately. Ludwig Wittgenstein, *Philosophical Investigation*, New York, 1945 sect. 67.

[3] The species are 'neighbouring' in the sense of being near each other in taxonomic space.

to evolve, for not until all the species which must be distinguished from each other have ceased to evolve can it be decided which and how many properties are sufficient to distinguish them *once and for all.* For example, very few properties are needed to distinguish modern man from any other known species. However, if a species of ape were to begin to develop along the same lines as man, acquiring comparable properties, the definition of *Homo sapiens* would have to be expanded to exclude this new form if *Homo sapiens* is to be kept minimally monophyletic. Even if a taxonomist wanted to, he could not supply these distinguishing properties in advance. Besides, until such an unlikely event occurs, there is no reason to complicate the definition. Taxonomists cannot be prepared in advance for all contingencies. All that they need do is to accommodate the contingencies that do arise as they arise.

In the case of entirely extinct species, it is at least in principle possible to define the names of these species once and for all *if* a complete fossil record is present for the species concerned and its neighbouring taxa. If the fossil record is not complete, the definition of the name of an extinct species must be changed as fossils of similar species are discovered. Thus, the definitions of taxa names as cluster concepts are peculiar in a second respect. Unlike traditional definitions, they cannot be forever insulated against empirical findings. As more evidence is accumulated, they will have to be altered to accommodate this evidence.

(*To be concluded*)

Reprinted from *Br. J. Philos. Sci.,* **16**(61), 1–18 (1965)

THE EFFECT OF ESSENTIALISM ON TAXONOMY— TWO THOUSAND YEARS OF STASIS (II) *

David L. Hull

5 *The Species Problem*

THUS far all that has been shown is that with respect to taxa names taxonomists have rejected Aristotelian definition. It has yet to be shown that they have failed to eliminate completely their predisposition for Aristotelian definition and that this failure has been at least in part responsible for the persistence of the species problem. Species will be treated in this paper only from the point of view of phylogenetic taxonomy; that is, from the point of view that classification must have some systematic relationship to phylogeny and that the unit of classification must be the unit of evolution. In order for such a position on the status of ' species ' to be justified, not only must an adequate definition of ' species ' as an evolutionary unit be given but also the phylogenetic programme itself must be shown to be feasible and significant. Only the former will be attempted in this paper.

G. G. Simpson defines an evolutionary species as ' a lineage (an ancestral-descendant sequence of populations) evolving separately from others and with its own unitary evolutionary role and tendencies'.[1] Unfortunately, Simpson's definition itself does not provide any explicitly formulated criteria for determining exactly how unitary an evolutionary role is unitary enough for species status. He defines roles in terms of niches and niches in terms of whole ways of life. Simpson's definition is important because it brings to the fore one of

[1] Simpson, 1961, p. 153

* Part I appeared in the previous number.

the basic principles of phylogenetic taxonomy (that the unit of classification must be the unit of evolution), but it does not contribute much toward determining what level of evolutionary unity is to be considered specific. In short it is not 'operational'. The purpose of the following sections will be to provide criteria to implement Simpson's definition.

Dobzhansky provided one such criterion in his biological definition. When a group of organisms which usually reproduce by interbreeding interbreeds consistently and produces reasonably fertile offspring, this group of organisms is as distinct an evolutionary unit as there is in phylogeny. The members of the group are *genetically* affecting each other's phylogenetic development. But the biological definition is not without its faults. Cain summarises the major difficulties confronting the criterion of actual interbreeding as follows: ' The bio-species is a definable concept only if time and allopatric populations are ignored and asexual forms are excluded from consideration '.[1] These are not the *only* difficulties confronting a successful definition of ' species ', but they are certainly three of the major ones. If they can be surmounted, the others will be relatively easy to account for.

Before each of these major difficulties is treated, reference must be made to Dobzhansky's second criterion for species status. Dobzhansky was well aware that actual interbreeding applied to only a small percentage of organisms. (Our ability to observe such actual interbreeding directly applies to an even smaller percentage.) To accommodate all other cases (that is, to accommodate a majority of the cases) he introduced the criterion of potential interbreeding. In doing so he adopted a non-traditional form of definition, a disjunctive definition. He did not, however, depart very radically from traditional definition, since the two disjuncts were considered to be the only pertinent conditions. Each was sufficient, the fulfilment of at least one necessary. Dobzhansky's definition has much to recommend it. One of the criteria is at least the basis for a sufficient condition for delineating species as units of evolution. The form of the definition, although not completely adequate, is more appropriate than the form of all previous definitions. Unfortunately, Dobzhansky chose potential interbreeding as his second criterion.

If it had not other faults, the criterion of potential interbreeding would be undesirable on the grounds of vagueness alone. It is intended to cover too many too varied exceptions to the first criterion.

[1] Cain, 1954, p. 24

In one sense a population of mice on one island is potentially inter-breeding with a population of mice on another island. They would interbreed if they could get at each other. In a second sense a population of Drosophila living in 1942 is potentially interbreeding with a population of that species living in 1922 or 1962. If they had lived at the same time in the same area, they would have interbred. In still another sense, two interfertile sibling species which are both sympatric and synchronic are potentially interbreeding. They could interbreed if they were so inclined. In another sense all the breeds of domestic dogs are potentially interbreeding. They would (and do) interbreed whenever their masters permit. The list could be extended indefinitely.

There is, however, a more fundamental philosophical reason for abandoning potential interbreeding as a criterion for species status. Bertrand Russell says, for example:

> The concept of potentiality is convenient in some connections, provided it is so used that we can translate our statements into a form in which the concept is absent. 'A block of marble is a potential statue' means 'from a block of marble, by suitable acts, a statue is produced'. But when potentiality is used as a fundamental and irreducible concept it always conceals confusion of thought. Aristotle's use of it is one of the bad points in his system.[1]

Whether or not such a blanket indictment of the concept of potentiality is completely justified, there are reasons peculiar to evolutionary taxonomy for avoiding it. What is important in evolution is not which organisms could interbreed but which organisms do interbreed. The fact that two groups of organisms *cannot* interbreed (regardless of the isolating mechanism) is important only in the respect that it follows deductively that they *are not* interbreeding. On the other hand the fact that two groups of organisms can or could interbreed even though they are not so interbreeding (regardless of how this is to be ascertained) is important in only two respects. First, it means that the two groups of organisms have not diverged appreciably from each other in interbreeding habits since they had a common ancestry which was actually interbreeding. Second, it means that if in the future the isolating mechanisms are removed, then the two groups would interbreed. But taxonomists are not obliged to predict the future course of evolution. Taxonomists are obliged to classify only those species that have evolved given the environment that did pertain, not to classify all possible species that might have evolved in some possible

[1] Bertrand Russell, *A History of Western Philosophy*, New York, 1945, p. 167

environment. Until potentially interbreeding organisms actually use this potentiality, it is of only ' potential ' interest in classification. In evolutionary taxonomy *unrealised* potentialities don't count.

A. *Allopatric Populations*

Synchronic populations can be geographically separated in two ways. Either they can be separated but connected by intermediate populations or else they can be completely isolated from each other. Chains of contiguous or overlapping populations are termed geographic *Rassenkreise*. Such chains may vary with respect to any property or type of property, but the two most important kinds of *Rassenkreise* are those that vary with respect to morphological similarity and those that vary with respect to interbreeding. Douglas Gasking defines a morphological species as all those forms that are serially very like each other[1] and a biological species as all those populations that are serially crossable with each other.[2] A serial relation is a relation such that the simple relation holds between any two consecutive terms in the series but need not hold between any two terms that are not consecutive.

For example in a morphological *Rassenkreis*, population *A* may be very like population *B*, which is very like population *C*, which is very like population *D*, and so on, but *A* and a distant population, say, *G* may not be very like each other at all. Such continuous variation among contemporary populations presents no problem for the biological definition because interbreeding status is the criterion for species status among contemporary populations, not morphological similarity. However, interbreeding *Rassenkreise* do present a minor difficulty. In some cases population *A* is interbreeding with population *B*, *B* with *C*, *C* with *D* and so on; but not only is it the case that *A* is not interbreeding with a distant member of the chain, but also it is sometimes the case that they are not even interfertile. Nevertheless, genes are exchanged via intermediate populations. All members of the interbreeding *Rassenkreis* belong to the same ' gene pool ' and are evolving with a sufficient degree of separateness and unity to be classed as species. They are genetically affecting each other's evolutionary development.

The second respect in which two synchronic populations can be separated geographically is by complete isolation. In such cases the populations are neither interbreeding nor serially interbreeding, and

---

[1] Douglas Gasking, ' Clusters ', *Australasian Review of Psychology*, 1960, **38**, 13, 18
[2] Gasking, 1960, p. 38

yet taxonomists class these isolated populations in the same species if they are morphologically similar to each other and distinct from other species; that is, if they possess a degree of morphological similarity and difference usually indicative of species status in organisms of that type. The degree of morphological similarity and difference usually indicative of species status is determined by the degree of morphological similarity and difference present among contemporary interbreeding species.

The question of greatest interest to the biologist is how good morphological similarity and difference is at indicating species status if species are to be units of evolution. Although this is primarily an empirical question and can be answered only after extensive empirical investigation, its solution has been hindered by logical and philosophical confusions. The phylogeneticists themselves have been responsible for some of the confusion by treating consistent interbreeding with the production of fertile offspring as both a necessary and a sufficient condition when it is obviously only sufficient. For example, true sibling species have been extremely troublesome to the phylogeneticists. From a practical standpoint, taxonomists would like to treat them as single species although they do not interbreed even when given every opportunity. On the other hand, from a theoretical point of view, classing them as a single species seems to run counter to the biological definition.[1] Classing two groups of organisms which are morphologically and ecologically quite similar as a single species although they never interbreed conflicts with the biological definition only if interbreeding is mistakenly considered to be a necessary condition. As Simpson has pointed out, a pair of sibling species which are distinguishable neither morphologically nor ecologically are evolving as an evolutionary unit—albeit without the aid of genetic interchange.[2] As will be seen shortly, the same can be said for species of asexual organisms.

A second confusion must be laid at the doorstep of the opponents of phylogenetic taxonomy. Although the point has been made often and well, it bears repeating: it does not follow from the fact that morphological similarity and difference are used as the evidence from which species status is inferred that the morphological definition of ' species ' has been substituted for the biological definition. Morphological similarity and difference is only the *evidence* being used to

[1] Mayr (1957), p. 376; note Mayr, 1942, p. 200, for his treating interbreeding as if it were a necessary condition at least with respect to sibling species.

[2] Simpson, 1961, p. 160

determine species status. How similar is similar enough is determined by the criterion of interbreeding and *this* is what is logically important.

Finally, A. J. Cain voices a common complaint against inferring species status from morphological similarity when he says, ' We can determine by observation the specific or merely varietal status of partially or completely sympatric forms, but can only guess at the status of wholly allopatric ones '.[1] Several factors contribute to this view, including such basic philosophical problems as the justification of induction and the role of deduction in science. The inferences taxonomists make from morphological similarity to species status are not readily put into a form which lends itself to easy manipulation within any of the various theories of probability which have presently been devised. This fact says more against the present development of probability theory than it does against such scientific inferences. Most of the inferences scientists make cannot be accounted for in probability theory. It might also be fruitfully mentioned that the most scathing critics of inferring that two populations belong to the same species from morphological similarity advocate a comparable inference that two different instances of a property are instances of the same property.[2]

The importance of justifying the inference from morphological similarity to phylogenetic relationship should not be underestimated. If it is not justified in a good percentage of the cases, then the entire phylogenetic programme becomes untenable since in most cases morphological properties are *all* the taxonomist has to go on. But before such a harsh judgment is passed, one should make sure that phylogenetic taxonomy is not being measured against an unrealistic standard. On the one hand, science is not as empirical as many scientists seem to think it is. Unobserved and even unobservable entities play an important part in it. Science is not just the making of observations: it is the making of inferences on the basis of observations within the framework of a theory. On the other hand, most of the inferences made by scientists are not deductions as many logicians and philosophers seem to think they are. All inferences made by scientists need not match the accuracy possible in certain restricted areas of physics to be justified.[3] Inductive inferences are not deductively certain.

---

[1] Cain, 1954, p. 73

[2] For example, Sokal and Sneath, 1963. Either both types of inference are justified or else neither is.

[3] Michael J. Scriven, ' The Key Property of Physical Laws—Inaccuracy ', H. Feigl and G. Maxwell (eds.), *Current Issues in the Philosophy of Science*, New York, 1961

If the inferences made by phylogeneticists are guessing, then so are those of meteorologists, economists, historians, pollsters and so on. According to the definition of 'guessing' implied by Cain's comment, most of what is known as science, including all of the social sciences, becomes guessing. Perhaps the scepticism with which Cain and others view inference from morphological similarity to species status arises from the confusion wrought by the criterion of potential interbreeding. If the status which taxonomists are to determine for wholly allopatric forms is whether or not they are potentially interbreeding, then perhaps the critics are justified in terming such inference 'guessing'. If taxonomists are expected to predict the future development of the organisms being classified, then they are guessing in the strictest sense of the word, since both gene and evolutionary theory are not predictive but retrodictive theories. If on the other hand taxonomists are expected only to infer what has actually happened, what species have actually evolved, what groups were actually interbreeding, then these inferences are well outside the range of guessing.

In any case the purpose of this paper is to present a *type* of definition appropriate for evolutionary taxonomy. Even if the opponents of phylogenetic taxonomy can show that phylogenetic relationships cannot be inferred with reasonable accuracy from the type and extent of evidence that the phylogeneticists have at their disposal, this fact will have no bearing on the *logical* assertion which is the thesis of this paper that Aristotelian definition in terms of a set of necessary and sufficient conditions is inadequate for defining 'species' if species are to be the units of evolution.

B. *Allochronic Populations*

Taxonomists are unanimous in their opinion that temporal isolation presents a more serious problem for the biological definition of 'species' than geographic isolation presents. A. J. Cain says, for example:

> The palaeospecies is an expression of the attempted imposition of a hierarchy developed for classifying discrete groups, on to a continuous evolutionary series. Because of the imperfections of the fossil record many fossils do fall into morphologically discrete groups and can readily be incorporated into the hierarchy. Nevertheless, the whole concept of the species as a morphologically (and by implication genetically) discrete group is based upon the observation of present-day animals, and holds only for short periods of time which on the evolutionary scale are mere instants.[1]

[1] Cain, 1954, p. 123

65

Evolving lineages form what might be called temporal *Rassenkreise* both with respect to morphological similarity and with respect to interbreeding. Each successive generation in a progressively evolving lineage changes only slightly. Each generation is serially very like all of its ancestral generations. Similarly, each generation of interbreeding forms is serially interbreeding with all of its ancestral generations. Thus, ' species ' cannot be defined in terms of a serial relation unless a temporal restriction is imposed on pain of classifying all organisms in a single species.

Morphological *Rassenkreise* among contemporary forms presented no problems for the biological definition because interbreeding status could be determined directly. In temporally separated populations, however, whether there is or is not a complete fossil record, interbreeding status cannot be determined directly. Yet phylogeneticists must find some way to divide progressively evolving lineages into evolutionary units. In the case of lineages broken by fossil gaps, the task is easy. In the case of lineages for which there is a reasonably complete fossil record, the task is not so easy. Even so, there is a solution to the problem of dividing progressively evolving lineages objectively and non-arbitrarily, and the key to the solution is again interbreeding.

The importance of interbreeding for determining species status has been emphasised time and again, but the extent of the criterion's significance has not been fully appreciated even by its strongest proponents. Mayr, using a suggestive metaphor, compares the biological definition to a ' yardstick ' for determining species status, and he rightly maintains that division by such a yardstick is both objective and non-arbitrary.[1] Further, he sees that what difficulties there are concerning the biological definition are not ' with the yardstick but with its application '.[2] A further development of Mayr's spatial analogy comparable to Simpson's analogy of a string gradually changing colour proves quite enlightening in the determination of the roles of interbreeding and morphological similarity and difference and placing them in their proper perspective.

The paradigm case of objective measurement is the measurement of objects in space or of the distances between spatially separated objects. Space as such is an amorphous continuum with no intrinsic metric.[3] What this means is that there is nothing about space itself to indicate

---

[1] Mayr, 1957, pp. 15, 16, 18, 19   [2] Mayr, 1959, p. 375
[3] Adolf Grünbaum, *Philosophical Problems of Space and Time*, New York, 1963

how long to make the unit of measurement or at what point to begin measuring once the unit of length has been chosen. With respect to objects in space, the choice of the unit of length is primarily a matter of convenience. Bacteria are measured in microns, rugs in feet (or yards or metres), roads in miles or kilometres, and interstellar distances in light years. One highly advantageous property for a system of measurement is to have the units commensurable. A mile can be divided evenly into yards, feet, or inches. At what point we begin to measure is a matter of convenience. We could begin to measure a rug by laying down our ruler anywhere on it, although it is most convenient to begin at one corner and measure one edge. Nothing about space itself dictates either the length of the unit of measurement or the point at which to begin measuring, but it does dictate what type of unit is appropriate—a spatial unit.

Comparable points can be made about what might be called 'taxonomic space', but it must be emphasised that everything that is said in terms of taxonomic space is meant merely to be explanatory and suggestive. Talk of taxonomic space, like talk of gene pools, is strictly metaphorical. Before either metaphor can actually function in taxonomic theory, a rigorous development in exclusively taxonomic terms is required. Taxonomic space is constructed by plotting 'morphological distance' on the horizontal axis and development in time on the other. 'Morphological distance' means morphological similarity and difference. Taxonomic space, like physical space, is an amorphous continuum with no intrinsic metric; there is nothing about taxonomic space to indicate how long to make the unit of measurement or at what point to begin measuring once the unit is chosen.

With respect to the objects in taxonomic space, the choice of the unit of length is neither arbitrary nor a matter of choice for the phylogeneticists. (This is not the case for the classificationists and their numerical progeny.) The unit of taxonomic space is the morphological distance usually indicative of interbreeding status among contemporary organisms which usually reproduce by interbreeding. However, interbreeding is not the unit of taxonomic space; interbreeding merely determines the length of the unit of taxonomic space. In terms of Mayr's metaphor, the yardstick is morphological distance. Interbreeding determines how long a yard of morphological space is. Nor is the choice of the point at which to begin measuring lineages arbitrary or purely a matter of convenience. In the case of lineages which terminate in contemporary species, it is certainly most convenient to begin laying down our yardstick with them; but there are also theoretical reasons to begin with contemporary species, for only with them can we check the accuracy of our yardstick. The purpose of the yardstick is to delineate evolutionary units. The rationale for making the yardstick one length rather than another is that for the group of organisms in question a particular morphological distance is usually indicative of interbreeding status, which is indicative that the group is evolving as a unit and is, hence, rightly called a species. The nature of taxonomic space as we constructed it determines what type of unit is appropriate for measuring lineages—morphological distance. In the case of lineages which are entirely extinct, measurement begins at the point of extinction or with the most recent fossil. These points may or may not coincide. In the case of lineages which are known only by isolated groups of fossils, the length of the object to be measured is usually less than the length of the yardstick so no division is necessary.

One rather disconcerting property of both physical and taxonomic space, which has been referred to only tangentially, is that fact that the length of the unit of measurement varies. Just as spatially extended objects determine the contours of physical space, evolutionary lineages determine the topography of taxonomic space. To stretch the analogy to its breaking point, taxonomic space is 'non-euclidean'. The vertical temporal axis is divided evenly into segments, but the horizontal axis which indicates morphological distance is not. The units of morphological distance vary in length depending on what morphological distance is indicative of species status for the contemporary members of the general type of organism. Some organisms interbreed even if there is great morphological dissimilarity; others permit almost none. If the properties under consideration are weighted, still another dimension of complexity is added. The logic of the situation remains unchanged, however.

Taxonomists use the yardstick of morphological distance to indicate species status among contemporary allopatric populations. There is no reason why its use cannot be extended to allochronic or even to allochronic and allopatric forms.[1] Although Simpson feels that the resulting divisions will be arbitrary, he condones chopping a progressively evolving lineage into segments by use of morphological distance. He goes on to say, however, 'In practice all that is needed is some criterion as to how large (and in what sense " large ") to make the

[1] Mayr, 1957, p. 120, and Cain, 1954, p. 111

68

segments. . . . Successive species should be so defined as to make the morphological differences between them at least as great as sequential differences among contemporaneous species of the same or closely allied groups '.[1]   In progressively evolving lineages there is no sudden discontinuity which can be used as a specific boundary, just as there is none in a synchronic morphological *Rassenkreis*; but there *is* a reason in both cases to make a break in the continuous series at one point rather than at another.

C. Asexual Populations [2]

Taxonomists universally agree (if universal agreement among taxonomists is possible) that organisms which never reproduce by interbreeding, whether contemporary or ancestral, present an insurmountable difficulty for the biological definition which no amount of modification could accommodate. The following quotations are typical:

> In summary, the existence of the species as an objective biological unit is not impaired by morphological indistinctness or by the continuity of the evolutionary process. The loss of sexuality, on the other hand, removes the very foundations on which the species exists as a type of breeding population. As a result biological species do not exist in asexual groups.[3]

> The essence of the biological species concept is discontinuity due to reproductive isolation. Without sexuality this concept cannot be applied. Asexuality then is the most formidable and most fundamental obstacle of a biological species concept.[4]

> The agamospecies represents an advance on the morphospecies, since the mode of reproduction is known. Unfortunately, it is a mode which allows no possibility of framing a definition of the species which is any less arbitrary than the morphospecies.[5]

In the case of asexual forms, taxonomists feel they have come to an impasse in applying the yardstick they have devised to determine

[1] Simpson, 1961, p. 165

[2] Mayr disapproves of calling groups of asexual organisms ' populations '. Simpson has no reservations concerning the term. For example, see his evolutionary definition of ' species ' as quoted in this paper.

[3] Verne Grant, ' The plant species in theory and practice ', *The Species Problem,* Washington, 1957, p. 61

[4] Mayr, 1957, p. 379   [5] Cain, 1954, p. 123

species status, for it is logically impossible for a non-interbreeding species to be interbreeding (not to *become* interbreeding but to *be* interbreeding). What they have neglected is that the yardstick is not interbreeding status but the degree of morphological distance usually indicative of interbreeding status. When a taxonomist says that a certain asexual species possesses a degree of morphological similarity and difference comparable to that of contemporary interbreeding species, he is not saying something that is logically impossible, although it may be empirically false. Mayr says, ' It is possible to use the same kind of inference to classify asexual organisms into species. Those asexual individuals are included in a single species that display no more morphological difference from each other than do conspecific individuals in related sexual species '.[1]

Although T. M. Sonneborn wants to retain the word ' species ' to refer to the unit of identification and coins the word ' syngen ' to refer to the unit of evolution as determined by the biological definition, he says, ' The question of whether asexual equivalents of syngens exist and can be recognized is more difficult, but not hopeless. The key to progress in this direction is to recognize in the syngen of sexual organisms a distinction between the means of ascertainment and that which is ascertained '.[2] He goes on to say in more detail:

> The preceding attempt to generalize the biological species or syngen runs counter to the view of proponents of the biological species concept . . . that biological species do not exist among obligatory inbreeders or asexual organisms. This denial, as indicated above, is based on an operational definition of biological species. Since the operation, testing gene flow, is impossible in asexual organisms, they deny the existence in them of the thing this operation discovers in sexual organisms, i.e., the biological species or syngen. Their statement of the situation thus implies an abrupt change in the organization of nature and in the units of evolutionary divergence correlated with an abrupt change from outbreeding to obligatory inbreeding and asexual reproduction. By subordinating the method of ascertainment to the thing ascertained and by seeking methods of ascertainment in asexual reproduction, the concept of biological species or syngens was generalized.

[1] Mayr, 1957, p. 381. Happily organisms which reproduce sexually are scattered throughout the animal kingdom from Protozoa to Chordata enabling taxonomists to establish the morphological yardstick without making unreasonable inductive leaps.

[2] T. M. Sonneborn, ' Breeding Systems, reproductive methods, and species problems in Protozoa ', *The Species Problem*, Washington, 1957, p. 290

This implies the absence of an abrupt change in the organization of nature and in the units of evolutionary divergence with changes in breeding systems or method of reproduction.

No such abrupt change is in fact found in the present review of conditions in Protozoa.[1]

E. A Disjunctive Definition of ' Species'

If the yardstick used to determine species status among allochronic and allopatric interbreeding species is accurate enough to indicate evolutionary units, and if it can be extended to apply to asexual species without any great loss in accuracy, then it would seem that the phylogeneticists at least are in a position to formulate a definition of ' species' adequate for their purposes. ' Species' could be defined *disjunctively* as populations that:

(1) consistently interbreed producing a reasonably large proportion of reasonably fertile offspring, or

(2) consistently serially interbreed with synchronic populations producing a reasonably large proportion of reasonably fertile offspring, or

(3) do not fulfil either of the first two conditions but have not diverged appreciably from a common ancestry which did fulfil one of them, or

(4) do not fulfil any of the first three conditions because they do not apply but are analogous to populations which do fulfil at least one of the first three conditions.

Conditions (1) and (2) are quite straightforward and require no application of the yardstick of morphological distance. In fact they are the basis for determining the length of the morphological yardstick. However, they apply only to contemporary sympatric populations of organisms which usually reproduce by interbreeding. Condition (3) applies only to populations which usually reproduce by interbreeding, but there are no temporal or spatial restrictions. How much divergence is ' appreciable' is determined by the morphological yardstick. Condition (4) applies only to non-interbreeding populations with no temporal or spatial restrictions. How analogous the populations have to be is determined again by the morphological yardstick.

As in the case of all disjunctive definitions, the fulfilling of *any one* of the conditions is sufficient and the fulfilling of *at least one* is necessary. Like the disjunctive definitions of taxa names, it is not insulated against

[1] T. M. Sonneborn, 1957, p. 296

71

empirical considerations, both because the objects in taxonomic space determine the length of the morphological yardstick and because new methods of reproduction might arise or be discovered. For example, some asexual forms exhibit a phenomenon called 'parasexuality', in which all or some of the genetic material of one individual is transferred to another. If it is found that these non-meiotic mechanisms of gene flow are sufficient to ensure evolutionary unity and separateness, then either an additional condition would have to be added to the disjunctive definition of 'species' or else the meaning of 'interbreeding' would have to be expanded to encompass parasexuality. The former is the more probable move.

However, instead of taxonomists concluding that 'species' can be defined, albeit disjunctively, they have concluded just the opposite. 'Species' cannot be defined because there are several *kinds* of species. Mayr says, for example, 'Two facts emerge from these and other classifications. One is that there is more than one species concept and that it is futile to search for *the* species concept'.[1] The reasons which taxonomists give for refusing to accept a disjunctive definition of 'species' and the moves they make to avoid defining it disjunctively are exactly the reasons that the traditionalists give and the moves they make for avoiding disjunctive definition of *any* term. According to the advocates of traditional Aristotelian definition, whenever a word can be defined only disjunctively, either one or more conditions must be accepted as necessary and sufficient or else the fuzzy concept must be divided into terms that can be defined traditionally. The first alternative is not open to phylogeneticists given evolutionary development as it is. Sonneborn outlines the possibilities given the second alternative.

(i) Apply the word 'species' to all the various kinds of species, including species as the unit of identification and as the unit of evolution.

(ii) Retain the term to apply to the unit of evolution as determined by the biological definition.

(iii) Continue to use the term to apply to the unit of identification as determined by the morphological definition.[2]

Sonneborn rejects the first alternative 'on the grounds that a technical term should have a single meaning, and the second alternative on the grounds of priority and generality'.[3] Thus, 'species' is to be reserved

---

[1] Mayr, 1957, p. 10   [2] Sonneborn, 1957, p. 201   [3] Ibid., p. 201

for the units of identification and groups of organisms which fulfil the requirements of the biological definition are to be termed 'syngens'. V. Grant opts for the second alternative and suggests the term 'binom' for groups of organisms which do not fulfil the requirements of the biological definition.[1] Cain suggests adopting either (i) or (ii). He says, 'One can either restrict the name to one meaning (presumably the biological species) or use it with appropriate prefixes for all'.[2] Regardless of how it may sound, these biologists are *not* arguing about words. 'Species' has no magic power, and they are well aware of it. What they are arguing about is whether the unit of identification or the unit of evolution will be the unit of classification and, thus, will remain intact as higher taxa are constructed. In order for the purposes of phylogenetic taxonomy to be fulfilled, the unit of evolution must remain intact.[3]

As is usually the case with disjunctive definitions, taxonomists feel two opposing pulls. On the one hand, since several alternative conditions are each sufficient, they feel that several different terms are being defined. Thus, they conclude that there are several different kinds of species. On the other hand, these different kinds of species seem to function with amazing similarity in both evolutionary and gene theory. Almost everything that a biologist would want to say about one kind of species, he would want to say about the other, with the exception of statements directly pertaining to their defining criteria. Thus, G. G. Simpson says, 'The evolution of uniparental and biparental populations is different in many important ways. That does not alter the fact that both form species and, by appropriate definition, the same kind of species'.[4]

Such a situation is not unique to taxonomic terms. For example, since some grapefruit have yellow, sour flesh and others have pink, sweet flesh, the fuzzy concept 'grapefruit' could be replaced by two precise concepts . . . 'Florida-grapefruit' and 'Texas-grapefruit'. But in most contexts in which the word 'grapefruit' is used, everything that is said about one kind of grapefruit is true of the other. In other contexts the distinction between the two slightly different fruits might be important and the distinction could be made. However, 'grapefruit' cannot be defined traditionally so that it is impossible to make a true statement about grapefruit in general which is false with respect to some individual grapefruit.

[1] Grant, 1957, pp. 46, 61   [2] Cain, 1954, p. 106   [3] Hull, 1964, pp. 1-11
[4] Simpson, 1961, p. 163

An example which is more like ' species ' is the word ' dishonesty '. There are at least three different criteria for dishonesty—lying, cheating, and stealing. The fulfilment of any one of these criteria is sufficient for proper application of the predicate ' dishonest '. If someone lies, he is being dishonest. If someone cheats, he is being dishonest. If someone steals, he is being dishonest. But it does not follow that if someone performs a dishonest act, he has stolen. He may have lied or cheated or both. Thus, a traditionalist would say that there are three kinds of dishonesty and want to abandon the word ' dishonesty ' for three more precise words. In a sense there are three kinds of dishonesty, but it is not a sense in which the term ' dishonest ' is fuzzy, meaningless, or indefinable. M. J. Scriven says of this example:

> There are cases of special interest here where we are led to apply the same term even when no natural cluster exists; the classic example is that of dishonesty, where we may discover that lying, cheating and stealing, the three main criteria, are not correlated with each other. This does not destroy the social utility of the term, though it may impair its value for personality-theory.[1]

There are several criteria for determining species as evolutionary units. Several criteria are required because evolutionary development is extended in time and space, because numerous factors affect this development, and because there are various ways in which species reproduce themselves. This does not destroy the general utility of the term ' species ' in biology, though it may impair its value in particular areas.

To some the ' solution ' to the species problem presented in this paper may seem no solution at all (which means it's not the kind of solution they had in mind). Instead it might seem merely philosophical sleight of hand. All that is necessary to solve any problem in definition is to trot out a disjunctive definition. Two examples in which this procedure cannot be used may help to dispel this illusion of fakery. In the early days of genetics, genes were held to be the units of heredity. For each gross trait such as eye colour there was supposedly a discrete particle which controlled it. When a radical change occurred in a trait, a gene mutation was postulated as the cause. As genetics developed ' gene ' was also defined operationally as the smallest unit of recombination. It was assumed that the smallest units of heredity, mutation, action, and crossing over were discrete units and one and the same unit. However, as larger and larger numbers were taken into

---

[1] Scriven, 1959, p. 867

consideration as more conveniently studied organisms were investigated, the limits of what had been envisaged as a gene were passed right through. The progression stopped only at the molecular level with the nucleotide pair (in the case of DNA), and no one wanted to call a pair of nucleotides a ' gene ' in its original sense.

In place of the classic gene several new units have been introduced. The smallest unit of mutation is termed the muton and consists of one nucleotide pair. The smallest unit of recombination is termed the recon and is also one nucleotide pair long. The unit of information, the codon, is most probably three nucleotides long. What comes closest to the classic gene is the cistron, the unit of function, which averages about five hundred nucleotide pairs in length. But the product of one cistron is not one trait but one protein. And the whole situation is complicated further by the possible existence of operators which control one or more cistrons, providing a larger natural unit, the operon. In any case nothing approximates the classic gene. This fact presents no serious barrier to the definition of ' gene '. Scientific words often acquire additional or even radically different meaning as science progresses, but in the case of the word ' gene ' all but two of the meanings happen to conflict. Almost nothing a geneticist would want to say about a muton or recon would he want to say about a codon, a cistron or an operon, and almost nothing he would want to say about any of the new units would he want to say about the classic gene. The fate of the word ' gene ' in modern genetics is that except in general discourse or in the first few chapters of an introductory text (and its use here is debatable), its function has entirely evaporated. Using such a truly ambiguous term like ' gene ' in intermediate or advanced discourse can lead to nothing but confusion.

' Protoplasm ' is an earlier example. It has already passed out of scientific discourse. Not too many years ago protoplasm was thought to be the stuff of life. If only its complex structure could be analysed, the secret of life would be revealed. As it turned out, it was primarily the nucleic acid constituents (a relatively simple molecule) that were of importance in heredity. Perhaps ' protoplasm ' could be defined now that there is so much knowledge of the molecular make-up of the cell, but it is doubtful whether any scientist would take the time to try since the concept of protoplasm is no longer of any use in biology. Its original function has been entirely usurped by other concepts.

The fate of ' gene ' and ' protoplasm ' has not befallen ' species '. On appropriate definition it is not ambiguous, and it is still an important concept in biology. Thus, the defining of it disjunctively is both possible and justified. The definition of 'species' presented in this paper may prove inadequate for the purposes of evolutionary taxonomy, but its formulation will have shown at least in what respects a definition of its kind is superior to the typical Aristotelian definitions of 'species' thus far offered in the literature.

6 *Conclusion*

It is commonly held that Darwin shattered the essentialist or static concept of species. Darwin shattered something all right, but it was only the first two tenets of essentialism, the ontological and methodological assertions. Darwin did not alter taxonomists' predisposition for Aristotelian definitions, either for species names or for 'species'. Contemporary taxonomists have finally abandoned attempts to define taxa names traditionally, but they still refuse to accept any but an Aristotelian definition of 'species'. To be sure, there are many objections to abandoning the clear-cut analytic-synthetic distinction which the adoption of cluster concept analysis implies, not the least of these being that it has broad philosophical ramifications; but taxonomists have already committed themselves to the necessity of defining taxa names as cluster concepts. No new logical or philosophical obstacles stand in the way of their extending this practice to include 'species'.

ADDENDUM BY D. L. HULL (1974)

In the decade since I wrote the preceding paper, considerable improvement has taken place both in the conceptual foundations of taxonomy and in my understanding of these foundations. For example, three schools of taxonomy have emerged where originally there were two. These schools are now commonly termed the phylogeneticists (cladists), the pheneticists (numerical taxonomists), and the evolutionists. The phylogeneticists propose to classify on strictly cladistic grounds (i.e., according to sequence of phylogenetic branching alone). The pheneticists argue that classifications should be constructed solely on the basis of overall phenetic similarity (i.e., any measure of similarity that does not depend on knowledge of phylogenetic development or evolutionary theory). The evolutionists attempt to combine both considerations in a single classification (i.e., considerations of order of splitting, amount of diversification, and degree of divergence are all combined somehow).

My argument concerning taxa names (such as *Bos bos*) depends on evolution usually proceeding gradually. In most cases it does. Occasionally, however, species arise in a single generation, e.g., some cases of polyploidy. The names of such species could perhaps be defined in the classical manner. In all other cases, the names of species as temporally extended lineages, if defined at all, will have to be defined as cluster concepts. The argument for "species" itself being a cluster concept is not so direct. I should have made it clear that the four criteria which I suggested for defining "species" were not *all* the relevant criteria. I intended the definition of "species," like the definitions of the names of taxa, to be an indefinitely long disjunctive definition. However, the greatest weakness in my paper was that I did not distinguish clearly enough between "species" as a unit of classification and "species" as a unit of evolution. Evolutionary taxonomy has a recording function. The criteria of potential interbreeding in the biological species definition is irrelevant to this function. If two populations did not interbreed, then whether or not they could have makes no difference. Hence I argued against potential interbreeding in defining "species" as a unit of classification. But "species" also plays a role in evolutionary theory. Potentiality in such a context is justified, since the notion of what could have happened (though it did not) is central to the notion of normic necessity. It might be noted that Ernst Mayr in his latest version of his biological species concept omits any reference to potential interbreeding (E. Mayr, *Principles of Systematic Zoology,* 1969, New York: McGraw-Hill, p. 26).

The important biological issue is whether or not there are any units of evolutionary development, whether there are different levels of evolutionary unity functioning differently in evolution, and the mechanisms responsible for the unity that does exist. Incorporated in the biological species definition is the assertion that gene exchange is important in promoting evolutionary cohesiveness. Recently, doubts have been raised as to the effectiveness of gene exchange in contrast to selection pressures in performing this function; i.e., evolutionary distinctness can be maintained in the face of considerable gene exchange, and evolutionary unity can be maintained in its absence. I must also note that I guessed wrong concerning the future development of the term "gene." Instead of "gene" dropping out of usage and one or more of the molecular terms taking over, just the opposite has taken place. The term "gene" has come to denote whatever the units of molecular function turn out to be. I must also add that I now believe that evolutionary theory is both predictive and retrodictive and suspect that species are better treated as individuals than as classes, but both of these contentions require a greater degree of explanation than I can give here (see David L. Hull, *Philosophy of Biological Science,* Englewood Cliffs, N.J.: Prentice-Hall, Inc., 1974).

Part II

ARE SPECIES REAL?

Editor's Comments
on Papers 5 Through 7

5 **BLACKWELDER**
   Animal Taxonomy and the New Systematics

6 **BURMA**
   Reality, Existence, and Classification: A Discussion of the Species Problem

7 **GREGG**
   Taxonomy, Language and Reality

The question of the reality of species is something that needs to be approached on several different levels. One important distinction that must be made is the difference between the species as a category and the species as a taxon. As a category, the species is an artificial construct no different from categories such as genus, family, order, class, and phylum. All these categories are units of classification and do not refer to actual organisms. In the classification hierarchy, the category species is below the category genus and above the category subspecies. The only attribute the species as a category has is a definition, which provides a method for deciding whether a given group of organisms should be placed in the classification hierarchy at that category level. The definition may be thought of as being analogous to the rule of a function in mathematics. A definition may state: all x that have the property y are species. Taxa, or the actual groups of organisms themselves, are compared against this definition to see if they can be considered species. If a given taxon satisfies the definition, it is considered a species. If it does not satisfy the definition, it must belong to some other category in the classification scheme. An example of a definition is that of the biological species, as expressed by Mayr (Paper 15): "Species are groups of interbreeding natural populations that are reproductively isolated from other groups." By this definition, any taxon that is composed of interbreeding natural populations reproductively isolated from other groups belongs to the category species in the classification scheme. The species as a category and as a taxon is a point discussed by Blackwelder (Paper 5).

On another level is the question of whether the taxa themselves

80

form natural groupings that correspond to species, i.e., whether or not real species exist in nature. The question then becomes: do we group taxa into species because there really are species in nature, or are we simply lulled by the existence of a category species into thinking that there are real species in nature when actually the whole concept of species is entirely artificial?

Complicating the matter are several major problems. One is that we do not have a universal definition that will in all cases specify the set of conditions necessary for a group of organisms to be considered a species. Another problem is that of variation along the time dimension. We know very little of the past history of most taxa, and nothing of their future. Even if groups of organisms diverge morphologically, physiologically, behaviorally, or reproductively, evolution can be reticulate, and populations that have differentiated can reunite. For a static concept of species, variation through time presents no difficulties. Taxa that have diverged to a certain point, be it morphological, reproductive, or ecological, can be called separate species. For a dynamic concept of species, however, variation through time is a more difficult matter to deal with. Some of these problems are discussed by Burma (Paper 6), who comes to the conclusion in Paper 6 and in Burma (1949a, 1949b) that species are not real but are simply units of convenience. This illustrates the point of view that the species may exist as a category (because we have set up this category for classification purposes) but that species do not exist as taxa. This view of species has been expressed by such students of evolution as Charles Darwin (1859) and J. B. S. Haldane (1956).

Another aspect of the question of the reality of species deals with semantics. On this level, an attempt is made to show that species must either be real or not-real with reference to a framework of logic and the semantic connotations of words. This approach is illustrated by part of Burma's (Paper 6) discussion, and by Gregg's (Paper 7) analysis of the reality of species. An interesting idea brought out by Spurway (1955) and Haldane (1956) is that our concept of a species results from the structure of our language and the structure of our brain. This is a view of species that fits well with structuralist philosophy, which holds that human behavior and perception are determined to a large extent by deep structures within the brain (see Stent, 1975). Such structures cannot be directly observed with our senses, and may lead to an innate predetermined view of the world. A structuralist philosopher might maintain that we perceive species as being real because our minds have been programmed, at some point in our evolutionary history, to divide a collection of objects into groups and form an abstract, generalized concept of each resulting group. The structure of language would then reflect this innate structure.

In practice, most biologists perceive species as real units existing in nature. Whether or not such units actually exist, the perception of species as real units provides both a convenient way of dealing with the diversity of organisms, and a useful generalization for studying evolutionary, ecological, physiological, genetic, and behavioral processes. Such generalization allows biologists to predict the ecological, physiological, and genetic behavior of groups of organisms. Predictions of this type are particularly important in applied fields such as biological control of pests, where minute differences in behavioral responses may determine the success or failure of a control agent.

5

Reprinted from *Surv. Biol. Prog.*, 4, 31–35, 53–57 (1962)

ANIMAL TAXONOMY AND
THE NEW SYSTEMATICS

R. E. Blackwelder

[*Editor's Note:* In the original, material precedes this excerpt.]

3. The Nature of Species

In *The New Systematics* (1940, p. 269) Hogben remarks that "we need not prolong a barren controversy about the various definitions of species." Later writers apparently disagree as to whether the subject is barren. Much further has been written, but if agreement on a definition of species, or on what the bases of "species" are to be, is taken as the criterion, the more recent discussions have been as barren as the old. It would seem that this was inevitable, because the arguers have never settled the preliminary problem of what it is that they are arguing, what it is that the argument is designed to settle. [The symposium on *The Species Problem* (Mayr, 1957) did not even attempt to define the problem or the issues.]

We cannot hope to get anywhere in a discussion of any subject unless we take the trouble to distinguish between the multiple meanings of key words. "Species" is such a word; its meanings are several and rather distinct, including these: (1) "Species" without any article would usually be plural and mean the various populations of organisms which we recognize by some means. These populations are groups of individuals. (2) "A species" would refer to one of the populations or groups. (3) "The species" would sometimes be singular but collective and denote the general concept covering all the groups which are known as species. [It would sometimes be plural and have the same meaning as (1).] (4) "The level of species" or "the category species" refers to the hierarchical level at which we choose to place these populations or groups.

The first of these refers to groups of individuals, groups which may have reality, objectivity, importance, or a definite relationship to nature, if we so define and distinguish them. The second refers to one of the same groups and thus has the same reality and basis. The third as a plural is the same as the first, but as a singular it refers only to the idea of groups which fit the prescribed conception. There is nothing objective or real about this idea; it has no relationship to the nature of organisms or to the nature of the groups. (It doubtless does have a relationship to the mind and to the sense-impressions which gave rise to it.) The fourth is a man-made thing, or more properly a man-selected position. It has a definite relationship to the other categories in the hierarchy, but it bears no relationship to nature. It is not objective, natural, or significant in itself. As part of the hierarchy it has significance that was given to it by the act of placing it between two other categories.

There are other meanings than these of the word "species." Apparently, however, most meanings will fall into one of the two types illustrated by (1) and (2) or by (3) and (4). When the word refers to actual particular populations, groups of individuals, or even hypothetical groups or populations defined by some attributes (1 and 2), then these particular individual species may have reality, objectivity, and significance and be natural in the sense of existing in nature. On the other hand, the general concept species and the hierarchical level of species (3 and 4) have no reality, no objectivity, no inherent significance, and no naturalness. They are correctly described as mental constructs which represent nothing concrete in nature.

If we now go back and examine some of the statements about species, to see how this distinction applies to them, some interesting things appear. We will be constantly in the presence of the misuse of the word category for group, and we will have to take this into account. Dobzhansky (1941, p. 368) states that "the category of species is more 'natural' than other categories used by systematists." If he really meant categories, his statement would be wrong, because the categories are all exactly alike in their nature and are all completely artificial. If he means the actual groups or populations, as we can be sure from the context that he does, then he is correct *if* the particular species (plural) referred to are ones which are delimited on natural grounds.

There is no question that the concepts of breeding populations and gene pools enable us to fix the groups at one level more clearly than at any other, and the groups which correspond with such concepts are unquestionably more natural, objective, and significant.

Simpson (1953, p. 338) writes, "The species, with its included subdivisions, is a different sort of group from those above it." Here the references to "subdivisions" and to "group" make it seem that "the species" refers to "a species." If so, he is right if the species in question is based on some natural phenomena that are different from those used for the groups at higher levels. On the other hand, the category species cannot have subdivisions; it consists of groups that consist of subgroups clear down to individuals, but the level is fixed and indivisible.

Mayr (1942, p. 281) states that "species are real and objective units, because the delimitation of each species is definite. . . ." Here the individual groups are obviously intended, and the statement is correct if the qualification about the definite delimitation is true. In 1953 (p. 23) Mayr *et al.* write, ". . . the species occupies a unique position in the taxonomic hierarchy." Here there can be no question that reference is made to the level known as the species level, the level to which species are assigned. The basis for the statement is given thus: "Essentially there are three kinds of categories: 1. The species. 2. Groups of populations within species. . . . 3. Groupings of species. . . ." This is the same as saying that the species level is unique because it occurs between the next lower level and the next higher level. No other category can make that statement! In this case, of course, the imputation of greater reality or significance to one level in the hierarchy is unjustified. The level has no reality, which can be ascribed only to the groups placed in it.

In another example, Grant (1957, p. 43) states that "an objectively defined species concept is available to take its place" (that of the typological species concept). This apparent imputation of objectivity to a concept is false by definition. Apparently what may have been meant and what might have been true is that there is new interest in objectively defined individual groups that can be placed at the level in the hierarchy called the species level. Grant claims that the species of the typological concept can be defined only subjectively.

Here, then, is a clear case in which two things are contrasted because one is objective (the objective species concept) and the other is subjective (the species of the typological concept). No useful comparison can be made between a concept and a species which is a group of individuals. The concept cannot be objective by definition, and the group is not subjective except in some particular specified sense.

The only thing objective about the new species concept is the delimitation of the groups placed in it. But on this basis the groups of the older concept are on exactly the same foundation as those of the new concept, *provided* that the same basis is used in delimiting the groups. If the newer groupings are based on more clearly definable features, then the new groups may be more objective to that extent, regardless of whether they are species or families.

Part of the confusion over species is due to the fact that some persons believe that they are classifying actual animals into groups having like attributes, whereas others believe that they are classifying species produced by evolution. The taxonomist is called upon to record the structures, behavior, distribution, and other relations of groups of individuals. He finds that correlations between these things are useful and meaningful. The phylogenist is called upon to interpret the probable evolution of groups. He is little concerned with individuals and their attributes but more with the ranges of characteristics and the factors that cause groups to remain separate. Each of these specialists has called certain of his groups "species," but they may have in common only this name. The concept which the taxonomist calls by the name species is based on data gathered from individual organisms by means of his senses and used for the business of taxonomy, which is discovery and systematization of data. The concept which the phylogenist calls by the name species is based on data drawn from populations by means of inferences and used for the business of phylogeny, which is the deduction of the past history of the group.

Nothing whatever is gained by denying the existence of these two very different concepts. No solution has been attained by the alternative scheme of claiming the existence of many other concepts of species, which turn out to be mere variants of these. No end to the arguments over species concepts can be reached until it is recognized that at the present time there is no way to correlate the species composed of individuals having attributes with the species composed of populations supposedly phylogenetically related. To accept the one is not to deny the other. They both exist; they both serve useful purposes; but they are not necessarily correlated. At the present time we can deal with each separately, but we cannot yet combine them into a single concept in practice.

This leaves us with two things represented by a single term. Misunderstanding and confusion are inevitable. Taxonomy may again be forced to surrender and abandon an established term to a new group of zoologists who use it for a more recent concept, as happened in the case of the term genotype. Such an unreasonable eventuality might actually be necessary in order to counter the illogical arguments of the speciationists that the species are not properly understood by the scientists who discovered and distinguished a million of them!

Sonneborn recognizes this difficulty, and so do others, but their voices are lost in the chorus that considers semantics as a part of philosophy and therefore of no value. A little attention to semantics would prevent a substantial waste of time, energy, and ink by making clear the lack of a common ground for argument.

[*Editor's Note:* Material has been omitted at this point.]

X. CONCLUSION

Taxonomy has in one sense always been the most inclusive of the biological sciences. It has attempted to classify the million or more kinds of animals *and* to make it possible to keep track of all the data of whatever sort about these kinds that is discovered by any zoologists. Considering the immensity of this task, the success of taxonomy is nothing less than phenomenal. Its systems survived unscathed the conceptual upheaval of the Darwin revolution and likewise the tremendous expansion in horizons produced by experimental biology in this century. It is increasingly important to other branches of biology, where some persons were slow to realize the necessity of knowing all the living and extinct forms upon which other work was being done.

Taxonomy has not been able to keep up with the demands of these other fields. This is not because of inadequacy of its classifications or its concepts, but largely because the labor involved is far beyond the limitations of the few professional taxonomists, even with the assistance of the more numerous nonprofessionals. This situation has been made worse by the lack of respect for taxonomy that is often voiced by other zoologists. Taxonomists are usually too busy to take much note of these uninformed criticisms.

A few biologists have recently attempted to force taxonomists to abandon the methods and concepts that have been the basis of its successes. They have insisted that the taxonomists *must* study the origins of the kinds of animals they have been studying. This so-called "modern" approach is firmly entrenched in the sense that it is being actively proclaimed, and giving results that justify the labor. These results are not part of taxonomy, although they should interest taxonomists; they are a part of a new science of speciation.

This "modern" approach has *not* produced a revolution in taxonomy. Recent publications show that only a few taxonomists have really accepted the views of the speciationists *as they apply to taxonomy* to the extent of weighing the evidence presented. Certainly many taxonomists have been passive or completely aloof. Others have been actively opposed to certain implications, and this group is larger than is usually realized.

Those taxonomists who have accepted the recent statements have seldom given any evidence that they have themselves examined the arguments, the logic, and the conclusions and are willing to say that they actively agree in the implications. There is no reason to suppose that the casual quoter of the new ideas sees all their implications and accepts them all. It is certain that the implications have not all been brought out for him to examine at leisure, and there is good evidence for believing that a few important implications have not been faced even by the proponents.

Some of the ideas that are challenged herein have implications or validity in other fields than taxonomy. It is not intended that these remarks shall be applied to these other implications of the ideas. A statement that can be shown to be inapplicable to taxonomy may still be of great importance in speciation or ecology. Only the validity in relation to taxonomy is challenged. In fact, the need to keep separate for certain purposes the various fields that deal with kinds of organisms is one of the major theses advanced. There are, of course, other purposes for which it is desirable to bring fields together and study their interactions.

An unsound premise or argument does not necessarily make an unsound conclusion. The conclusion may be right on other grounds even when the argument is false. But no one can afford to leave a conclusion "supported" by a false argument. This is an invitation to criticism. It is just as important to root out false argumentation as false documentation. If we will take the trouble to use only proven foundations and build upon them with faultless logic, we need not worry about the resulting generalizations.

The writer has here tried to show that the application of speciation ideas to taxonomy has not been universally accepted and not even widely practiced, that the arguments purporting to show that these ideas must be adopted by taxonomists are far from conclusive and in fact often illogical and unfounded, that the purpose of taxonomy is to classify animals and our knowledge about them rather than to illuminate their evolution, and that current use of language falls far short of adequacy for discussion of the methodology of taxonomy.

It is specifically not intended to deny evolution or that species have had histories (phylogenies), or even that the phylogenies are somehow related to the present nature of the species; nor the importance of the study of speciation, populations, genetics, evolution, or any other biological subject; nor the desirability of finding and using data from all fields of biology in our classifications.

There is nothing but language and certain acceptances standing in the way of recognition of the real goals and uses of classification. If we can make the language adequately rigorous and free from rhetorical obfuscations, we should be able to deal with the acceptances on the basis of fact and logic. If we refuse to consider semantics and epistemology in our discussions of methodology, we can expect no end to the "problems" of taxonomy.

REFERENCES

Dobzhansky, T. 1941. "Genetics and the Origin of Species," 2nd ed., 446 pp. Columbia Univ. Press, New York.

Grant, V. 1957. The plant species in theory and practice. In "The Species Problem," Publ. Am. Assoc. Advance. Sci. No. 50: 39-80.

Hogben, L. 1940. Problems of the origins of species. In "The New Systematics" (J. Huxley, ed.), pp. 269-286. Oxford Univ. Press, London and New York.

Mayr, E. 1942. "Systematics and the Origin of Species," 334 pp. Columbia Univ. Press, New York.

Mayr, E. (ed.) 1957. "The Species Problem," *Publ. Am. Assoc. Advance. Sci.* **No. 50**, 395 pp.

Mayr, E., Linsley, E. G., and Usinger, R. L. 1953. "Methods and Principles of Systematic Zoology," 328 pp. McGraw-Hill, New York.

Simpson, G. G. 1953. "The Major Features of Evolution," 434 pp. Columbia Univ. Press, New York.

6

Reprinted from *Madroño*, 12(7), 193-209 (1954)

REALITY, EXISTENCE, AND CLASSIFICATION: A DISCUSSION OF THE SPECIES PROBLEM

BENJAMIN H. BURMA

INTRODUCTION

In 1949 the writer published a short paper setting forth certain views concerning the species concept, which elicited several other papers on the subject. One of these (Gregg, 1950) observed that writers on the subject of the species concept had in general been guilty of lack of clarity in the formulation of the ideas and definitions involved. The writer fully agrees with this view, and the present paper may be regarded as an attempt to survey, in a relatively short space, the basic philosophical assumptions and definitions involved in this phase of biology, and their application to the subject at hand. This has not proved a simple task and I doubt that the aim of clarity has always been achieved. On the other hand, a number of the concepts involved are rather difficult, and often I have had to choose between greater clarity or brevity, and had to choose brevity.

It may be well to point out at once that the ensuing discussion will, at different times, proceed on different levels. (On one level of discourse it is perfectly legitimate to refer to a table top as solid. In a discourse on the atomic level, such an assertion would be absurd.) The different levels have not in general been labeled, but every effort has been made to avoid confusion of the level of discourse. In the more strictly biological part of this paper, it will be apparent that the general level is that of a "picture-of-Nature," in which phenomena are interpreted in terms of "models." The physical sciences, and particularly physics, have gone beyond this level, and eventually biology will also, I am quite certain. If the state of the science were sufficiently advanced, it seems very likely that the discussion in the last part of this paper might well have been in terms of open energy systems in a field of energies, in something of an analogue of a physical field theory. For the present, however, we must be satisfied with less precise methods of dealing with the phenomena in question.

Several people, all members of the staff of the University of Nebraska, have been kind enough to read the entire manuscript and offer helpful criticism. For this I am indebted to Dr. Dwight D. Miller, of the Zoology department; Dr. Adam Skapski, Physics department, and Drs. William H. Werkmeister, Thomas F. Storer, and Bruce Waters, Philosophy department. I am particularly indebted to Dr. Storer, especially for his advice concerning the use of existence as a predicate. Nathan Mohler assisted in the preparation of the illustrations.

STATEMENT OF THE PROBLEM

The question before us may be stated as "Are species objectively real units existing in the real world?" This innocent seeming question has in it several words which are exceptionally difficult of definition and which are notoriously used by different persons in different ways. Our first task, then, shall be to attempt to definite, or at least describe the usage, of certain words or phrases in the above question in such a way that there will be a minimum of uncertainty in the mind of the reader as to the manner in which each is used in this paper.

It may be well first to say a word concerning verbal definition as such. It must be realized that any definition attempted can never be anything except the beginning of an infinite regress, at least within the limits of the language used in the definition. Thus we might define "beer bottle" as "brown glass container." This, of course, merely substitutes three undefined words for two. Each of these must then be defined, then each of the words in this definition and so on, theoretically without limit, hence an infinite regress. Since the language has a finite number of words, however, the regress will not actually be without limit as to *new* words introduced. A point will be reached where the available words are exhausted and new definitions will involve only reused words. Thus, in actual practice, we will be faced by circular definitions of the type of "Feature means peculiarity, peculiarity means characteristic, characteristic means feature." In any case, the essential point is that, in the last analysis, there is no such thing as a final definition, such being impossible unless one wishes to assume the existence of terms whose definitions exist in-the-nature-of-things. The mystic or theologian may have such but the scientist does not. In the problem at hand, then, definitions will be stopped at least this side of the point of diminishing returns.

Meaning of "Real"

Our first task will be to specify the meaning to be ascribed to the word "real," as it will be used in this paper. The word is used in so many senses that it is of first importance to make certain that its usage is always as clear as possible.

In this paper the word will be taken in its usual, or what I take to be its usual, "scientific" sense. All scientific inquiry has as a basis some postulate, or postulates, concerning reality and the relation of perceptual data to this reality. The following postulates and definitions are those on which this paper is based, and, I believe, they would be very widely recognized as being usual postulates. They are:

(1) There is a physical reality. (This is an unprovable assumption, but whether true or not, all the sciences proceed *as if* it were a fact and not an assumption. Sensory data may also consistently be explained on the basis of such a postulate as — The total reality is mind, and matter is a non-physical construct of the mind, that is, that reality is non-physical. Both postulates have been the basis of philosophic systems concerning the universe, and probably with equal success. Why then should we postulate a physical reality? There are a variety of reasons, some logical and

some not. The non-logical reasons are certainly of great force and are expressed in such statements as "If there were no physical reality, then science would be impossible," or "I would see no reason to study the sciences." Such attitudes place a powerful bias in minds of the type that would be interested in the physical and biological sciences in favor of the postulate of a physical reality. In addition, however, there are more logical reasons. If there is more than one mind in the universe, then, the argument runs, is it not strange that two minds would reach agreement regarding some "physical" fact in the absence of some underlying physical reality. It is easy to argue against this view, but to some minds, mine among them, such arguments are unconvincing.)

(2) There is some sort of relation between perceptual data and total reality. (This, again, is unprovable. Perceptual data may in themselves be reality—Berkelian idealism and similar epistomologies. However, if there *is* a physical reality, it would be completely outside the range of any knowledge unless there were a relation of some sort between perception and total reality.)

(3) Perceptual data give us our only first-hand data of the real world. (This is unfortunate truth, rather than assumption. It is merely the universally acknowledged fact that, for example, sight is a subjective, not an objective experience.)

(4) There is some sort of a *systematic, regular* relation between perceptual data and total reality. (If relation between the two were haphazard and unsystematic, it hardly seems likely that there would be any orderliness to the world of the senses. Such a postulate, though again unprovable, is probably a necessary basis for any theory of communication.)

(5) The real world, as the term will hereafter be used, is the reflection of total reality in perceptual data, and such that two or more observers may reach agreement in correlating their individual perceptual data. (This is, of course, a definition rather than a postulate. It is simply a more precise statement of the generally accepted idea that anything real will be perceptible to two or more observers in such a fashion that mutual agreement may be reached concerning the nature of the object. Note that the definition specifically excludes the perceptual data of the insane, the "abnormal," and the mystic. This does not deny the validity of these percepts, but any reality involved falls outside the "real world" of science.)

(6) Since total reality is non-perceivable, data received by our senses give us our only knowledge of the real world of total reality, and, for the individual observer, constitutes the real world. [This final postulate is, of course, the basis of relativism, whether in physics, philosophy, or elsewhere. The first known statement of this principle was made about 450 B.C. when Protagoras said that "Man is the measure of all things." It means that the first (logically) task of any observer is to discover the

rules for transforming the data from his observational system (physical, not notational) into that of another observer, and vice versa. This is actually a necessary precondition to point (5) preceding. The appreciation and successful solution of this problem for systems in non-linear relative motion is one of the greatest accomplishments of relativistic physics. Although it is not generally appreciated, the biological sciences are not, by some divine fiat, exempted from these necessities. |

(7) In addition to the above six postulates and definitions, I would add the following — that only is real which possesses extension in space-time. This is to say that reality is at least four-, not three-dimensional. The neontologists have consistently treated the species problem as though the organisms involved had only extension in space and not in time, the usual reason given being that "although paleontologists may have to deal with time in connection with organisms neontologists deal with such short spans of time, comparatively, that the time factor may safely be ignored as of no importance." However, no one espousing this view has *ever* given any reason why one should ascribe reality to the three-dimensional shadow-pictures they describe or why the objects of their study should be exempted from the canons of reality applying to the other physical and biological sciences. Until such convincing reasons are given, and I know they will not be, we are justified in rejecting as entirely unscientific any views on the species-problem which are not discussed in terms of the space-time continuum.

The Meaning of "Exists"

The word "exist" has also been fruitful of misunderstanding. To say that a thing exists is to say that it is not fictitious, but an actuality, and since actuality embodies acts or events in the real, physical world, the world of things, it embodies a set of characteristics peculiar to that thing. One of these characteristics is the extension in the space-time continuum. That which does not have such extension cannot be said to exist in the sense used in our statement of the problem.

The use of "exists" is important in a consideration of Gregg's paper, "Taxonomy, language and reality" (Gregg, 1950). Since the difficulties in which Gregg finds himself in this paper are not uncommon, it may be useful to analyze certain of his arguments in some detail (p. 421 *et seq.*).

First, he examines the proposition "All species exist," a proposition of the type "all fish swim," which may be recast as "for any x: if x is a fish, then x can swim." A similar recasting of the first proposition gives "for every A: if A is a species, then A exists." The contrary of this is then given as "not (for every A: if A is a species, then A exists.)" This, Gregg says is inconsistent as implying the contradictory statement "there exists an A such that A does not exist." I cannot agree with this. It is true that the last statement is superficially, at least, contradictory, but I do not regard it as legitimately following the contrary. The contrary statement may be transcribed in ordinary language as "It is not true that for every A, if A is a species, then A exists." This statement becomes contradictory *only* if the "is" is taken itself to mean "exists," which does not follow.

A similar difficulty is involved in his analysis of the proposition "some species exist" which he inferentially, by example but not directly, recasts as "there exists an A, such that A is a species, and A exists." Here again, "exists," the first one, is improperly substituted for "is." The difficulty lies in the failure to distinguish between what we may call logical existence and real existence. The meaning of the two terms may be illustrated as follows: Consider the class of unicorns. We erect the class definition — unicorns are those animals with the head, neck and body of a horse, chin tuft of a goat, legs of a buck, tail of a lion and a long straight horn on the middle of the forehead. This class is properly constructed; it may be used in syllogisms, etc., and may be said to have logical existence. On the other hand, no such animal ever lived, there is no actual animal of the real world meeting this description, and for this reason, the individual unicorn is said to be without real existence in the sense defined in the first part of this section.

If "exist" of the propositions "All species exist" and "Some species exist" is of the type of logical existence only, then the discussion of these topics is *purely* theoretical and of no possible application to the discussion in this paper and in my former paper (Burma, 1949) which is concerned only with real existence, nor is it of any particular interest to biologists as biologists, whose concern is also with real, not logical existences. On the other hand, if "exist" in the two propositions refers to real existence, or has any flavor of it, then Gregg's conclusion that both propositions are necessarily true is certainly false since the statements he cites. "There exists an A such that A does not exist" and "there exists an A, such that A is a species and A exists" involves contradictions *only* if it is not realized that the first "exists" refers to logical existence and the second to real existence. For this reason, the logical contraries of the two original propositions: "It is not true that for every A, if A is a species, A exists," and "There is an A such that A is a species and A does not exist," where *only* the words "exist" refer to real existence, contain no internal contradictions at all, exactly opposite the conclusion of Gregg.

When (p. 423) Gregg says that the statement " 'There exists no A such that A is a species' [better stated as "There is no A such that A is a species and A exists"] is *false* for there *are* species: *Homo sapiens* is one, *Escherichia coli* is another, and *Anopheles quadrimaculatus* is another", he is in error in his reasoning. Let us recast this statement of Gregg's in syllogistic form:

> The taxonomic unit *Homo sapiens* exists
> *Homo sapiens* is a species
> Therefore, species exist

Put thus baldly, it is apparent that we are again faced with a confusion in the usage of "exists." If, in this syllogism, "exists" refers only to logical existence, we need not quarrel with Gregg but the syllogism then has nothing to do with our problem.[1] The *apparent* proving of the (real) existence of species arises when the first "exists" refers to logical, and the second to real existence. However, since the two "exists" are actually different words which happen to be spelled the same, the conclusion "Therefore species exist" does not follow from the major and minor premises. If both "exists" are taken to refer to real existence, nothing is actually proved since the major premise then *assumes* the very point we are supposedly out to establish! In short, this apparently convincing argument is sophistical and false. (Parenthetically, it may be pointed out that since the above arguments are basic to Gregg's thesis, we must conclude that his thesis is not proven.)

No one can deny that the units of the taxonomic system have logical existence, so does a mathematical line. Our problem concerns the real existence of species and Gregg's paper does not help us in this problem. Let us now consider some aspects of the general problem of classification.

The Process of Classification

Classification, as a process, is a fundamental necessity in human life. We are presented from birth with a bewildering variety of sensory images, and the infant's first task is to bring some sort of order out of this chaos. Among the first of these orderings is the recognition that one particular group of sensory images belongs to a class that provides food and comfort. The first vocalization of the infant often names this class — mama —, in this case a class of one member. By the time the child is a few months old, the class, mama, is firmly identified. The very development of skill in vocalization depends on and develops with this ability to classify. The infant learns that the word "dog" is associated with a certain group of sensory images, and that when he points to a member of this class, and says "doggie," he will be rewarded.

Indeed, we can see that this ability to classify is necessary to the ability to communicate. Nouns and adjectives, our chief classifiers of the world about us, are an absolute necessity for the exchange of information. Consider the number of sensory images, inherent or implicit, in the noun "Man." Consider the time saved by classifying this mass of images in the one word. Indeed the very process of vocalization is one of classification, for when I say, "men," I have placed a certain group of sensory and conceptual data in the class "men." Because classification is necessary for communication, it does not follow that: (1) precision is gained thereby, or (2) that classification is a feature of the world itself rather than our own mental processes.

---

[1] Actually, the "syliogism," and the argument so formalized, have certain peculiarities which, apart from other considerations, render the validity of the argument doubtful.

The first usable formalization of classification must be credited to Plato and Aristotle. The "archetype" of Plato may be thought of as a spiritual prototype of the objects of the material world. (Plato's εἶδος which is almost invariably translated as "idea" I have here rendered as "archetype." "Idea" inevitably, and especially for non-philosophers, carries with it a connotation on non-materiality. However, the εἶδος of Plato was the very essence of reality and in every sense material. The world of matter was, in fact, considered to be only a pale reflection of the world of the εἶδος.) Thus, there was an "archetype" of "dog." Matter, by partaking of this "archetype" became a dog. Thus the process of classification became merely a process of recognizing the "dogginess" inherent in any dog. (Observe the essential identity of this process with the process of recognizing a species by means of its essential characters.) Similarly, one recognizes the class of bears by recognizing the inherent "bearness" of certain animals. Thus the physical world was considered to be neatly compartmented into classes corresponding to "archetypes" and the process of classifying consisted only in the more or less intuitive recognition by the philosopher of the indestructible "archetype" behind the shifting veil of the physical world.

Aristotle's views were basically quite different although in practice the results were about the same as with Plato's system. According to Aristotle, every material object is the result of the union of two principles, matter (material) and form (non-material). Matter is regarded by him as possessing the capacity for form or being potentially formed matter. However, form has being only insofar as it is expressed in material objects. Thus the dog is a "dog" because the matter of which the animal is composed had the potentiality, the form, of "dog." From this point classification proceeds by recognizing "forms" as we before recognized "archetypes."

This general view of classificatory process was regarded, during revival of Aristotelianism, as being compatible with Christian dogma, and as such passed into western philosophy, either explicitly or implicitly. Linnaeus' classification was almost certainly Aristotelian in its basis, yet it is equally certain that in practice he leaned strongly to the Platonic view. Thus in his *Philosophia Botanica* he states "species tot numeramus quot diversae formae in principio sunt creatae" (freely rendered as "our classification contains just as many species as there were different *forms* originally created"), an unexceptionably Aristotelian statement. However, in his *Classes Plantarum* he states "species tot sunt quot diversas formas ab initio produxit infinitum Ens" ("there are as many species as there were different forms produced in the beginning by the Infinite Being"). Here it is quite plain that his species are archetypal, fixed and immutable from the day of creation.

Such a mixed Platono-Aristotelian view of the species generally lurks in the background of classifications even today. Thus, when the native Papuan (Mayr, 1949, p. 371) recognized a given individual bird as a fantail, he compares this individual with a composite mental image of all fantails of his experience, checks to see that the individual in question conforms in essential characters, and, if it does, announces, "This is a fantail." In so doing, the Papuan is a reasonably accurate facsimile of a Platonic philosopher. He extracts from the *changing* appearances of ever-changing matter, the eternal "archetype" of "fantail" — the veriest essence of "fantailness." One might say, by definition, that any individual conformation of matter partaking strongly of the "archetype" of fantail *is* a fantail. Avowed Platonists are rare in the world today; unavowed, unconsciously Platonic Platonists are indeed legion, perhaps to the extent of including all mankind.

Such a process of abstraction, identification, is the basis of classification. The chief danger is in the unconscious use of "archetype" as the basis of classification, a piece of mysticism productive of many difficulties, not the least of which is the according of the word "species" with a connotation of "If I recognize A as a species, I must be recognizing something, and that something is real, otherwise I wouldn't recognize it, therefore species A is a reality," the reality in the last analysis being the "archetype" of species A.

Sources of Ambiguity in Classification

One difficulty with almost any scheme of classification is that, sooner or later, uncertainty arises as to whether some particular individual should or should not be referred to a particular class. Such ambiguous cases may arise from two rather distinct, though sometimes not necessarily distinguishable causes. We may refer to them as extrinsic and intrinsic ambiguities respectively.

Extrinsic ambiguities are those external to the objects being classified and inherent in the *class* involved. They are essentially difficulties in the *definition* of the class. For example, it is difficult to state exactly whether or not viruses belong to the class of living things. This ambiguity is primarily due to the lack of certainty about the definition of *life* and not about the pertinent characteristics of the viruses.

Intrinsic ambiguities exist in the individuals being classified rather than in the definition of the class involved. These exist primarily where the individual is a member of a continuously variable series and a class is set up for a portion of this series. In this case, the *definition* of the class may be perfectly unambiguous, but uncertainty will of necessity exist regarding the assignment of individuals on the border of the defined class. Such ambiguity is inherent in the situation.

The Individual

The basic unit of a biological taxonomic system is the individual. The individual may be made of cells, organelles, etc., etc., and these constituent structures will be important in understanding the individual, but they do not in themselves take part in the taxonomic hierarchy. Let us first, then, seek an understanding of *what* an individual is.

To avoid unnecessary complications, we may restrict our discussion to non-colonial organisms. Introduction of such ancillary problems would lead us far from our present purpose. Biologically the individual is important as the unit through which life maintains itself in space-time. It is the smallest unit which can, either by itself, or through cooperation with another unit, ensure that a given kind of life persists from generation to generation. As such, an essential function is the passing on of hereditary factors so that a genetic continuum is maintained from ancestor to descendant. The simplest way to consider this aspect, and others, of the individual, is by reference to the "world line" of the individual. ("World line," as will be seen below, refers not to the fully relativistic world line of Minkowski, but to a simplified version useful to our purpose. Specifically, we will use as coordinates x, y, z, t rather than x, y, z, ict.".)

Since the concept of the world line may be unfamiliar to some readers, a short explanation is in order. The world line of an object is the path that an object takes in space-time. If one wishes to plot such a world line, four coordinate axes are necessary, three spatial and one temporal. (For a good, reasonably non-technical, discussion of Minkowski's world line, see d'Abro, pp. 195-200, 1950.) Considering the difficulties involved in drawing a tesseract on a sheet of paper, we need not attempt to plot a line, or volume, in one. Again, for the sake of simplicity, we may adopt one axis for the space coordinates combined and a second for the time coordinate, as in Figure 1. For our examples we shall plot the world lines of individuals as lines. Thus Figure 1 shows the world line of a given individual from time T_1 to T_2.

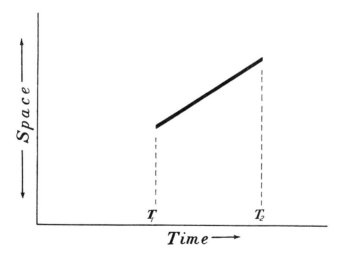

Fig. 1. World line of an individual in space-time during time-segment T_1 T_2.

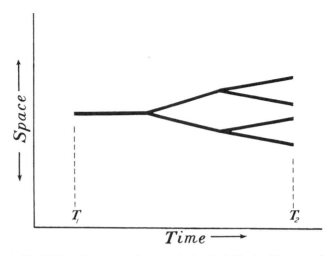

Fig. 2. World line of an asexually reproducing individual with two episodes of reproduction by binary fission.

If our organism reproduces by fission we may, starting at time T_1 show it and its descendants as in Figure 2. Notice that we have reached a point where the unambiguous designation of an individual in terms of its world line becomes difficult, and for much the same reason that we have difficulty in precisely designating individuals in highly colonial animals; that, viewed over-all, we have continuity, and it is only at specified time segments that individuals have their world lines sharply differentiated. (The ordinary view of bodies in space-time is that they are bodies with three spatial dimensions traveling through space-time. In this view, the line of Figure 1, and 2, is actually a composite of an infinite number of points so that the continuity shown in Figure 2 is effectively real but not physically real. An alternative view is that objects are actually four dimensional, although for some reason our preception only reveals three-dimensional cross sections. In this view, the continuity would be in the highest degree physically real. I know of no exploration that has been made of this extremely interesting alternative view, although it has a number of intriguing consequences.) [While this paper was in manuscript, Dr. Werkmeister called my attention to a paper (Williams, 1951) in which one aspect of this interesting view is examined.]

Sexually reproducing organisms may similarly be shown by world line plots. In Figure 3, where such an example is given, sex cells are shown arising from the parents, fusing, and giving rise to new individuals. Note that this monogamous couple has produced two offspring. In the case of such sexually reproducing diploid organisms it is somewhat easier to designate the individual, but difficulties remain. The individual may be said to come into existence when the chromosome sets of the haploid sex cells combine. Even this definition is less precise than it seems. What is.im-

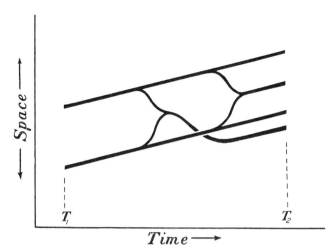

Fig. 3. World lines of two sexually reproducing individuals with formations of gametes, zygote, and new individuals.

portant is not the definable separateness of the individual but the continuity between parent and offspring, i.e., the continuity of germ plasm— and of cytoplasm, too, if cytoplasmic inheritance is of importance.

The Breeding Population

Although we have been unable thus far to say precisely where, in space-time, one individual begins and another leaves off, let us proceed to a consideration of the next larger aggregation of organic units. In sexually reproducing organisms, any given individual will ordinarily be within the range of activity of a considerable number of individuals of the opposite sex who could, if the opportunity arose, mate with this first given individual and produce viable offspring. Such a group, composed of one individual together with its immediately potential mates, we may refer to as first order breeding populations. Obviously, first order breeding populations will be highly unstable, rapidly changing in composition in space-time, and are more valuable as analytic units than anything else. By definition, there are in the world as many first order breeding populations as there are sexually mature individuals, and each such individual might be a member of several thousand first order breeding populations.

Within a first order breeding population, gene flow is, by definition, actually or potentially complete and free. If we survey all the first order breeding populations to which a given individual belongs, and pass from these to other connected breeding populations, we will find certain geographic areas within which gene flow is actually or potentially as free and complete as within a single first order population. However, sooner or later we will come to a boundary, geographic or some other kind, across which gene flow is restricted. The nature of the barrier to free gene flow will, of course, depend on the organisms involved. For land snails, a small river might well constitute such a barrier; the same stream would be no barrier whatever to most birds. The aggregate of first order breeding populations within which gene flow is relatively free and unrestricted and between which there is some restriction of gene flow, we may call second order breeding populations. Here again we are dealing with a unit that is useful for purposes of analysis but which we would probably find was impossible to define *precisely* in nature.

Barriers between adjacent second order breeding populations will often be temporary in character. When such barriers are removed, the second order populations involved will, of course, merge and become one. Let us now examine the world lines involved in these second order populations.

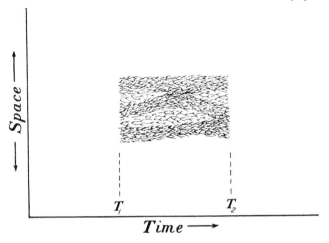

Fig. 4. Temporary separations and fusions of related second order breeding populations in space-time. (See text.)

In Figure 4, which is highly simplified, individuals are shown as lines. Because genetic separation of these second order populations is incomplete and impermanent, such second order populations will not maintain any significant genetic differences over any period of time, and as a consequence morphological differences between the populations involved will be minor and transitory. If two such complexes of second order populations become separated to the extent that gene flow is markedly restricted and over such a length of time that barriers to gene flow, inherent in the animals themselves, develop, gene flow will still be restricted when contact between populations is renewed, or may even be actually or essentially nil. Such groups of second order populations we may refer to as third order breeding populations. A third order of populations will tend to evolve independently of other such populations since exchange of genic material will be restricted wholly or mostly to individuals within the population.

With the third order breeding populations we reach the end of our natural hierarchy. All such populations which are in themselves unable to exchange genic materials will be different. Any further building of a hierarchy will be based on decisions as to *amount* of differences between these populations. Such a decision is a *value* judgment, and is not part of the real world. Third order breeding populations are *different*. Only the human mind makes an issue of *how* different they are.

Note that the foregoing analysis is essentially independent of the mechanism by which the hereditary principle is passed from parent to descendant. In the discussion we have, for convenience, spoken in terms of the gene theory of inheritance, but this is *only* a convenience and in no wise necessary to the argument. Only two major assumptions are made in the foregoing analysis — (1) that offspring resemble parents because of some physical "principle" which they receive from their parents, and (2) that, in the course of the passage of this hereditary principle from one generation to the next, hereditable differences may arise and be passed on to further offspring. I do not believe that any reputable biologist would quarrel with either of the above assumptions today. They are among the most ancient of bases of evolutionary biology. Anaximander and Empedocles, nearly 2,500 years ago were familiar with these tenets. Note also that no special theory of evolution is here assumed, only evolution in its most general sense.

Biological Taxonomy

We may now inquire as to where, in the preceding hierarchy of breeding populations, the usual taxonomic hierarchy fits. It is apparent, I believe, that all rest within what we have just defined as third order breeding populations except for subspecies. Subspecies seem to be second order breeding populations, if they have real existence at all, a matter we shall discuss below. According to the usual definitions, subspecies, in general, interbreed more or less freely if allowed to mix in nature and will, with such continued opportunity, become indistinguishable. All the other categories must then be third order populations between which gene flow is restricted or absent.

Let us then examine the species to see if any reality may be ascribed this supposed biological or taxonomic unit. First of all, be it clearly understood that the *logical existence* of species as a taxonomic unit is not in question. Whatever definition one may wish to use, species will be a defined class of some sort, and as such may be said, no more and no less, to exist in precisely the same sense that the class of unicorns may be said to exist. But, as I have intimated before, this is not our problem, which is — "do species have real existence, and if so, in what manner."

Classes, as such, have no real existence. They are, as we have seen, mental constructs and as such lack actuality in the sense here defined. No one ever saw a mental construct walking down the road. Species, *as classes,* thus are obviously without real existence. To construe the actuality and the existence of classes thus rigidly, however, may seem overly severe, and might be said to beg the question insofar as our central problem is concerned. In what sense at all can any class be said to have real existence?

Since we have seen that classes cannot be said to have real existence in actuality, any tincture of reality ascribed to them must be *analogical* and comparable to the reality of the individuals making up this class. As a neutral example, let us examine the class of "tables." We may define a table as a manufactured object consisting of an essentially flat top supported by one or several legs or pillars. (Note that this is a structural, not a functional definition.) This definition is quite unambiguous and any residual ambiguity will be largely extrinsic, rather than intrinsic, as defined above. (It must be understood that this applies primarily to structural definitions. I would hesitate to estimate how many problems needlessly plague biologists because of their fondness for functional rather than structural definitions.) What canons must we now specify in order that we may ascribe some aspect of real existence to this class. I would specify the following: (1) the class definition must be essentially unambiguous and any residual ambiguities must be extrinsic and not intrinsic; (2) the class must have at least one member which has real existence; (3) the member or members of the class must have a demarcable boundary, at least theoretically, in space-time. I will now discuss these specifications in order.

(1) The class definition must be essentially unambiguous, and any residual ambiguity must be extrinsic and not intrinsic. Members of a class may be designated in one of two ways. They may be designated by individual specification. For example, I may say, and touch with my finger, "this desk, this chair and this bookcase constitute the class of whingdings." Such denumerable, individually specifiable classes are a distinct minority insofar as practicability is concerned. To so specify the class of dollar bills, for example, would be not only wearisome but downright impossible if one wished to include those bills of the past which have since been destroyed. Thus the commoner method of designation of the members of a class is to describe the characteristics an individual must have to be considered a member of that particular class. The specification above, concerning unambiguity of definition, is necessary to fulfill the fifth canon of reality discussed in the section "Meaning of 'real'" above, which, in essence, states that reality must be communicable. Any ambiguity of definition, and particularly an intrinsic ambiguity, will result in a failure of communication. If Smith cannot describe a given phenomenon with essential unambiguity to Brown, Brown will never know whether or not he made observations comparable to Smith's. Yet such agreement is necessary before reality may be ascribed to the phenomenon. An ambiguously described phenomenon may be real, theoretically, but in actuality, no one

can prove it and it is thus effectively without reality. Since the definition of "table" is essentially unambiguous, or can be made so, it has satisfied the first canon.

(2) The class must have at least one member that has real existence. This simply says that reality can be ascribed only to real things. Thus the class of unicorns *might* possibly be unambiguously defined, but since there are no unicorns and never have been, it is an empty class and has no tincture of reality as defined above. Not all cases are so simple, however. The class of man-carrying space-ships is today an empty class, and so one without reality. I would hate to have to bet very much that it would be an empty class, say, five years from now. Since we do not know the future, as a practical matter we must understand that the one member necessary to ascribe reality to a class may be of past or present existence, with all bets off where the future is concerned. Similarly, I would hesitate to stake my life on the contention that there are not unicorns somewhere in the universe. Here again, as a practical matter, we must restrict ourselves to things within the possible present knowledge of man. In any case, the class of "tables" has at least one member, so that it fulfills this canon also.

(3) The member or members of the class must have a demarcable boundary, at least theoretically, in space-time. This specification is closely linked with the preceding ones. What it says is that a "real" class must in some sense be a naturally existing unit. Let us test the class of "tables" in this respect. At some time and place in the past, the first table was manufactured. The world line of this individual table could be plotted from its inception to its dissolution. Similarly world lines for all subsequent tables could be plotted. And similarly, sometime in the future, the world line of the last table will end. Thus we might draw a four-dimensional boundary around the entire class of "tables." This means that it is in a very real sense a natural unit strictly analogous to an individual. Since the real existence of a class is only by analogy to real existence of an individual, such a class may be said to have this analogical reality. Observe that such a unit is possible only if the class is unambiguously defined.

So we see that the class of "tables" fulfills all three canons and we are now justified in saying that the class of "tables" has real existence.

We may now ask if a biological species, any one, fulfills these three canons. It probably fulfills the second one, since if it is a "valid" species it has or had real individuals for members. The other two canons are a different matter, however. Consider Figure 5, in which the zone of short lines is a diagrammatic representation of the world line of the individuals making up a third order breeding population, a single phyletic line. At times a and b there existed two populations, which, we shall assume, were different enough to be considered two "species," a and b respectively, by ordinary standards. We may also assume, for the sake of simplicity, that no other species would be recognized in the interval between times a and b. Can a and b be unambiguously defined in such a way that individuals of

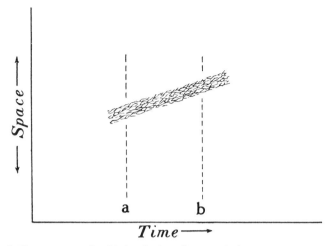

Fig. 5. Time segment of a third order breeding population.

the time interval *a b* can be unambiguously distributed between *a* and *b* and so that *a* and *b* will be demarcable units? It must first of all be observed that *a* and *b* are components of a biological continuum. (The succeeding discussion is based on the assumption that evolution on the "species" level took place in minute, usually unmeasurable, stages. I know of a great amount of actual evidence from the fossil record that this is true. I know of *no* evidence that it is not usually true. "Species formation" in the plants by the processes of hybridization and polyploidy are not considered. These processes would require the recasting of details of the argument of this paper insofar as it affects plants, but not animals. The general line of argument is not affected.) If we have an intracharacter continuum, there are obviously, even by definition, no natural demarcable units within it. Any definition attempted will be *intrinsically* ambiguous. Thus species as classes do *not* fulfill the first and third canons and cannot be said to have real existence in any sense.

We may now ask, if species as classes are without real existence, what have biologists been talking about all these years? Judging by descriptions of individual species, all too many did not know what kind of a unit they were talking about. However much lip-service has been paid by biologists to the dynamic philosophy of evolution with its Heraclitean flux, almost all biologists have dealt with species in terms of the outmoded, static, Platono-Aristotelian philosophy. In discussions of evolution, the following type of phrase is commonplace — "species *a* evolved into species *b*." This, *as it stands,* means that there was some sort of a definable unit, species *a*, which changed without any particular intermediate phase into species *b*. Such one-step speciation is possible in plants by hybridization or polyploidy. In animals, it is apparently rare and unimportant. In any case, the author of the phrase would probably say that he had no such thing in mind, that, of course, he did not intend to say there was any such jump from *a* to *b,* but he would go right on talking in these terms, and, linguistics being what they are, those who talk in such a fashion are almost certain to think in these same terms. Anyone who looks through evolutionary literature with this in mind can quickly locate literally hundreds of examples where it is obvious in context that the writer was thinking of species as discrete, objective, real units, regardless of any protestations the author may have that he realized the subjective character of biological classification. What all these workers, neontologists and paleontologists, have actually been dealing with is an arbitrarily set-off segment of a continuous phyletic line. For those who say, "Well, of course, but what of it?", I can only reply that it is extremely improbable that anyone who *thinks* in terms of the static species concept fails to appreciate the full implications of a dynamic philosophy such as evolution. It would be easy to quote examples to support this contention, but I prefer not to do so.

In this situation, the most obvious thing to do is to discard such a term as "species" with its overpowering load of undesirable connotations, and use or coin a new word for these phyletic-line segments which have been hitherto called "species." I do not think any such course will be adopted, the International Rules of Zoological Nomenclature being one of several reasons. To minimize these effects, however, I would suggest the following steps. First, all taxonomic units of whatever kind should be recognized explicitly for what they are—arbitrarily erected, man-made constructs, incautious use of which may result in obscuration to a degree which outweighs the convenience of recognizing such units. Secondly, the idea of the reality of evolving populations of individuals should always be kept in the forefront of any discussion of the evolutionary process. Such highly abstract fictions as "species", in the conventional abstract sense, will only continue to obscure such discussions.

Department of Geology,
University of Nebraska, Lincoln

LITERATURE CITED

BURMA, B. H. 1949. The species concept. Evolution 3:369-70, 372.

D'ABRO, A. 1950. The evolution of scientific thought. 2nd. ed. Dover.

GREGG, J. R. 1950. Taxonomy, language and reality. Am. Nat. 34:419–435.

MAYR, E. 1949. The species concept. Evolution 3:371-372.

WILLIAMS, D. C. 1951. The Sea Fight Tomorrow, *in* Structure, method and meaning, edited by Henle, Kallen, and Langer. Liberal Arts Press, New York, 306 pp.

7

Reprinted from *Am. Nat.,* **84**(819), 419–435 (1950)

TAXONOMY, LANGUAGE AND REALITY

JOHN R. GREGG

COLUMBIA UNIVERSITY, NEW YORK

I. SOME recent discussions in *Evolution* (Mayr, 1949; Burma, 1949) have reopened the old controversy whether species are *objectively real.*[1] The lay biologist, browsing in the literature and hoping to come on his account to a satisfactory resolution of this puzzle, is confronted with an immense record of apparently irreconcilable but at the same time irrefutable views, each claiming a basis in solid taxonomic fact. The history of this controversy, therefore, might suggest that intelligent analysis of the relevant factors presupposes intimate acquaintance with the foundations of taxonomy and intensive first-hand experience with the methods of taxonomic inquiry, and that criticism of the authoritative opinions that have been advanced is not an activity in which mere amateurs may profitably engage.

But to a stubborn inquirer the issues of this controversy sooner or later may come to appear less profound than muddled. There is much ground for the accusation that participants in it seldom have clearly formulated their ideas about the kinds of entities that are referred to by taxonomic class-expressions, or of the kinds of attributes that sensibly may be predicated of them, or of the sorts of relations that significantly may be said to hold between them. Taxonomic writing, therefore, frequently is guilty of *ambiguity of reference;* and the failure to distinguish explicitly between entities of such diverse taxonomic and logical types as organisms, classes of organisms, and classes of classes of organisms entails the sometimes very puzzling problem of deciding just what entities are being discussed. Furthermore, the liberal and semantically uncontrolled use of

---

[1] Detailed accounts of the controversy are given by Mayr (1942) and in the articles edited by Huxley (1941).

expressions like " objective," " real," " natural," " exist,"
" arbitrary," " subjective," " abstract " and " artificial " has
introduced into taxonomic theory much regrettable *ambiguity of meaning,* for these are among the most equivocal
of English expressions, and in taxonomic contexts it is not
always easy to see in which of several equally probable but
not equally defensible senses they are being employed.
Finally, there does not appear to be anywhere in taxonomic
literature a clear statement of the precise conditions that
would furnish grounds for decision whether or not species,
or any other taxonomic groups, are correctly to be characterized by using one or more of these expressions.   Taken
all together, the circumstances under which the controversy
has been conducted may seem to justify the suspicion that
little progress has been made because the basic issues have
never been clearly conceived.

The general tenor of the controversy suggests that taxonomists in attempting to support their various theoretical
views may be confusedly fighting a battle of hazily formulated private ontological dogmas when they might with
greater profit be appealing to methodological rules governing the construction of acceptable taxonomic systems.   This
suggestion will be developed further in the body of this
essay, which is offered as a preliminary step toward a
clearer, less ambiguous treatment of the problems of taxonomic methodology.   But it is one thing to recognize an
ambiguous situation and another to rectify it, and we shall
not claim to have done more than proceed a little way on
the road to clarity.

II. Whatever else taxonomists may be doing, we shall
suppose it correct to say that since the appearance in 1758
of the tenth edition of Linnaeus' *Systema Naturae* they
have been engaged in the business of *classifying* living and
extinct organisms; that is, they are concerned with constructing a system of *classes* of organisms in accordance
with some more or less explicitly formulated general principles that are designed to implement certain tacit or stated

taxonomic aims. We shall take it for granted, therefore, that species, genera, families and other taxonomic groups are classes of organisms; and that familiar expressions like "Arthropoda," "Chlamydomonas," "Diptera," "Canidae" and others are *class-names*.

Now, although there has been much discussion about the "existence" of entities named by these expressions, we can not concur in the view that this is a significant biological problem. But let us inquire, nevertheless, what it is that statements to the effect that taxonomic groups of various sorts exist are asserting; let us consider, for example, the statement:

(1)   Species exist.

As it stands, (1) is ambiguous: it may mean either that *all* species exist, or only that *some* (an unspecified number) of species exist. Suppose we consider the former case first. The problem now is to see just what it is that (1) may be asserting about species, if it is taken to mean:

(2)   All species exist.

We know what we mean by *other* statements of this same grammatical form. By "All fish swim," for example, we mean "For any x: if x is a fish then x can swim." If (2) is translated similarly, we arrive at:

(3)   For every A: if A is a species then A exists.

But unlike our statement about fish, which clearly provides us with the factual information that they are swimming things, (3) gives us no factual information whatever. The reasons are these. The negation of (3):

(4)   not (For every A: if A is a species then A exists)

is *inconsistent,* for it entails the self-contradictory statement:

(5)   There exists an A such that A does not exist.

Since (5) is self-contradictory, and therefore trivially false, it follows that (4) also must be false. But if (4) is false, then *its* negation, namely (3), must be *true;* and this solely by virtue of its linguistic form, not because it asserts any empirically verifiable fact. To say, therefore, that all species exist is to utter a trivial truth that, like " all red things are colored " and " $2 \times 2 = 4$," is certifiable on purely logical grounds; and to deny that all species exist is to be self-contradictory. Taxonomists anxious to defend the view that all species exist are also committed, therefore, to the view that all genera exist and that all families exist and indeed to the view that all unicorns exist (embarrassing though this may seem to be) for to deny it is to defend an inconsistency.

Suppose, on the other hand, that by (1) is meant only that:

(6)   Some species exist.

Now we might be tempted to translate (6) to read: " There exists an A such that A is a species and A exists "; for it is certainly correct to translate " Some fish swim," which has the same grammatical form as (6), to read: " There exists an x (at least one, perhaps thousands) such that x is a fish and x swims." But we shall argue that it is not a good idea to construe (6) in this way. The *subcontrary* of " Some fish swim," *i.e.*, " Some fish do not swim " means simply that " There exists an x such that x is a fish and x does not swim "; and this, whether true or false, is at least not self-contradictory. But the contrary of " Some species exist," *i.e.*, " Some species do not exist," when construed in this manner to read: " There exists an A such that A is a species and A does not exist," *is* self-contradictory, for it entails that there exists something that does not exist. If " exists " is used in this way, therefore, the subcontraries of statements like (6) have the queer property that they are inconsistent. We shall have to find some other way of employing " exists " if we are to preserve consistency in our language.

Now we all know what is meant by statements like: " Fish do not exist." We would never misconstrue this false statement to mean: " Some fish do not exist," for this is self-contradictory, as we have seen. Nor would we construe it queerly to mean: "All fish do not exist," that is, to mean: "Everything that is a fish does not exist." On the contrary, we would know it to mean mistakenly but exactly: "There is no x such that x is a fish." Similarly, we are always willing to construe:

(7)   Species do not exist

to mean the same as:

(8)   There is *no* A such that A is a species.

Now if we were to deny (7), and to assert that species *do* exist, then we must mean:

(9)   There *is* an A such that A is a species,

and this says all that legitimately can be asserted by "Species exist." Now (9), we shall claim, is a proper translation not only of (6), but exhibits the form of all existential statements like it. But note that (9), unlike "There is an A such that A is a species and A exists," does not assert that anything has the characteristic of existing, but only that something has the characteristic of being a species.

If these considerations mean anything, then the question whether taxonomic groups of various kinds exist is not very hard to settle. For, if the statement:

(10)   Species do not exist

means the same as:

(11)   There exists no A such that A is a species,

then (10) is *false*, for there *are* species: *Homo sapiens* is one, *Escherichia coli* is another, and *Anopheles quadrimaculatus* is another. Furthermore, if:

(12)   Families do not exist

is to mean the same as:

(13)   There is no A such that A is a family,

then this, too, is clearly false; for there are taxonomic families: Canidae is one, Drosophilidae is another, and Cicadidae is another. In general, *all* statements of the form of

"F's do not exist" are false, where "F" is substituted for by the name of any of the official taxonomic categories: "Species," "Genus," "Family" and the others. This being the case, all statements of the form of:

F's exist,

i.e.:

There is an A such that A is an F,

are *true,* whenever "F" is substituted for by any taxonomic category-name. In such statements, ostensible reference to existence as a *characteristic* of taxonomic groups does not occur. Certainly, no problems worthy of many decades of heated debate are posed by assertions such as this.

But the pseudo-problem of existence is not the only one that has been generated in taxonomy by the misuse of language: we may add also the question whether taxonomic groups are "abstract" entities, or whether they are objects discoverable, like organisms, "in nature." Now if it is correct to say that taxonomic groups are classes of organisms, then the question whether taxonomic groups are abstract entities is an instance of the more general question whether *classes* are abstract entities. Let us see what may be said on this topic.

One objection to the view that classes of organisms are spatiotemporal entities "in nature" is that adherence to it robs us of one of our most useful modes of expression. Among our most common expressions, in and out of technical biology, are statements like "Jones is a member of the class of humans," which are of the form of "The object x is a member of the class A." But if the view that class-expressions are names of spatiotemporal *objects* of some sort is correct, then in uttering expressions of this form we are guilty of uttering nonsense. For it is literally meaningless to say, in any usual sense of "is a member of" (see section III of this essay), that an object is a member of another object. Objections that it is not nonsense to say this seem based upon the notion (advanced independently by two different taxonomists reading an earlier version of this paper) that species are composed of organisms just as organisms are composed of cells: according to this argument a species is just as much a concrete, spatiotemporal thing as is an individual organism, though it is of a less integrated, more spatiotemporally scattered sort. This argument sounds fairly plausible, until one reflects that it contains an equivocation upon two common meanings of " is composed of." It is true that an organism is composed of cells; it is also true, but in a different sense, that species and other taxonomic groups are composed of organisms. The relation of a cell to the organism in which it is located is the relation of part to whole. But the organism–species relation is that of member to class; and these are entirely different sorts of relations. Let us suppose, for example, that there is a cell x which is a part of an organ y, and that y is a part of an organism z. It follows that x is part of z: part–whole is a *transitive* relation, like " less than." But given that some object x is a member of some class A and that A is a member of another class F, it does *not* follow (see section III) that x is a member of F; *i.e.*, membership is *not* a transitive relation. Therefore, " is composed of " can not be construed in the same context in the sense of " has as members " and in the sense of " has as parts." But we may go further than this.

Suppose that there is a cellular organism O. Let us mean by " C " the class of all the cells of O. On the view we are refuting, O and C are identical, *i.e.:*

(1) $O = C.$

Now, if the view that an individual is composed of a class of parts allows us to identify the individual and the class, then we may identify O with the class M of the *molecules* which compose O, *i.e.*, to assert:

(2) $O = M.$

From (1) and (2) we are now entitled to infer:

(3) $C = M,$

i.e., to infer that the class of cells composing O and the class of molecules composing O are identical. But this is

114

patently absurd, for these are *mutually exclusive* classes: no cell is a molecule and no molecule is a cell. We must admit, therefore, that:

(4) $C \neq M,$

but this contradicts (3).

In general, *classes and concrete entities can not be identified* and the part–whole relation used interchangeably with the member–class relation without engendering inconsistencies. Classes are *abstract, non-spatiotemporal* entities; and statements of the form of " x is part of y " should not be confused with statements of the form of " x is a member of A," where x and y are individual physical objects and A is a class.

Appeal to the ontological dogma that classes are spatiotemporal entities " in nature " in support of the view that certain taxonomic groups are " objectively real," while others are not, is thus seen to be ill-conceived. For all classes of objects (and classes of . . . classes of objects) are abstract, non-spatiotemporal entities. *This* problem, then, is a pseudo-taxonomic one which is to be resolved by reference to the semantic structure of language, and upon which no purely biological evidence (geographical distribution, interbreeding relations, etc.) has the slightest bearing whatsoever.

The supposition made by some taxonomists that classes of organisms *could be* spatiotemporal entities seems to have at least three sources: (a) The ambiguity of expressions like " is composed of," that confuse the part–whole relation with the member–class relation; (b) The historical accidents of everyday language in which classes metaphorically are referred to as *objects; e.g.,* " the *limits* of species are *blurred,*" " the *borderline* between species," " drawing a circle *around* species," etc.; and (c) The insidiously misleading use of class-expressions in place of individual-expressions; *e.g.,* " This species nests in oak trees" for " *The members of* this species nest in oak trees," and " This species is sexually active the year round " for " *The members of* this species are sexually active the year round," to use two actual examples from the literature that are wholly trivial in themselves, but nevertheless are indicative of the sort of linguistic ambiguity that does, finally, lead to disaster in exact theoretical discussion.

Whatever are the biologically interesting aspects of the controversy we have been discussing, it should be apparent by now that they are not associable in any literal sense with what is assertable by statements employing the expressions " objective reality in nature " and " existence." The misuse of expressions like these, as we have claimed earlier, has led taxonomists to confuse ontological pseudo-difficulties with genuine methodological problems facing them in the building of adequate taxonomic systems. It is time now that we turn to a discussion of the latter.

III. Before we can give an account of the most general features of some methodological problems confronting taxonomists, we must arrive at a clear understanding of the structural features of the system of classes they are engaged in constructing. We may begin by recalling some elementary logical distinctions that in ordinary language are expressed in various idioms of the verb " to be."

" Polaris " and " The North Star," we know, are expressions that refer to a single individual (namely, a certain bright object that appears at night above the northern horizon); and " Polaris is the North Star " is a statement that asserts this fact. Likewise, " Cicero " and " Tully " name the same individual; or, as we commonly say, " Cicero *is* Tully." In these examples, " is " is being used as a sign of *identity;* and to distinguish this usage of it from others we shall mention shortly, we shall write:

(1) $x = y,$

whenever we wish to assert that x and y are the same individual, using " = " (read " is identical with ") in place of " is "; *e.g.,* " Polaris = The North Star," and " Cicero = Tully."

Unlike " Cicero is Tully," the sentence " Arthropoda is the largest phylum " asserts the identity of reference not of two individual-names but of two expressions referring to a *class* of individuals; it tells us that "Arthropoda" and "The largest phylum" are expressions designating the same class of joint-legged invertebrates. We may write this in the manner of (1) to read: "Arthropoda = the largest phylum." In general, we shall write:

$$(2) \qquad\qquad A = B$$

whenever we wish to say that "A" designates the same class as "B."

A second use of "is" is illustrated by the statement: "Reynard is a fox." "Reynard," we know, refers to a single vulpine individual, while "fox" on the other hand refers to a whole *class* of such individuals. What "Reynard is a fox" is telling us, then, is that Reynard *is a member of the class of* foxes. We may write "Reynard is a fox" to read: "Reynard ε Fox," where "ε" (read: "is a member of the class") is written instead of "is a" not for esoteric reasons, but simply to distinguish this use of "to be" from its use as an identity sign. In general, whenever we want to say that an individual x is a member of a class A we can write an expression of the form of:

$$(3) \qquad\qquad x \, \varepsilon \, A.$$

In taxonomy, for example, there are many statements having this form: "x ε *Homo sapiens*," "x ε Arthropoda," "x ε Artemia" and others. "x ε A," therefore, corresponds to the common idiom "x *is an* A"; while "x = y" corresponds to the idiom "x *is* y."

The sign of class-membership "ε" may stand not only between an expression designating an individual and one designating a class of individuals—as in "x ε A"—but also between an expression designating a class and one designating a class of classes; as, for example, in "*Homo sapiens* ε Zoological Species," "Artemia ε Genus," and "Arthropoda ε Phylum." In general, we may write expressions of the form of:

$$(4) \qquad\qquad A \, \varepsilon \, F$$

to indicate membership of a class A in another class (of classes) F.

It should be noted here that given "$x = y$" and "$y = z$," it is always correct to infer "$x = z$"; but given "$x \,\epsilon\, A$" and "$A \,\epsilon\, F$" it is *not* correct to infer "$x \,\epsilon\, F$." For example, given "Jones ϵ *Homo sapiens*" and "*Homo sapiens* ϵ Zoological Species," it is not correct to infer "Jones ϵ Zoological Species." *Homo sapiens* is a class of organisms and thus may contain the organism Jones as a member, while Zoological Species is a class of *classes* of organisms (of which *Homo sapiens* is only one), and thus does not contain as a member the organism Jones, who is not a class of organisms. Membership thus differs from identity and from part–whole (as we saw in Section II) in being a non-transitive relation.

A third use of "to be" corresponds to the idiom "A's are B's"; as in "frogs are amphibians." What this latter expression says is that everything that is a frog is also an amphibian; *i.e.*, it says that for any x, if $x \,\epsilon\,$ Frog then $x \,\epsilon\,$ Amphibia. In general, when to be a member of a class A insures membership in another class B, then we shall say that A *is included in* B. If we write "$\subset$" to mean "is included in," then where A and B are classes:

(5)   "$A \subset B$" means the same as "For any x,
       if $x \,\epsilon\, A$ then $x \,\epsilon\, B$."

In taxonomy, for example, we have the statements: "Amphibia $\subset$ Vertebrata," "Drosophila $\subset$ Insecta," and others. Notice that it would not make sense to write "Amphibia ϵ Vertebrata" for (the class) Amphibia is not a *member* of (the class) Vertebrata; since Vertebrata is a class of organisms, and the class Amphibia is not an organism, but is itself a class of organisms. In general, given "$A \,\epsilon\, F$" it is not permissible to infer that any member of A is also a member of F.

We shall now employ the three relations designated by "$=$," "ϵ" and "$\subset$" in giving a brief account of the main structural features of the present-day system of biological classification, which for lack of a better name we shall call "L" (after Linnaeus, though his system has been considerably altered in the nearly two centuries since its proposal).

There is an important distinction to be made between what we shall call "taxonomic groups" in the Linnaean system L and what we shall call "taxonomic categories" in L. By "taxonomic group" we shall mean any class in L whose members are organisms, living or extinct; *e.g.*, Felis, *E. coli*, Reptilia, Hominidae, Echinodermata and others. By "taxonomic category" on the other hand we shall mean any class in L whose members are not organisms but are taxonomic groups; *e.g.*, Species, Genus, Family, Order, Class, Phylum, Kingdom and any subdivisions of these that may be introduced.

The relations holding between an organism, the various taxonomic groups of which it is a member, and the taxonomic categories of which the groups are members, are shown diagrammatically in Table I. If while consulting this table the reader will recall what is *meant* by statements in which "ϵ," "$=$" and "$\subset$" appear, he will note that while it makes sense to say that the membership relation holds between an organism and a taxonomic group or between a taxonomic group and a taxonomic category, it would *not* make sense to say that it holds between two organisms, two taxonomic groups, two taxonomic categories, or an organism and a taxonomic category. Similarly, the inclusion relation holds only between two taxonomic groups and never between two taxonomic categories or between an organism and the group to which it belongs. A little attention should make these facts clear; but should this not prove to be the case, the reader is invited to refer to Langer (1937) for a clear detailed elementary account of the theory of classes, and to Quine (1950) and Woodger (1937) for discussion of certain other logical matters touched upon in this essay.

We may now inquire what general criteria must be satisfied by a taxonomic group if it is to be admitted into the system L.

Simply by way of convention, let us agree to call a statement of the properties which an organism x must have in

TABLE I

Relations ordering the "Linnaean" system of classification. The organism designated by "x" in column 1 is a member of every taxonomic group named in column 3. Each taxonomic group is a member of the taxonomic category whose name appears in column 5 in the same row only. x is not a member of any of the taxonomic categories named in column 5. Turning to column 1, x is of course related to itself by identity, and is a member of the class *Organism*. In column 3, each taxonomic group named is included in (but is not a member of) every taxonomic group whose name appears above its name; and each taxonomic group named is a member of the class (of classes) *Taxonomic Group*. In column 5, each taxonomic category named is a member of the class (of classes of classes) *Taxonomic Category*. No direct ordering relation holds between the various taxonomic categories, for these are given in the system simply by enumeration (in particular, neither ε nor ⊂ relates them).

	1	2	3	4	5
	Organism		Taxonomic Group		Taxonomic Category
	ε		ε		ε
13	x	ε	Animalia	ε	Kingdom
12	=		⊂		
11	x	ε	Arthropoda	ε	Phylum
10	=		⊂		
9	x	ε	Insecta	ε	Class
8	=		⊂		
7	x	ε	Diptera	ε	Order
6	=		⊂		
5	x	ε	Drosophilidae	ε	Family
4	=		⊂		
3	x	ε	Drosophila	ε	Genus
2	=		⊂		
1	x	ε	Drosophila melanogaster	ε	Species

order to be a member of a particular taxonomic group A, a *group-description;* for example, a list of the properties which an organism must have in order to belong to the genus Daphnia, is a group-description. But we call attention to group-descriptions mostly to distinguish them from what we shall call *category-definitions.*

A category-definition, we shall say, is any list of the properties which a taxonomic group must have in order to be a member of a taxonomic category; a definition of "Phylum," for example, is a category-definition. Let us say, further, that a taxonomic group A *satisfies* a category-definition D when, and only when, A exhibits the properties mentioned in D. Arthropoda, for example, satisfies a certain definition of "Phylum" if, and only if, Arthropoda exhibits the properties mentioned in the definition; if so, "Arthropoda ε Phylum" is a true statement. But this must not be construed as meaning that just *any* definition of "Phylum" would be acceptable to taxonomists, for any such category-definition must meet certain requirements of adequacy relative to the purposes for which L is constructed.

For example, if L is being constructed simply as a *catalogue* of organisms, then the category-definitions of L must insure that the groups admitted to L meet one kind of criterion of adequacy; another kind of criterion of adequacy may have to be met by the groups admitted to L if L is being constructed to organize and exhibit our knowledge of certain specified *kinship* relations holding between organisms; and category-definitions need to be framed so that their employment shall result only in the admission to L of groups whose members exhibit these relations to each other and to the members of other admitted groups.

Let us suppose there is some set P of stated ends for which L is being constructed (in particular let us suppose that the statements of P formulate the modern aim of arriving at an *evolutionary* classification of organisms); and let us call a *requirement of taxonomic adequacy* a statement of the properties which the members of any taxonomic category must have if they are to further the ends mentioned in the statements of P. Let us suppose also that a requirement of taxonomic adequacy has been specified for the members of each category. Then we shall say that a taxonomic group A *satisfies* a requirement of taxonomic adequacy T when and only when A exhibits the properties mentioned in T. Let us then call *taxonomically adequate* any category-definition D such that every taxonomic group A satisfying D also satisfies a requirement of taxonomic adequacy for the groups that are members of the category defined by D.

Now we are in a position to state in quite explicit general terms what it is that taxonomists mean to assert when they apply to some taxonomic group A in L such terms as "natural," "objective," "real" and others: they must mean that

(6)   There is a D such that D is a category-definition, and A satisfies D, and D is taxonomically adequate.

And when they call some taxonomic group A in the system L "arbitrary," "subjective," "abstract," or "artificial" they must mean to say that the methodological conditions mentioned in (6) fail to hold for A. That is to say, if we are to make any sense at all of statements employing these ambiguous terms we must construe them as tacit references to rules of taxonomic procedure; not as appeals to various footless ontologies.

But if the foregoing is to stand as an acceptable analysis of such statements, then we must be able to account in terms of it not only for the generally held taxonomic view that genera, families and other groups belonging to the "higher" categories are best characterized by such terms as "subjective," "artificial," and "arbitrary," but also for the fact that there is widespread disagreement about a similar characterization of species.

Now, this analysis easily interprets the first view, that genera and other higher groups somehow occupy a taxonomic status different from that of species. It is commonly admitted by taxonomists there are no known definitions of "Genus," "Family," "Order," and so on, that are taxonomically adequate in the "evolutionary" sense—that is to say, whose use insures that among other things genera, families and orders will be established whose members bear to each other and to the members of other such groups certain specifiable evolutionary relations. There are many genera, families, etc., now listed in the Linnaean system that are arbitrary with respect to the requirements of an "evolutionary" classification; and this is sometimes expressed in the misleading ontological mode of speech by saying that they are not " objectively real." But it is obvious that a more defensible and adequate expression of these same facts can be made by reference to taxonomic criteria.

Our analysis also provides a ready interpretation of the species-controversy. For there *are* definitions of " Species " for which a limited taxonomic adequacy may be claimed, but most if not all of them have certain features about which disagreement can arise. For example, given a definition of " Species," it may be charged (we withhold opinion here) that it is inadequate because it is *vague* (*e.g.,* the definition: " A species is a group of morphologically similar organisms " may be said to be vague, for there are situations in which, given two organisms, it would be impossible to decide save by fiat whether or not they were sufficiently similar to belong to the same species) ; or that it is inadequate because it is *difficult practically to apply* (*e.g.,* the definition: " A species is a maximal group of interbreeding organisms " may sometimes be difficult to apply, since it is not always an easy matter to demonstrate that a set of populations *is* such a group) ; or that it is inadequate because it is *not generally applicable* (*e.g.,* the last definition is inapplicable to asexually reproducing organisms and to fossil organisms) ; or there may be still other reasons upon which may be based the charge that it is taxonomically inadequate.

Now whether or not any of the species-definitions now available are taxonomically adequate; and whether the species and other taxonomic groups now listed in taxonomic systems do as a matter of fact meet requirements of the sort mentioned in (6) is not our business to discuss; for these are genuine taxonomic problems upon which purely methodological considerations have little or no bearing. Indeed, probably no general statement one way or another would be correct, for taxonomic analysis in future may reveal that some taxonomic groups now listed in the Linnaean system are unsuitable while others are entirely acceptable. Such analysis profitably can be carried out only with respect to (a) specified taxonomic groups, (b) specified category-definitions, and (c) specified criteria of taxonomic adequacy; that is, under conditions in which it may be clearly recognized when an answer has been obtained, which only taxonomists are competent to specify. We *shall* claim, however, that problems of this kind (irrespective of whether we have given an adequate formulation of their general nature here) are the only taxonomically relevant issues raised by the question whether taxonomic groups, be they species or whatever, are objectively real; but to most biologists these may seem to offer a sufficiently stimulating challenge.

ACKNOWLEDGMENTS

My indebtedness to Professors Theodosius Dobzhansky, Ernest Nagel, and George Gaylord Simpson, and to Drs. A. J. Cain and Ernst Mayr, for detailed criticism and advice is considerable; but this grateful expression of it is not intended to provide the slightest clue to their opinions of my views.

LITERATURE CITED

BURMA, B., 1949 The species concept: a semantic review. Evolution **3:** 369–370.

HUXLEY, J., ed., 1940 The new systematics. Oxford University Press.

MAYR, E., 1942 Systematics and the origin of species. Columbia University Press.

1949 The species concept: semantics versus semantics. Evolution **3:** 371–372.

LANGER, S. K., 1937 An introduction to symbolic logic. Houghton Mifflin Company.

QUINE, W. V. O., 1950 Methods of logic. Henry Holt.

WOODGER, J. H., 1937 The axiomatic method in biology. Cambridge University Press.

Part III

MICROBIAL, PARTHENOGENETIC, AND PALEONTOLOGICAL SPECIES

Editor's Comments
on Papers 8 Through 10

8   COWAN
      The Microbial Species—A Macromyth?

9   DeBACH
      Uniparental, Sibling and Semi-species in Relation to Taxonomy and Biological Control

10   IMBRIE
      The Species Problem with Fossil Animals

The three papers in this section were chosen primarily because they illustrate the inapplicability of the biological species concept to situations where sexual reproduction occurs only rarely, if at all, or to situations where it is impossible to observe sexual reproduction and gene flow. Microorganisms present a problem for species definition not only because of their use of asexual reproduction, but also because environmental factors play a large role in determining their morphological and physiological responses. In bacteria, some genetic exchange is known, but the prevalent reproductive strategy is asexual division. Identification of species is often done by scoring the responses of cultures to various culturing techniques and to different enzymes, and the results are analyzed by numerical taxonomy methods, using computers. Sherman (1962) has suggested that each bacterial culture be treated as a natural unit, a concept that is somewhat similar to the local population concept in higher animals and plants. Some of the problems of defining species in microbes are discussed by Cowan (Paper 8), who concludes that the species is not a useful concept in microbial studies.

Similar problems are found when attempts are made to apply species concepts to blue-green algae and fungi. Blue-green algae reproduce asexually, although there is a possibility that genetic transfer may take place in one genus (Van Baalen, 1973). As in bacteria, species limits are set by the methods of numerical taxonomy (Desikachary, 1973; Komarek, 1973). Although fungi can reproduce sexually, much of their reproduction is asexual, which precludes any study of interbreeding among populations. Ciferri (1932) listed a number of criteria for defining fungal species. These included morphological characteristics, biological characteristics such as symbiotic relationships and localization of the fungus on a host, and cultural characteristics based on the behavior of the fungus on an artificial medium. Unfortunately, morphological, biological, and cultural characteristics appear to be greatly influenced by environmental factors (States, 1969), making them generally unreliable as criteria for species determination. Among the morphological characters, the reproductive spores appear to be the least variable (States, personal communication), a situation that provides a pathway to a typological species concept. The problem of asexual reproduction also arises in protozoans, sponges, and coelenterates. Although a sexual cycle is known in most bryophytes and lichens, asexual reproduction is very common.

The parthenogenesis discussed by DeBach (Paper 9) is a specialized form of asexual reproduction in which embryos develop from unfertilized eggs. This is the type of asexual reproduction found in higher animal groups. Plants are more versatile in their asexual reproductive methods. Stebbins (1950) lists three types of apomixis (asexual reproduction) found in plants: (1) vegetative reproduction, by means of runners, buds on bulbs, or vegetative propagules; (2) adventitious embryony, in which an embryo develops from nucellar cells or the integument of the ovule without the development of a gametophyte; and (3) gametophytic apomixis, in which a diploid gametophyte is present. Gametophytic apomixis in plants can be further subdivided into two types: (1) apogamety, in which an embryo develops from a somatic diploid cell of the gemetophyte; and (2) parthenogenesis, in which an embryo develops from a diploid egg cell of the gametophyte. Regardless of the mechanism, asexual reproduction allows genetic material to be passed from parent to offspring but does not allow genetic material to be exchanged between members of the parental generation. As an evolutionary strategy, this may be a very successful form of reproduction for organisms that have short generation spans which allow mutations to accumulate. The more rapid accumulation of mutations promotes variability in organisms that have low vagility, cannot search out mates, and live in reasonably stable environments which are still capable of change. As a factor to be taken into account in species definitions, asexual reproduction raises serious problems for any unified species concept that is based on lateral gene flow between parents.

In paleontological work, no direct observation of interbreeding is possible. All conclusions concerning interbreeding populations must be made through inference, primarily from morphological and stratigraphic data. Some of the problems and methods of species delimitation are discussed by Imbrie (Paper 10), who identifies *transient species* as "reproductively isolated groups of individuals living during a single instant of geologic time" and *successional species* as "segments of phyletic lineages." Imbrie points out that, in practice, neontologists (those who study present-day organisms), and most paleontologists describe transient species. Unfortunately, in the absence of experimentation or direct observation of reproductive relationships, a discussion of reproductive isolation becomes a matter of probability, bolstered by the hypothesis that morphological divergence parallels reproductive divergence. In such cases, taxonomists often make inferences concerning reproductive isolation on the basis of their intuitive feel for the reproductive significance of a given degree of morphological divergence. Nor are paleontological species always susceptible to the more quantifiable methods of numerical taxonomy and multivariate analysis, since skeletal materials of some groups of organisms may undergo varying degrees of deformation within strata. It must be pointed out, however, that given the nature of fossil materials, most problems in delimiting paleontological species and applying a criterion of interbreeding are methodological, rather than conceptual problems relating to the nature of species.

8

Reprinted from *Symp. Soc. Gen. Microbiol.,* **12** (*Microbial Classification*),
433–455 (1962)

THE MICROBIAL SPECIES—
A MACROMYTH?

S. T. COWAN

*National Collection of Type Cultures, Central Public Health
Laboratory, Colindale Avenue, London, N.W. 9*

> Je m'en vais chercher un grand peut-être—
> Last words attributed to François Rabelais, 1553
> (Cohen & Cohen, 1960)

If this Symposium had been on Chemical Classification, it would have been relatively simple to define the different units such as element, salt, organic compound and so on, but in biology our units are much less precise, and the species, which is probably referred to most of all, is an enigma. Mine is the twentieth and last contribution to the Symposium; each of the other nineteen papers will have contained the word species, and—writing without seeing any of them—I am sure the word has been used to cover at least nineteen concepts. The word 'species' may have been used in nineteen different ways, but it will have been readily understood by the readers of this book, although to each reader, just as to each contributor, the concept behind it will be different. Among biologists there are those who are confident that they know what a species is, and these are people living in the twentieth century, not in the pre-Darwinian era as you might imagine. Let me quote from a hand-book on evolution, of anonymous (1959) authorship but published with the authority and prestige of the Trustees of the British Museum: 'the reproach that such species are subjective concepts and have no existence outside the mind of the scientist who "made" them...cannot be levelled at the biological criterion of the species, which is that of a group of organisms reproductively isolated from all other organisms'. But the anonymity of the hand-book clearly conceals the plurality of its authorship, for a less dogmatic assertion appears only two paragraphs later: 'species are not necessarily the end-products of finite changes, but stages in a continual process of potentially infinite change' so that in two paragraphs the hand-book skips a hundred years. The size of the problem is indicated by Hillaby's (1960) statement that there are about three-quarters of a million known species of insects, and that 20 million specimens of insects have been lodged in the Natural History Museum.

129

With species a source of confusion to the less categorical botanists and zoologists, how much more difficult it must be for the micro-biologist, dealing with populations that normally do not increase by sexual reproduction and are seldom isolated (reproductively or otherwise) from other microbial populations. To review the subject of microbial species it seems logical to study the use of the word 'species', both historically and biologically, and to consider the kind of biological unit to which it may be applied; this will demand consideration of the problems of classification in an evolving population, and it is certain that I shall go over ground that has already been covered more adequately by the other contributors to the Symposium.

USE OF THE WORD 'SPECIES'

Species is an old word and has been used with various (but perhaps related) meanings. Genus and species are two of the Five Predicables of Porphyry's Isagoge or Introduction to the Categories, genus being a group of things that is divisible into subgroups of species, and species the groups into which a genus may be divided. The biological use of 'species' derives from that of the logician, and John Locke (1689), in *An Essay Concerning Human Understanding*, gave definitions which, although not intended to be applied to the then undiscovered microbe, have hardly been bettered. Here is an example: '*genera* and *species*... depend on such collections of ideas as men have made, and not on the real nature of things'. This definition goes to the heart of the problem. Except for certain pathogens, where cause and effect can easily be proved and the species characterized by its specific pathogenicity, microbial species are populations of small cells, each of which is made up of a cell-wall (with its own characteristics) and the contents of the cell (with another set of characteristics). In the past both the cell-wall and the cell constituents have been analysed serologically, but in more recent years attention has been directed to their chemical nature. Biochemists may look upon microbes as bags of enzymes and to this concept another of Locke's definitions seems applicable: 'our distinct species are nothing but distinct complex ideas, with distinct names annexed to them'.

Biologists have not improved on Locke's definitions. In a book entitled *The Origin of Species* we might expect a definition of the subject but Darwin did not attempt one. In the following quotations the page numbers refer to a modern reprint of the last (6th) edition of *The Origin of Species* (Thompson, 1958):

Nor shall I here discuss the various definitions which have been given of the term species. No one definition has satisfied all naturalists; yet every naturalist knows vaguely what he means when he speaks of a species. Generally the term includes the unknown element of a distinct act of creation (p. 50).

Hence, in determining whether a form should be ranked as a species or a variety, the opinion of naturalists having sound judgment and wide experience seems the only guide to follow (p. 54).

The term species thus comes to be a mere useless abstraction, implying and assuming a separate act of creation (p. 56).

From these remarks it will be seen that I look at the term species as one arbitrarily given, for the sake of convenience, to a set of individuals closely resembling each other, and it does not essentially differ from the term variety which is given to less distinct and more fluctuating forms (p. 59).

Undoubtedly there is one most important point of difference between varieties and species; namely, that the amount of difference between varieties, when compared with each other or with their parent-species, is much less than that between the species of the same genus (p. 64).

Often 'species' is defined in terms of 'genus', so that the definitions of genus and species are interdependent. This concept of dividing a large group into subgroups which are themselves divisible into sub-subgroups was used in the third century by Porphyry in constructing his Tree, and the same principle is used by the biologist to draw up trees of the usual biological classification. Unfortunately, at this stage the microbiologist, even more than the biologist, is deceived by his own works. Remembering his history books he thinks of these trees in terms of kinship or relationship, and he goes on to draw the unwarranted assumption that the tree he has drawn reveals the phylogenetic relations of the organisms. As used in microbiology the trees are generally made as an aid to diagnosis or identification, and are based on easily ascertainable characters; if they were to show true relationships much more fundamental characters (probably obscured by the ones we use for diagnosis) would need to be found and used in the tree.

BACTERIAL EVOLUTION

It is not my purpose to suggest here that different bacteria have all evolved from a single primordial kind, each adapting to its own surroundings so that after millions of years they have acquired individual characteristics. We now recognize that micro-organisms are not static units; they show a continuous adaptation to their environment, and it is pertinent to ask why, when they are transferred to new surroundings, they do not immediately become unrecognizable. If they made this change suddenly and completely they would achieve something equivalent to a transformation of species. We must suppose that on transfer to unfavourable surroundings most of the organisms die and only a small proportion of the inoculum survives. The survivors may be able to cannibalize the bodies of their less fortunate fellows and so utilize compounds synthesized by their kind. Meanwhile, adaptation is taking place, slowly at first, but with gradually increasing tempo. In this evolving microcosmos we are indeed looking for trouble when we try to arrange the individuals in an orderly manner, and before we start on such a project we should find out what considerations are involved.

We should consider whether our arrangement is intended to show a progression of adaptations from source-form to end-form, or whether it is to show (or to try to show) a series of relationships each of different degree as in the genealogical trees. Is our arrangement intended to be didactic, erudite or strictly practical? Since we do not normally ask ourselves these questions, they remain unanswered.

Enumeration or cataloguing hardly comes into classification, as each specimen may be a separate subdivision or unit within the catalogue. We should also distinguish between classification and identification. Identification demands the characterization of a single specimen so that it can be compared with previously identified specimens; a characterization for diagnosis is based on certain selected characters (differentiae) which are known to have special value; unlike classification, where large numbers of characters of equal weight are compared, as few as eight characters are sufficient to make a diagnosis (to the level of genus) of the common bacterial pathogens (Cowan & Steel, 1961). When specimens have been identified by using the differentiae, several specimens may be sorted into groups of similar and dissimilar units and form the basis of a classification. This is where microbiologists forsake principle for expediency; the limited number of differentiae are often regarded as adequate for characterization, and characters believed to be unimportant are either not investigated or not recorded. The truth of this statement can be seen not only in the seven editions of *Bergey's Manual of Determinative Bacteriology* (1923–57), but in the papers describing bacteria, the papers on which the *Manual* is based.

To make a classification we must create units into which the specimens can be sorted; a decision must be made whether these units are to be of equal value or whether they are to be graded in the form of steps or ranks. The decision will be based on convenience and, to some extent, on the purpose of the classification. The names of the units will also be determined by convenience; they can be as simple as a numerical sequence, as in first-, second- and third-class railway travel, or they can be as complicated (and definitive) as the deme terminology of Gilmour & Heslop-Harrison (1954) for plants. When a classification deals with living things it is usual, but not essential, to cast the units in terms of a hierarchical system and use a terminology based on a genealogical tree, with names such as family, genus and species. Other names have been suggested instead of species, but whatever we call our working unit, we define it to suit our purpose.

'The boundaries of the species, whereby men sort them, are made by men' (Locke, 1689) is as true in microbiology today as it was in a philosophical sense three hundred years ago. Since it is a conception that exists only in the mind of the beholder, the biological species is a unit without parallel in any other science. Just as no two observers see the same rainbow, so no two biologists conceive exactly the same species. Yet to most biologists the species, although indefinable, is something real; this sense of reality may be a relic of an upbringing which involved a literal interpretation of what was clearly a poetic description of the origin of the world. We know that it cannot be a divine creation because, like all living things, the species as it exists today consists of survivors of an earlier population, survivors that have adapted themselves to their surroundings, often adverse. A microbial species is a population, not a particular specimen; it follows that, like any other population, it is made up of many different individuals each of which shares certain features with its fellows. Camp (1951) prefers to call the unit a 'binom' until such time as its genetic relations to other units have been defined; this is a compromise between the older static species of special creation and the post-Darwinian dynamic unit which shows an evolutionary pattern and has indefinable limits. It can be combined with the 'type' concept of classical taxonomy, the type acting as the centre of the unit (which we call species or binom according to our whim), the less typical individuals being grouped about the type, their distance from the centre being inversely proportional to their community with the type (Fig. 1).

The main unit of a biological classification is the species which is intended to be an assemblage of specimens so similar that experienced workers would say they were alike. This is much the same as defining a species as what a competent worker says is a species. The futility of this type of definition was well illustrated by Camp (1951) in quoting three 'competent' systematists (two of whom were past presidents of the American Society of Plant Taxonomists and were thus entitled to be described as competent specialists) who classified the same material, the blackberries and raspberries (*Rubus*) native in North America, and divided them into 494, 205 and 24 species! Between the extremes of these

133

three experts there is a 20-fold difference in the number of species recognized, which means that, in a population that one would call homogeneous, another found twenty different kinds. It is interesting to note that *Rubus* did not present any taxonomic difficulties to Linnaeus (Ramsbottom, 1938).

Julian Huxley (1940) says that species are natural units which: (*a*) have a geographical distribution area; (*b*) are self-perpetuating as groups; (*c*) are morphologically (rarely only physiologically) distinguishable from other related groups; and (*d*) normally do not interbreed with related groups.

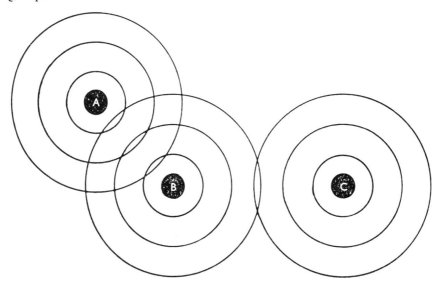

Fig. 1. Diagram to illustrate the use of the type concept, by which an unknown organism B is shown to have a closer affinity to type A than to type C.

To quote Huxley (1938) again, the chief effect of geographical isolation is the insertion of 'biological discontinuities of different degrees of completeness into populations showing continuously-varying adaptive differentiations, thus accentuating the closeness of adaptation' and also, by adding some degree of non-adaptive differentiation, increasing the diversity. A species distinction created by geographical isolation is shown by two gulls (*Larus argentatus* and *L. fuscus*) native in the British Isles where they do not interbreed (Fisher & Lockley, 1954). Both are probably derived from a form found in the Behring Straits; from there it is assumed the gulls migrated both eastward and westward encircling the North Pole as a 'ring species' with ten intermediates differing mainly by colour of legs and mantles. Because the ends of the chain do not interbreed we have two apparently different species in the British Isles, but the dividing line between the species has to be made arbitrarily between two interfertile intermediates. In this connexion it is interesting to note that Breed, Conn & Baker (1918) wrote that 'the living species (of bacteria) represent only the ends of evolutionary lines, and that one modern form must not be considered the ancestor of another'.

Most biologists will today accept the theory that geographicaily separated groups may evolve into different species (Smith, 1958), but the effect of the environment is more debatable. That acquired characters can be transmitted to the progeny is a view that is not generally accepted, though Cannon (1958, 1959) thinks that Lamarck's ideas have been distorted and grossly misrepresented. It is possible that microbiology may provide the evidence that Lamarck's followers have been seeking, for a microbial population (a strain) that acquires a property in a new environment may retain it for some time when transferred back to the old (Penfold, 1911; Klieneberger, 1927) though a re-adaptation may sometimes occur within five generations (Spiegelman, 1951). Examples of complete and permanent adaptation (or mutation) are seen in strains of *Brucella abortus* which, when first isolated, need CO_2 for growth but quickly lose this character on subculture; and some strains of *Haemophilus* species become less fastidious after prolonged subculture and no longer require X and/or V factor(s). Such strains have become completely adapted to a non-parasitic existence and may well provide good reasons why Lamarckism should not be summarily dismissed. If the change affected many characters the adaptation to the new environment might make the strain appear to change from one species to another, but in such cases it would be debatable whether the original strain had been 'pure' or composed of two populations each of which became dominant in turn in the different environments. Shimwell (1959) goes so far as to say that 'the majority of *Acetobacter* cultures are, or soon become, mixtures of two or more "species"'. Extending their observations beyond the genus *Acetobacter*, Shimwell & Carr (1960) found such variation in colony form on different media that they concluded that 'existing classifications, based on the study of cultures under different chemical and physical conditions, may be nothing more than the classification of mixed and composite cultures, which may vary in cell composition according to the tests applied'.

THE TYPE CONCEPT

Buchanan (1955), the authority on bacterial nomenclature, is a firm
believer in the type concept and says that: 'A bacterial species may then
be defined as the type culture together with such other cultures or
strains of bacteria as are accepted by bacteriologists as sufficiently
closely related. The designation of type cultures of the type species of the
various bacterial genera is a matter of major importance.... The delimitation of the boundaries of the species is not attempted, the circumscription of the species is the task of the systematist; it is not nomenclature.' The last sentence shows that Buchanan has in mind the species
name; but the species itself must be delimited before the nomenclaturist
has a right to give it a name. Omission of the essential characterization
is the cause of so many synonyms for one organism.

This definition acknowledges the fact that the type strain of a species
need not be the most characteristic strain of that species just as a type
species need not be the best known of a genus. The rules for the selection
of bacterial types are laid down in the Bacteriological Code (1958)
and the annotations to Rule 9d indicate that in order of preference the
type strain is (1) one designated by the original author of a name (holotype); (2) if he failed to designate a holotype then one of his strains may
be chosen by a later worker (lectotype); (3) a strain selected by subsequent workers when none of the original author's strains is available;
most type strains are of this kind and are called neotypes. The type concept can also be criticized on the grounds that a single strain cannot
indicate the variation admissible in a species; according to Braun (1953)
a 'typical' representative of a species is the particular mutant pre-
dominating under laboratory conditions of growth.

The type concept is not entirely theoretical but it is more complex than
a series of circles drawn around the type centres as shown in Fig. 1. In
reality it is multidimensional and can best be shown, though still only
incompletely, in the form of models such as those constructed by
Lysenko & Sneath (1959) to show the complex relations of the intestinal
and other bacteria we call the Enterobacteriaceae.

The subdivision of bacteria has not followed any particular plan;
each group has been considered in isolation and not in relation to its
fellows. To some extent the degree of subdivision can be correlated with
the importance of the organism in some field; for example, the finer subdivisions (serotypes and phage types) of the Salmonella group are of
importance in epidemiological surveys, but they contribute little to the
treatment of the individual patient. They are thus important to the

epidemiologist and the Medical Officer of Health, but hardly at all to the family doctor. Because bacteria often form a series of intergrading forms arbitrary decisions must be made about the allocation of a single isolate to one or other of the subdivisions, a good example being the arbitrary placing of certain bacteria in the Salmonella or Arizona groups (Seligmann & Saphra, 1951); other examples are given in Cowan (1959 a).

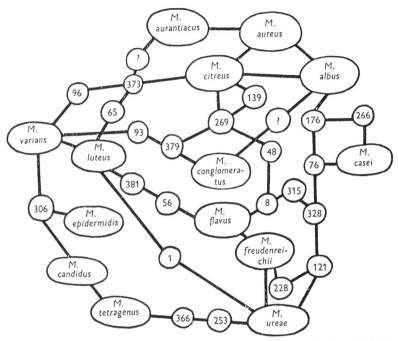

Fig. 2. Diagram to show relations between micrococci in Hucker's collection. A difference of one character separates each circle. Numbers are those of strains in Hucker's collection, and the species names are those used by Hucker. (From Rahn (1929) by permission of Gustav Fischer Verlag.)

Since micro-organisms share many features in common, they resemble a spectrum of gradually changing form; if there are breaks in the spectrum divisions can be made at these breaks, but if the change is continuous it is difficult to know where to draw the lines demarcating the different units. Rahn (1929) thought that species were defined too completely. Taking an example from Hucker's (1924 a, b) monographs on micrococci, in which many intermediates were found in spite of the recognition of a large number of species, Rahn arranged the species and intermediates as circles in a complex figure, each circle differing from its neighbour by only one character (Fig. 2). In Hucker's collection Rahn found representatives for each, except two, of the circles in his figure.

The plan for making subdivisions may be likened to the subdivision of a group of people of varying height. Adult men and women show every variation from about 4 ft. 6 in. to 7 ft.; if we plot the number or proportion against height we shall get a typical Gaussian distribution curve, but the absence of useful dips or peaks prevents us from breaking up the series. However, if we combine height with colour of hair, in a particular group we might find that among the tall (T) most were fair (F) and among the short (S) most were dark (D); by combining these features we could arrange our series as say, TF 35, SD 30, TD 20, SF 15, giving us two main groups TF and SD. In each of these main groups we could find the mean height (say 5 ft. 9 in. and 5 ft. 1 in.) and make our central figures (or types) as 5 ft. 9 in. and fair and 5 ft. 1 in. and dark. Individuals of other heights would be grouped about these centres. In this argument I have simplified matters by recognizing only two colours of hair with height as the only variable. In practice we should find some people of doubtful colour and observers would vary in their descriptions of the pigment. So it is in microbiology; different observers will score the same character in different ways. To add to the subjectiveness of the observations (and this can only be eliminated by making all measurements quantitative), we find a subjectiveness in interpretation; for example, one observer might put 5 ft. 3 in. people in the tall group, another would put them in the short group. Thus, even when the observation is exact (as in height) the allocation of that observation depends on the standard, which is subjective. Four subgroups are now recognizable in the population we are sampling, people who form a series of gradually increasing height. If we now add a third character and choose sex we are complicating the picture. Sex is determined not by one character but by a series of anatomical, physiological and psychological factors, so that between the complete male and female there are at least 15 intersex types (Armstrong, 1958). The addition of sex divides our 4 subgroups not into 8 (as the layman might suppose) but into any number from 4 (if they are all of one sex) to $4 \times 17 = 68$. In this example we have used only three main features, height, colour of hair and sex. The more features we use, or the more ways in which the features can be expressed, the more numerous will be the subdivisions unless certain of the features are linked with other features. The more features we use, the more exactly will the ultimate unit be defined.

Shimwell & Carr (1961) distinguish between the type concept (based on an extant culture) and the Linnaean concept (based on a description of an extinct culture), and point out that because characterization was so inadequate the Linnaean concept should not be applied to micro-organisms described before the twentieth century. Linnaeus is regarded as a protagonist of the fixity-of-species school, but Ramsbottom (1938), in reviewing his writings, showed that at least some degree of change and variability became acceptable in the later years of his life. Few now question evolution and because micro-organisms multiply rapidly, evolutionary changes take place more quickly than in forms of life with generation times reckoned in years rather than minutes. Are we, then, attempting the impossible in trying to define a species, and wasting our time in trying to characterize constantly changing features? Braun (1953) thinks that a description of a bacterial species should indicate its potential mutational range.

It is clear that we cannot apply to microbes Huxley's (1940) criteria for species because in laboratory studies sexual reproduction seems to be a rare event in the life of most micro-organisms. van Niel (1955), after quoting Babcock & Stebbins as saying 'The species, in the case of a sexual group, is an actuality as well as a human concept; in an agamic complex it ceases to be an actuality', goes on to say that we cannot hope to apply the modern concepts of biologists to micro-organisms 'so as to render the bacterial and myxophycean species "actualities" rather than merely "human concepts"'.

DEVELOPMENT OF NEW IDEAS ON MICROBIAL SPECIES

In 1946 van Niel advocated the discontinuance of the terms genus and species for bacteria, and the development of multiple diagnostic keys; later he (van Niel, 1955) supported Winogradsky's (1952) 'biotypes' untrammelled by type species, the type concept and other restrictive practices enjoined by the Bacteriological Code.

The Société Française de Microbiologie had a discussion on the species concept, and Lwoff (1958) in opening pointed out that because bacteria are, in general, asexual, it is difficult to find a starting-point. The descendants of a single strain would all be considered to be of the same species in spite of the fact that, by mutation and selection, the descendants might differ in several ways from the parent culture. In his view the species is merely a stage in an evolutionary process, a stage in a precarious equilibrium. Vendrely (1958) expressed a hope that analysis of DNA might show species differences; the relation between the amino acid content of DNA, particularly the ratio between adenine + thymine to guanine + cytosine, was thought to have taxonomic significance and to show species differences. Schaeffer (1958) thought that confusion would be lessened if authors of dichotomous keys used the terms group and subgroup instead of genus and species. In Thibault's (1958) view the subdivision of bacteria is too rigid, and a new nomenclature and a new taxonomy must be developed.

The discussion of the Société Française seemed to mark a turning point at which bacterial taxonomists began to take notice of genetics and to rely less on the older criteria. Also in 1958 at a Rutgers University symposium, after giving a paper on classification (Cowan, 1959a), I was assured by several biochemists that they were about to settle the whole problem, presumably because DNA is supposed to bear the genetic information transferred in transformation, transduction and conjugation (Ravin, 1960). I have not yet seen the solution of all our problems and there still seems to be plenty of work for taxonomists to do.

It was also in 1958, at the meeting of the International Committee on Bacteriological Nomenclature, that another discussion took place on what unit should be regarded as a species. This was followed by Kauff-mann's (1959a, b) proposal that among the Enterobacteriaceae the sero-type should be the species unit; a proposal that was later extended to the pneumococci (Kauffmann, Lund & Eddy, 1960), and by implication, to all other groups of bacteria that could be subdivided by serological analysis. I pointed out (Cowan, 1959b) that this was an extreme pro-posal, and suggested that it would be more logical to go to the other extreme and regard each group (Salmonella, Arizona, Escherichia, etc.) as a species of one genus (the present family Enterobacteriaceae). At that time both suggestions seemed to be extreme and since they would involve too many changes in nomenclature, would be quite unacceptable. Taylor (1959) also protested against the proposed synonymy of species and serotype.

In 1961 Kauffmann modified his definition of a species to read 'A species is a group of related sero-fermentative phage-types'. This definition is difficult for the non-specialist to understand and Kauffmann explains that 'sero-fermentative' refers to the *Salmonella* species that were characterized biochemically and serologically in the first Report (1934) of the Salmonella Subcommittee, and gives as an example the type species, *Salmonella cholerae-suis*. Certain salmonellas, for example *S. typhi* and *S. paratyphi*-B, can be subdivided into phage types, and these he calls 'sero-fermentative phage types'. However, it is not clear whether the species as now defined by Kauffmann is a sub-division of a serotype, or is the smallest unit that can be characterized by present-day techniques.

Genetics now play a greater part in the thought put into defining a microbial species and among the newer definitions Bryson (1959), with his tongue in his cheek, produced: 'A microbial species may be defined as a group of minute organisms possessing certain collective properties and limits of genetic and phenotypic variability, as established by a statistically unique but not necessarily uniform system of hereditary determinants'. At the same symposium I (Cowan, 1959 a) said that the argument about the fixity of species might 'end by providing a definition of a bacterial species as the lowest rank that cannot be altered by artificial means' but I did not explain what I meant by 'artificial means' and, looking back, the phrase is now as obscure to me as Robert Browning's poems were to him (Chesterton, 1903).

Ravin (1960) has pointed out that the living universe is not a vast community of genetically interacting organisms but is divided into populations between which 'gene flow' is impossible. The breaks in the gene flow form the barriers which separate the 'biological species' of the 'modern systematist trained in genetics'.

We need not be despondent at our inability to define species; the botanists and zoologists, although they deal more often with interbreeding forms, have equal difficulties. Consider for a moment the species *Paramecium aurelia* which has two mating types (corresponding to sexes). This 'species' is divided into a number of varieties (subspecies) which do not normally interbreed; when mating between different varieties does occur it has fatal consequences for the participants. It appears, therefore, that the varieties have the mating qualities of distinct species and that taxonomists have made a major error in assessing the rank of *Paramecium aurelia* as a species (Sonneborn, 1947).

HIERARCHICAL SYSTEMS IN MICROBIOLOGY

So far our attempts to define a microbial species have proved fruitless, and we may be able to shorten the argument by asking ourselves the simple question: do we need or want species? Various substitutes have been proposed for the species, the deme terminology (Gilmour & Heslop-Harrison, 1954), the binom (Camp, 1951), the biotype (Winogradsky, 1952) and the 'biological species' (Ravin, 1960) are examples, and none of them assumes that living things can be arranged in a hierarchical system.

Trees of Porphyry are not confined to biological problems of classification; they are equally applicable to the subdivision of motor cars (Cowan, 1957, 1959 a) or joiners—things that join (Fig. 3).

In a biological classification this type of tree shows subdivisions that are possible with the knowledge available and is thus an alternative

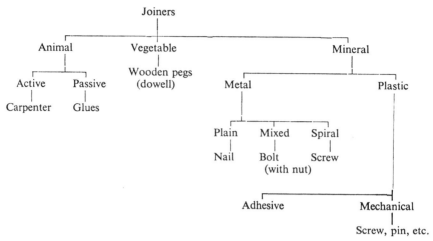

Fig. 3. Tree to show how joiners may be classified; an alternative scheme is shown in **Fig. 4.**

method of expressing a diagnostic key; it does not indicate the degree of relationship that would be shown by a genealogical tree. With increasing knowledge other relations may be found; for example, when we remember that beaten egg (white and yolk) is used in cooking as a binding agent, we realize that the passive animal adhesives need subdividing. We also see that the tree could be redrawn in many other ways; one of which, using different criteria, is shown in Fig. 4.

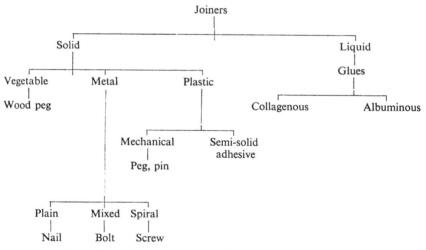

Fig. 4. Alternative tree for the subdivision of joiners (cf. Fig. 3).

The Tree of Porphyry is a device used consciously or unconsciously by all who classify by breaking down the larger unit. In biology we have tried to make it more meaningful by assigning ranks to the different levels and creating a hierarchical system, but by doing so we have added to our difficulties because many have assumed that it has magically developed a phylogenetic significance. Turrill (1952) would have us be more honest and admit that the trees only show resemblances. Rank depends on circumstances rather than on qualities, as was shown in 1960 when a Congolese Sergeant-Major became a General overnight. In orthodox taxonomy the rank of a bacterium cannot be expressed in a simple relation to other organisms, for every individual is treated as belonging to a number of categories of consecutive rank (*Bacteriological Code*, 1958, Principle 7(*a*)) of which, as Pirie (1955) has pointed out, only the individual organism is real. All higher ranks are figments of the imagination and occur only in the minds of taxonomists. The units larger than the individual are populations which we name colonies, strains, species and so on, and many taxonomists believe that the arrangement is natural (i.e. phylogenetic), and like a marriage made in Heaven. In fact, all these arrangements are artificial and are more like marriages of convenience. We should always bear in mind that the individual elements making up these taxonomic units are not necessarily alike but each, as Gilbert (1883) said, through the mouth of Sergeant Willis, 'is either a little Liberal or else a little Conservative', or in the more modern idiom of Orwell (1945), 'all...are equal but some are more equal than others'.

Steel (p. 419) has mentioned the relative merits of anabolic and katabolic analysis in identification, and, since only the individual is real, we might make better classifications by a building up rather than breaking down. This is the approach of the specialist and, working with a restricted range of organisms, he is able to make a satisfactory and workable classification. In practice we cannot characterize a microbial unit smaller than a strain (or isolate) and the range of variability of the individual strains in the next larger unit will depend on the particular worker; thus all these units (taxa) are subjective. To one the next larger unit will be a species, to another a subspecies (or variety), to a third a serotype, and to a fourth a phage type. What the unit is called does not matter in the classification of a restricted range, but when comparisons are made with other specialist ranges (I avoid the word 'group' deliberately because it has often been given a special meaning, sometimes, as in streptococci analogous to species, sometimes, as in the Enterobacteriaceae to genus) it is necessary to align the ranks of the classifications of two or more restricted ranges. Thus Kauffmann's (1959*a*, *b*) suggestion that *Salmonella* serotypes should be regarded as species might appeal to some, but not all (Taylor, 1959) of those working only with the enteric bacteria, but it appalled the more general taxonomist trying to classify all kinds of bacteria in a uniform scheme (Cowan, 1959 b).

It can be argued, as was done very forcefully and adequately by Dr G. S. Wilson at a meeting of the International Committee on Bacteriological Nomenclature at Stockholm in 1958, that it is convenient to have different qualities for equivalent ranks in different ranges of bacteria, and that we should subordinate general principles to convenience. van Niel (1946) pointed out that bacterial taxonomy has often been founded on convenience in identification, and advocated the development of multiple determinative keys without any major effort to reconcile them. This is a practical but anarchistic solution to a difficult problem, and we should remember that, although the abandonment of principles in wartime may lead to victory, taxonomic theorists are not yet at war. If we assume, and not all microbiologists are willing, that microbes can be arranged in a series of groups within groups, we should pause to consider the minimal differences between units of the same level (rank). Few have attempted to do this: Breed (1928) said that bacterial species 'should show several distinguishing characteristics, not one'. Sneath (1958) did not think it safe to divide a taxon unless at least five correlated features were different, and Bryson (1959) thought that 'one or two mutations, even though leading to conspicuous biochemical or morphological differences do not seem adequate...to establish a "new" species'. Barnett (1957) discussed the number of tests that need to be applied to distinguish between species and expressed his conclusions in a mathematical formula.

Interfertility among bacterial 'species' or 'genera' seems to be proved, and Schaeffer reviewed the evidence up to 1958; it is particularly common among the 'genera' within the family Enterobacteriaceae, where crosses between *Escherichia coli* and *Salmonella* species (or serotypes) are easily made. Zinder (1960) and Baron, Spilman & Carey (1960) provide two recent examples, but in earlier experiments Luria & Burrous (1957) produced progeny with characters found in the Arizona group (or genus) in nature. Not all *Escherichia* × *Salmonella* crosses are fertile but it seems clear that since *Escherichia* × *Salmonella* → Arizona and *Escherichia* × *Shigella* → A–D group that the *Escherichia*, *Salmonella*, Arizona and *Shigella* groups should be regarded as an interfertile unit which in botany or zoology would be called a species. On quite different grounds Ewing & Edwards (1960) subdivided the enterobacteria into four divisions, one of which contained the *Escherichia* and *Shigella* (ES) and another the *Salmonella*–Arizona–*Citrobacter* (SAC) groups. Interfertility has not yet been shown among other members of the Enterobacteriaceae, but should the *Klebsiella–Enterobacter–Hafnia–Serratia* (KEHS) subgroup be found to be interfertile but not able to cross with the ES and SAC subgroups, a great deal of reclassification of the family will be needed, and perhaps the large number of 'genera' will be collected into one genus with three or four subdivisions or species representing ES, SAC, KEHS and PP (*Proteus*–Providence) subgroups. It might be pertinent to ask whether the Enterobacteriaceae are more unstable than other bacteria? The answer can only be found by further work, but the papers of Shimwell (1959), and Shimwell & Carr (1960, 1961) suggest that not only are bacteria continually evolving, but that this happens at such a rate that the concept of a fixed species becomes sheer nonsense. It may well be that we are on the threshold of a new era in taxonomic reality in which the fixity-of-species concept will be finally abandoned, and we shall recognize that to describe a particular unit (species) in precise terms is attempting the impossible.

AND THE FUTURE?

'If it can be said of anyone that he brought order out of chaos it is most applicable to Linnaeus: *Deus creavit, Linnaeus disposuit*' (Ramsbottom, 1938). But the age of chaos is still with us and I shall try to indicate what steps I think are needed to bring some order into our affairs.

Cain (1959*a*) says that 'more pure nonsense has been talked (and published) about phylogeny in birds than in any other group of animals' and we could make the same remark about microbes, for we have no evidence of their phylogeny. We should forget all we have been told about the evolution of one form from another and assume that the primordial types are all extinct (Breed *et al.* 1918). From this it follows that the hierarchical system is inapplicable and with it the genealogical tree. Other kinds of tree may, however, have their uses in the shape of diagnostic keys.

In place of trying to classify micro-organisms by breaking down into orders, families, tribes, genera, species and strains, we should probably do better by building up from the smallest practical unit, the strain (isolate) or, if it had been derived from a single cell, the clone. Sneath (1957*a*, *b*) proposed a method of classification based on the correlation of all known features and not only on those considered to be important. This method used an electronic computor and when data from a wide variety of bacteria were fed to the machine, the sorting produced a classification not unlike that developed over the years by orthodox methods (Sneath & Cowan, 1958). Skerman (1961) thinks that we should make

more use of the memory of computors by storing for future consideration the results of certain specified tests carried out on all cultures. Once
in the machine the data could be reanalysed as occasion required and
would provide a means of finding out the relation of mutants to existing
forms.

What evidence there is suggests that the groups (or 'genera') of the
Enterobacteriaceae may be the equivalent of interfertile subspecies of
other biological sciences; but these would be suspect by those purists
who regard a species as the type strain and other strains like it. It seems
to me that the type concept has only nomenclatural value. It relates a
culture to a name; if the culture can be allotted to a taxonomic unit its
name can be considered (probably with others) as a label for the unit.
But a type strain does not indicate the plasticity of the unit and thus has
but limited use either in classification or diagnosis. I do not intend to
discuss the many difficulties of nomenclature; I have already indicated
(Cowan, 1956) how confusion could be reduced by adopting for bacteria
a suggestion made for fungi by Ainsworth & Ciferri (1955), namely by
setting up a Register of Names. But when we do turn our attention to
the principles of biological nomenclature, we should consider carefully
Cain's (1959b) proposal for a uninominal system.

As realists we recognize that the species concept is untenable in microbiology; as practical workers we must accept plastic units (with reasonably defined limits) to which we can attach names, not as an exercise in
nomenclature but for the purpose of identification. The codes of
nomenclature were drawn up when species and genera were regarded as
static (with an allowance for minor variation) and now may be more of a
hindrance than a help. A numerical system, or a combination of letters
and numbers might be more practical, and, best of all, a system of
punched cards bearing the description of the unit. With such a system we
should need to use standardized methods (Clarke, 1955) so as to avoid a
situation that arose in the seventeenth century in the days of Ray and
Willughby when, Cain (1959a) tells us, it was not only possible for the
descriptions of the same animal written by different authors to be mistaken for different species but also the different sexes of the same animal
were written up as though they were different. A punched card system
would bring together the major groups and quickly show the differences
between individuals. Skerman (1961) made a somewhat similar suggestion, though his plan calls for access to an electronic computer, and he
would try to work his scheme as an international effort.

While these ideas are suitable for the collection and analysis of data,
something else would be needed for day-to-day identification and charac-

terization. For this purpose we might adapt one of the diagnostic schemes that have been proposed. For bacteria the first successful and the only comprehensive scheme was one by Skerman and published in the seventh edition of *Bergey's Manual* (1957); this was a development of an earlier scheme (Skerman, 1949) and has since been revised (Skerman, 1959). If, instead of working out an unknown organism to the name of a genus, we used the sectional letters and numbers of his key of 1959 we could form a coded identification complex (CIC), e.g. 1,2:B6:D1,2,4,7,-15,17,19,23 = *Neisseria*. This CIC has a great many characters and records mainly a series of negatives but it should be possible, especially when dealing with a more limited group of organisms, e.g. medical bacteria, to use simple diagnostic tables of differentiae (Cowan & Steel, 1961) from which a simpler coding could be made.

If it is possible to give an adequate characterization for identification in the form of a CIC, a complete description would need the space available on a fairly elaborately coded punch-card. However, the CIC could be made more precise than a generic or specific name by recording certain characters of the strain under investigation; its use would have to be confined to the laboratory, and, for reporting, it would need translation into the nearest equivalent genus and species names, or after the introduction of a rationalized uninominal system, into the 'uninom'. Neither Skerman's diagnostic keys nor our diagnostic tables are intended to classify bacteria, though both may suggest affinities that have so far been overlooked.

AND SO WHAT?

This modern expression pithily puts the question that all who have read so far are entitled to ask, and it is only fair that I should try to summarize the conclusions reached. Because I am a bacteriologist my conclusions apply especially to bacteria and may not be wholly applicable to other microbes.

First of all I think we can answer the question posed by the title of this paper: the microbial species does not exist; it is impossible to define except in terms of a nomenclatural type, and it is one of the greatest myths of microbiology.

Next we can say with confidence that microbes cannot, on present knowledge, be arranged in a hierarchical system to show their phylogeny. The great unravelling of microbial relations awaits the results of more crossing experiments and it is to the geneticists that we must look for future advances in phylogeny.

On the other hand, better characterization and separation of microbial units will depend on the progress made by biochemists in analysing the different parts of microbes and substituting a biochemical characterization for the old biological one based on simple morphology, staining and sugar reactions, serology, and so on. A start has already been made by the analysis of cell-walls (Cummins & Harris, 1956), extracted whole cells (Mattick, Cheeseman, Berridge & Bottazzi, 1956), surface antigens (Kauffmann, Lüderitz, Stierlin & Westphal, 1960; Westphal, Kauffmann, Lüderitz & Stierlin, 1960), and DNA (Rolfe & Meselson, 1959).

Data will continue to accumulate at such a rate that punched card systems and electronic computors will be called for to help in their analysis, and when these aids are more generally available Adansonian principles can be applied to the sorting process.

We cannot apply names to microbes until we have solved the taxonomic problems, and since we cannot yet define the simplest microbial unit I have not discussed nomenclature except to indicate that the codes of nomenclature do not seem to be applicable. In revising these codes we should think seriously of dropping binomial nomenclature and work towards a uninominal system.

In the Society's 1954 discussion on classification I asked a simple question: 'are we wasting our time in trying to classify microbes?' (Cowan, 1955). After reading this paper there can be no doubt that I am *still* wasting my time.

REFERENCES

AINSWORTH, G. C. & CIFERRI, R. (1955). Mycological taxonomic literature and publication. *Taxon*, **4**, 3.

ANONYMOUS (1959). *A Handbook on Evolution*, 2nd edition. London: Trustees of the British Museum.

ARMSTRONG, C. N. (1958). The clinical diagnosis of sex. *Proc. R. Soc. Med.* **51**, 23.

BACTERIOLOGICAL CODE (1958). *International Code of Nomenclature of Bacteria and Viruses*. Edited by R. E. Buchanan, S. T. Cowan, T. Wikén & W. A. Clark. Ames, Iowa: State College Press. [Reprinted with corrections 1959. Iowa State University Press.]

BARNETT, J. A. (1957). Some unsolved problems of yeast taxonomy. *Leeuwenhoek ned. Tijdschr.* **23**, 1.

BARON, L. S., SPILMAN, W. M. & CAREY, W. F. (1960). Diploid heterozygous hybrids from matings between *Escherichia coli* and *Salmonella typhosa*. *J. exp. Med.* **112**, 361.

Bergey's Manual of Determinative Bacteriology (1923–57). Seven editions: 1st, 1923; 2nd, 1926; 3rd, 1930; 4th, 1934; 5th, 1939; 6th, 1948; 7th, 1957. Baltimore: Williams and Wilkins Co.

BRAUN, W. (1953). *Bacterial Genetics*. Philadelphia: W. B. Saunders Co.

BREED, R. S. (1928). The present status of systematic bacteriology. *J. Bact.* **15**, 143.

BREED, R. S., CONN, H. J. & BAKER, J. C. (1918). Comments on the evolution and classification of bacteria. *J. Bact.* **3**, 445.

BRYSON, V. (1959). Some contributions of genetics to microbiology. In V. Bryson (editor), *Microbiology Yesterday and Today*, p. 80. New Brunswick, N.J.: Institute of Microbiology, Rutgers, The State University.

BUCHANAN, R. E. (1955). Taxonomy. *Ann. Rev. Microbiol.* **9**, 1.

CAIN, A. J. (1959a). Taxonomic concepts. *Ibis*, **101**, 302.

CAIN, A. J. (1959b). The post-Linnaean development of taxonomy. *Proc. Linn. Soc. Lond.* **170**, 234.

CAMP, W. H. (1951). Biosystematy. *Brittonia*, **7**, 113.

CANNON, H. G. (1958). *The Evolution of Living Things.* Manchester: University Press.

CANNON, H. G. (1959). *Lamarck and Modern Genetics.* Manchester: University Press.

CHESTERTON, G. K. (1903). *Robert Browning.* London: Macmillan and Co.

CLARKE, P. H. (1955). The principles of microbial classification. Methods for determining the biochemical activities of micro-organisms as applied to classification. *J. gen. Microbiol.* **12**, 337.

COHEN, J. M. & COHEN, M. J. (1960). *The Penguin Dictionary of Quotations*, p. 294. Harmondsworth: Penguin Books Ltd.

COWAN, S. T. (1955). The principles of microbial classification. Introduction: the philosophy of classification. *J. gen. Microbiol.* **12**, 314.

COWAN, S. T. (1956). 'Ordnung in das Chaos' Migula. *Canad. J. Microbiol.* **2**, 212.

COWAN, S. T. (1957). A taxonomist looks at the Enterobacteriaceae. *J. Path. Bact.* **73**, 312.

COWAN, S. T. (1959a). Bacterial classification—problems and developments. In V. Bryson (editor), *Microbiology Yesterday and Today*, p. 54. New Brunswick, N.J.: Institute of Microbiology; Rutgers, The State University.

COWAN, S. T. (1959b). Nonconformism in nomenclature. *Int. Bull. bact. Nom. Tax.* **9**, 131.

COWAN, S. T. & STEEL, K. J. (1961). Diagnostic tables for the common medical bacteria. *J. Hyg., Camb.* **59**, 357.

CUMMINS, C. S. & HARRIS, H. (1956). The chemical composition of the cell wall in some Gram-positive bacteria and its possible value as a taxonomic character. *J. gen. Microbiol.* **14**, 583.

EWING, W. H. & EDWARDS, P. R. (1960). The principle divisions and groups of Enterobacteriaceae and their differentiation. *Int. Bull. bact. Nom. Tax.* **10**, 1.

FISHER, J. & LOCKLEY, R. M. (1954). *Sea-Birds; an Introduction to the Natural History of Sea-Birds of the North Atlantic.* London: Collins.

GILBERT, W. S. (1883). *Iolanthe*, Act II. London: Chappell and Co.

GILMOUR, J. S. L. & HESLOP-HARRISON, J. (1954). The deme terminology and the units of micro-evolutionary change. *Genetica*, **27**, 147.

HILLABY, J. (1960). Taxonomy: a neglected science. *New Scientist*, **9**, 262.

HUCKER, G. J. (1924a). Studies on the Coccaceae. II. A study of the general characters of the micrococci. *Tech. Bull. N.Y. St. agric. Exp. Sta.*, no. 100.

HUCKER, G. J. (1924b). Studies on the Coccaceae. IV. The classification of the genus *Micrococcus* Cohn. *Tech. Bull. N.Y. St. agric. Exp. Sta.*, no. 102.

HUXLEY, J. S. (1938). Discussion following the Presidential Address by J. Ramsbottom (1938). *Proc. Linn. Soc. Lond.* **150**, 253.

HUXLEY, J. S. (1940). Introductory: towards the new systematics. In Julian Huxley (editor), *The New Systematics*, p. 1. Oxford: Clarendon Press.

KAUFFMANN, F. (1959a). On the principles of classification and nomenclature of Enterobacteriaceae. *Int. Bull. bact. Nom. Tax*, **9**, 1.

KAUFFMANN, F. (1959b). Definition of genera and species of Enterobacteriaceae. Request for an Opinion. *Int. Bull. bact. Nom. Tax.* **9**, 7.

KAUFFMANN, F. (1961). The species-definition in the family Enterobacteriaceae. *Int. Bull. bact. Nom. Tax.* **11**, 5.

KAUFFMANN, F., LÜDERITZ, O., STIERLIN, H. & WESTPHAL, O. (1960). Zur Immunchemie der O-Antigene von Enterobacteriaceae. I. Analyse der Zuckerbausteine von Salmonella-O-Antigenen. *Zbl. Bakt.* (1. *Abt. Orig.*), **178**, 442.

KAUFFMANN, F., LUND, E. & EDDY, B. E. (1960). Proposal for a change in the nomenclature of *Diplococcus pneumoniae* and a comparison of the Danish and American type designations. *Int. Bull. bact. Nom. Tax.* **10**, 31.

KLIENEBERGER, E. (1927). Künstliche Gewinn- und Verluständerungen im Salizin- (bzw. Arbutin-) Vergärungsvermögen eines Coli-Bakteriums in besonders ausgedehnten Versuchsreihen. *Zbl. Bakt.* (1. *Abt. Orig.*), **101**, 461.

LOCKE, J. (1689). *An Essay Concerning Human Understanding*, book III, chapter VI.

LURIA, S. E. & BURROUS, J. W. (1957). Hybridization between *Escherichia coli* and *Shigella. J. Bact.* **74**, 461.

LWOFF, A. (1958). La notion d'espèce bactérienne à la lumière des découvertes récentes. L'espèce bactérienne. *Ann. Inst. Pasteur*, **94**, 137.

LYSENKO, O. & SNEATH, P. H. A. (1959). The use of models in bacterial classification, *J. gen. Microbiol.* **20**, 284.

MATTICK, A. T. R., CHEESEMAN, G. C., BERRIDGE, N. J. & BOTTAZZI, V. (1956). The differentiation of species of lactobacilli and streptococci by means of paper partition chromatography. *J. appl. Bact.* **19**, 310.

VAN NIEL, C. B. (1946). The classification and natural relationships of bacteria. *Cold Spr. Harb. Symp. quant. Biol.* **11**, 285.

VAN NIEL, C. B. (1955). Classification and taxonomy of the bacteria and bluegreen algae. In *A Century of Progress in the Natural Sciences*—1853–1953. San Francisco: California Academy of Sciences.

PIRWELL, G. (1945). *Animal Farm*, chapter 10. London: Secker and Warburg.

PENFOLD, W. J. (1911). Studies in bacterial variation with special reference to the chemical functions of the members of the typhoid-coli group. *J. Hyg., Camb.* **11**, 30.

ORIE, N. W. (1955). The principles of microbial classification. Summing-up. *J. gen. Microbiol.* **12**, 382.

RAHN, O. (1929). Contributions to the classification of bacteria. IV. Intermediate forms. *Zbl. Bakt.* (2. *Abt. Orig.*), **78**, 8.

RAMSBOTTOM, J. (1938). Linnaeus and the species concept. *Proc. Linn. Soc. Lond.* **150**, 192.

RAVIN, A. W. (1960). The origin of bacterial species. Genetic recombination and factors limiting it between bacterial populations. *Bact. Rev.* **24**, 201.

REPORT (1934). The genus *Salmonella* Lignières, 1900. Issued by the Salmonella Subcommittee of the Nomenclature Committee of the International Society for Microbiology. *J. Hyg., Camb.* **34**, 333.

ROLFE, R. & MESELSON, M. (1959). The relative homogeneity of microbial DNA. *Proc. Nat. Acad. Sci., Wash.* **45**, 1039.

SCHAEFFER, P. (1958). La notion d'espèce bactérienne à la lumière des découvertes récentes. La notion d'espèces aprés les recherches récentes de génétique bactérienne. *Ann. Inst. Pasteur*, **94**, 167.

SELIGMANN, E. & SAPHRA, I. (1951). An unusual enteric pathogen. *Publ. Hlth Rep., Wash.* **66**, 1369.

SHIMWELL, J. L. (1959). A re-assessment of the genus *Acetobacter. Leeuwenhoek ned. Tijdschr.* **25**, 49.

SHIMWELL, J. L. & CARR, J. G. (1960). Are species of bacteria unclassifiable? *Leeuwenhoek ned. Tijdschr.* **26**, 383.

SHIMWELL, J. L. & CARR, J. G. (1961). The type culture concept in *Acetobacter* and other genera. *Leeuwenhoek ned. Tijdschr.* **27**, 65.

SKERMAN, V. B. D. (1949). A mechanical key for the generic identification of bacteria. *Bact. Rev.* **13**, 175.

SKERMAN, V. B. D. (1959). *A Guide to the Identification of the Genera of Bacteria.* Baltimore: Williams and Wilkins Co.

SKERMAN, V. B. D. (1961). Species concept in bacteria. In *The Evolution of Living Organisms*, **1**, 213. Melbourne: University Press.

SMITH, J. M. (1958). *The Theory of Evolution.* Harmondsworth: Penguin Books Ltd.

SNEATH, P. H. A. (1957*a*). Some thoughts on bacterial classification. *J. gen. Microbiol.* **17**, 184.

SNEATH, P. H. A. (1957*b*). The application of computors to taxonomy. *J. gen. Microbiol.* **17**, 201.

SNEATH, P. H. A. (1958). Some aspects of Adansonian classification and of the taxonomic theory of correlated features. *Ann. Microbiol. Enzimol.* **8**, 261.

SNEATH, P. H. A. & COWAN, S. T. (1958). An electro-taxonomic survey of bacteria. *J. gen. Microbiol.* **19**, 551.

SONNEBORN, T. M. (1947). Recent advances in the genetics of *Paramecium* and *Euplotes*. In *Advances in Genetics*, **1**, 263. New York: Academic Press Inc.

SPIEGELMAN, S. (1951). The particulate transmission of enzyme-forming capacity in yeast. *Cold Spr. Harb. Symp. quant. Biol.* **16**, 87.

TAYLOR, J. (1959). Why christen a Salmonella? *Int. Bull. bact. Nom. Tax.* **9**, 159.

THIBAULT, P. (1958). La notion d'espèce bactérienne à la lumière des découvertes récentes. La notion d'espèce dans le groupe Shigella. *Ann. Inst. Pasteur*, **94**, 213.

THOMPSON, W. R. (editor) (1958). Charles Darwin: *The Origin of Species*. Everyman's Library, no. 811. London: J. M. Dent and Sons Ltd.

TURRILL, W. B. (1952). Some taxonomic aims, methods, and principles. Their possible applications to the algae. *Nature, Lond.* **169**, 388.

VENDRELY, R. (1958). La notion d'espèce bactérienne à la lumière des découvertes récentes. La notion d'espèce a travers quelques données biochimiques récentes et le cycle L. *Ann. Inst. Pasteur*, **94**, 142.

WESTPHAL, O., KAUFFMANN, F., LÜDERITZ, O. & STIERLIN, H. (1960). Zur Immunchemie der O-Antigene von Enterobacteriaceae. III. Analyse der Zuckerbausteine Kreuzreagierender Salmonella-Arizona- und Escherichia-O-Antigene. *Zbl. Bakt.* (1. Abt. Orig.), **179**, 336.

WINOGRADSKY, S. (1952). Sur la classification des bactéries. *Ann. Inst. Pasteur*, **82**, 125.

ZINDER, N. D. (1960). Hybrids of *Escherichia* and *Salmonella*. *Science*, **131**, 813.

9

Reprinted from *Israel J. Entomol.*, 4, 11-28 (1969)

UNIPARENTAL, SIBLING AND SEMI-SPECIES IN RELATION TO
TAXONOMY AND BIOLOGICAL CONTROL

By Paul DeBach*

Department of Biological Control
University of California, Riverside

ABSTRACT

Uniparental, sibling, and semi-species are defined and the taxonomic problems associated with them discussed, with special reference to parasitic Hymenoptera. It is emphasized that such species frequently are overlooked or ignored and considered to be so-called races or strains. Criteria are outlined concerning the recognition and naming of uniparental species of parasitic Hymenoptera. Such species are indicated to be much more common than realized and of considerable significance to biological control research. Likewise, sibling species of parasitic Hymenoptera are rather common and support is developed for their recognition and formal naming whenever possible. The importance of semi-species to biological control research and application is emphasized. Examples are presented relating to each of the taxonomic categories considered.

This paper was prompted by nomenclatorial problems encountered during biosystematic studies of the genus Aphytis. These taxonomic studies were correlative to research on the use of Aphytis species in biological control of diaspine scale insects.

Taxonomists and biological control investigators share a major common interest. The identification and classification of organisms is crucial to both and both have contributed significantly to the other's field. (see: Sabrosky, 1955; Schlinger and Doutt, 1964). However, viewpoints and objectives differ somewhat. The end point for the taxonomist, briefly and broadly speaking, lies in classification and the determination of phylogenetic relationships. For the biological control worker the beginning and necessary basis for his research start with an accurate knowledge of the precise taxonomic identity of the organisms involved. The taxonomist's interests tend to begin with and to range up-

---

* It is a pleasure to dedicate this to Prof. E. Rivnay, who, appropriately enough, was one of the first to work with Aphytis holoxanthus DeBach which at that time was most illustrative of the important problems involving sibling species dealt with in this paper.
The research reported herein was supported by NSF Grant GB-7444. It is a continuation of the JBP project: The Biological Control of Scale Insects.

wards from the species level to supraspecific categories; the biological control researcher's interests and needs stress the species level but tend to range from this more toward sub-specific categories.

From the standpoint of practical biological control, we are vitally interested in whether natural enemies differ from one another, regardless of our ability to tell them apart morphologically. All grades of specific or sub-specific gentically-based difference may be important. Obviously, different species which may be taxonomically indistinguishable can be quite distinct biologically. The importance of such sibling species to biological control has been discussed by DeBach (1960) and Schlinger and Doutt (1964). Many taxonomists tend to avoid, ignore or overlook sibling species because little can be done if only preserved specimens are available. Likewise, uniparental (or thelytokous) species are of real importance to biological control because they represent biological entities which are reproductively isolated. To taxonomists, they present thorny problems as far as the species concept is concerned; so frequently they are designated as so-called strains or races and not described or even considered to be species.

Sub-specific categories are not commonly dealt with by taxonomists, except in very thoroughly studied groups of fair-sized insects. Here, subspecies may be formally described. The term, semi-species, although not a taxonomic category, may be more useful in biological control research because it connotes partial reproductive isolation (Mayr, 1963; Rao and DeBach, 1969) which the terms race, strain or sub-species do not necessarily imply.

The following discussion regarding the aforementioned problem categories is primarily slanted towards the biological control workers' need to know whether populations of organisms are the same, or are significantly different genetically, regardless of how similar they are morphologically. In other words, the degree of reproductive isolation (with the concurrent implication of biological and/or ecological differences) is of most importance in biological control. I think most modern systematists have this opinion with respect to reproductive isolation and the usual biological species definition.

Before proceeding with the discussion it may be well to clarify briefly the concepts of species as we are considering them in this paper as shown in the following tabulation:

Biological species		Ethological (=uniparental, =ecological) species	
Main characteristics: Biparental reproduction; reproductive isolation from other species; free interbreeding within the species population.		Main characteristics: Uniparental reproduction; reproductive isolation from other species; significant differences in ethology or ecology from other species (see p.).	
Morphological species	Sibling species	Morphological species	Sibling species
Discernable morphological differences with other species.	No significant morphological differences.	Discernable morphological differences with other species.	No significant morphological differences.

From the preceding table it is clear that there are two types of biological species (morphological and sibling) and two types of ethological or uniparental species (morphological and sibling). Although the philosophical concepts concerning sibling and uniparental species are formidable, perhaps the practical procedure of applying taxonomic names is even greater in many cases. There are few practical problems when species exhibit significant morphological differences, whether they be either biological or uniparental species. However, with sibling species difficulties arise. When biological sibling species are involved, these difficulties can be solved by crossing tests where possible. In biological control research such is often the case. When uniparental sibling species are involved, more serious practical taxonomic problems arise, since reproductive isolation occurs among all individuals. The problem is compounded when there are two or more uniparental sibling species, each as alike as identical twins. A solution to this is suggested on p. 19 . Uniparental species will be discussed in the next section, keeping in mind that even though they can be either morphological or sibling species, the latter category will be emphasized in the subsequent section dealing with siblings. Here again, even though the discussion emphasizes sibling species, it should be noted that these can be either biological species or uniparental species, but not, of course, morphological species.

UNIPARENTAL SPECIES

Such species are doubtless much more common among parasitic Hymenoptera than is readily evident. Clausen (1962) states that some 30 genera of the parasitic Hymenoptera contain one or more species that reproduce uniparentally. From our own studies with the genus Aphytis and with species of the Signiphoridae it has been found, both from large series collected in the field and from live cultures maintained in the laboratory, that a surprisingly high proportion of species in these groups are uniparental. Table 1 shows

154

that of the 53 species of Aphytis whose sexuality is known, 16 (30 per cent) are uniparental. Other information supports this. Of the current Aphytis species cultures on hand at Riverside, which we have acquired from abroad at random with respect to sexuality, 8 out of 23 are uniparental, or about 35 per cent. An intensive one-year study of the Aphytis species present in southern Greece and Crete disclosed 9 uniparental species and 4 biparental species, or about 70 per cent uniparental (DeBach, 1964b). The study of 4 imported cultures of the Aphytis maculicornis species complex by Hafez and Doutt (1954) indicated that at least 3 sibling species were involved, of which 2 were uniparental. Uniparentalism also is common in the Signiphoridae. From live culture studies, as well as from specimens in our collection and literature records, sufficient data are available on the sexuality of 41 species of Thysanus or Signiphora. Sixteen of these are uniparental, or about 40 per cent.

Table 1. - Sexuality and sibling status of species of Aphytis[a]

| Group | Total | No. of Species | | | Siblings |
| | | Sexuality status | | | |
		Unknown	Biparental	Uniparental	
Vittatus	21	12	8	1	0
Proclia	15	2	7	6	6
Lingnanensis	21	4	15	2	8
Mytilaspidis	19	5	7	7	4
T o t a l s	76	23	37	16	18

[a] Based upon an ongoing revision by the author and Dr. David Rosen, hence figures are not final. About 24 of the 76 species have not yet been formally named.

Even if the preceding data were not indicative of the incidence of uniparentalism in other groups of parasitic Hymenoptera, it is obviously a much more general and important phenomenon in many respects than has been realized.

Uniparental species exhibit thelytokous parthenogenesis; females producing female progeny without fertilization by males. Occasionally males are produced by uniparental Aphytis and Signiphora, but thus far we have not found that they perform any required reproductive function. Rather, they appear to be genetic mistakes. Most current evidence indicates this to be the general rule. According to White (1964), "In this genetic system (thelytoky) fertilization is entirely suppressed. Males are absent from the population or are only produced as occasional, non-functional anomalies, frequently inter-sexual." I know of no hard data to dispute this statement. It has been shown that the proportion of occasional males produced by uniparental species can vary considerably with the season and that male production in some species can be considerably increased - even made entirely male in a given genera-tion - by subjection of young adult females, unemerged females, or perhaps even female pupae, to high temperatures (Wilson and Woodcock, 1960; McCoy, 1967). The evident explanation of this phenomenon is that abnormal temperatures interfere with either the automictic or apomictic mechanisms of thelytoky. Flanders (1945) has suggested that male production in uniparental species is correlated with nutrition through the influence of environmental factors on the primordial germ cells of the immature female. This hypothe-sis needs collaborative proof.

Under either natural conditions or normal insectary temperatures the proportion of males produced by uniparental species is low. Wilson and Woodcock (1960) record the production of 126 males and 6 gynandromorphs to 14,996 females in a normal insectary culture of Ooencyrtus submetallicus (Howard), or less than 1 per cent. In our uniparental culture of Signiphora "borinquensis" my colleague, Dr. José R. Quezada, observed only an occasional rare male, estimated at less than 1 per cent. A random check of 3,000 spe-cimens from this laboratory culture yielded no males. All of the uniparental species of Aphytis we have examined in any detail produce occasional males. Comparative figures have not been kept, but from observation I would estimate male production to range from about 1% to 5%. In Aphytis, any substantial field sample consisting of less than 10% males (or perhaps even 20% males depending on the season and temperature) could be considered to represent a uniparental species. This is substantiated by the fact that in the many bi-parental species of Aphytis studied, the average proportion of males is about 40 to 50 per cent.

In the parasitic Hymenoptera, I know of no valid records of cyclical parthenogenesis (hetergony) such as occurs in the cynipids or certain aphids. According to Flanders (1945), "The chalcid Ditropinotus aureoviridis exhibits a unisexual overwintering generation and a bisexual summer generation. (Phillips and Poos, 1921)" but all that Phillips and Poos (1921) actually state regarding this is, "No males (of D. aureoviridis) normally occur in the first generation of this species, and the females seem greatly to outnumber the males in succeeding generations." Rather than indicating cyclical partheno-genesis, their statement suggests thelytoky with high summer temperature-induced production of some unessential males.

Also, there have been statements or suggestions in the literature of reversal of uniparental parasite species to biparental reproduction or vice versa, but there does not appear to be any rigorous experimental verification of this. For example, Schlinger and Doutt (1964, p. 258) cite unpublished data by Schlinger and Hall to the effect that uniparental female Aphelinus, when cultured at 85°F (instead of the normal lower temperature), gave rise to 90% males "and thus a biparental stock was obtained". However, this statement does not mean what it seems. The authors have recently clarified this in conversation. Male Aphelinus were produced only when females were cultured at 85°F. These males were not known to be functional, but as long as the culture was maintained at 85°F a substantial proportion of males would be produced and it would appear to be a biparental culture. When the temperature was reduced to normal, only females were produced. Thus the stock actually never became biparental, it merely produced a high proportion of males at 85°F, presumably, as previously discussed (see Wilson and Woodcock, 1960; McCoy, 1967), due to interference of the high temperature with the automictic or apomictic mechanisms which otherwise result in thelytokous female production.

The occasional appearance of uniparental females in biparental cultures has been recorded by several authors (see Flanders, 1945). The possibility of accidentally mixed cultures in the laboratory or sympatric colonies (one being an "invader") in the field leading to competitive displacement of one or the other also is a likely explanation of a uniparental species "turning into" a biparental one or vice versa. In our experience it has occasionally happened in the insectary that one biparental species of Aphytis rapidly has "turned into" another morphologically distinct biparental species - due of course to accidental contamination and subsequent competitive displacement. Thus, it would appear to be safe to consider most, if not all, uniparental species of parasitic Hymenoptera to be essentially permanent entities in the sense that any species is permanent.

If a biological control specialist discovers a uniparental species, all is well from the immediate practical viewpoint. He can go ahead and treat it as a distinct species whether it is formally described or not. This was done with the mytilaspidis species complex in Greece (DeBach, 1964b, p. 13) wherein it was pointed out that apparently 4 sibling species occurred, all of which would run to A. mytilaspidis in the most authoritative key. Biological and experimental evidence indicated the 4 to be distinct species. One is biparental and the other 3 are uniparental. However, if a taxonomist acquires a large series from a field population which are all females, hence evidently uniparental, he may assign these to an already described biparental species, perhaps designating the uniparental population as a form or strain or even ignoring completely the fact that it is distinct biologically. It may thus remain buried for possible use in biological control for an indefinite time.

The major difficulty for the taxonomist is that uniparental species do not fully meet the most commonly accepted definition for biological species. The qualification of reproductive isolation obviously is completely met because presumably no crossing whatsoever occurs. The qualification of free inter-breeding among individuals of the species population is not met, obviously by the same token, because each individual reproduces itself without crossing with another. Thus, the dilemma arises that each individual meets a major quali-fication of the species definition, that of complete reproductive isolation.

What should be done about this from the standpoint of practicing taxonomy and biology? Some of the world's outstanding systematists consider that uniparental species should be recognized and described as good species, even though they admit difficult problems are involved. Ernst Mayr (1963) makes the following comments: "To draw conclusions from the degree of mor-phological difference on the probable degree of reproductive isolation is a method of inference that has long been applied successfully to isolated popula-tions in sexual organisms. There is no reason not to extend its application to asexual types. It results in the combining in a single species of those asexual individuals that display no greater morphological difference from each other than do conspecific individuals or populations in related sexual species. "(p. 28). "Another species class is represented by the 'parthenogenetic species' that occur in many insects and lower invertebrates. Among the sibling species of chrysomelid beetles described by Brown..., many are known only in the fe-male sex and apparently reproduce strictly parthenogenetically. The same is true of the so-called species of white-fringed weevils...., of psychid moths of the genus Solenobia..., and of isopods of the genus Trichoniscus... Some of the 'biological races' of Trichogramma minutum also seem to be, at least in part, parthenogenetic and reproductively isolated from each other.... Whether or not to list such clones as sibling species depends on the criteria adopted for 'species' in asexual organisms" (Chapter 15. p. 56). "Complete partheno-genesis poses a taxonomic problem. The orthodox species criterion of inter-breeding cannot be applied, because each clone is reproductively isolated not only from the parental species but also from every sister clone. How to treat clones and parthenogenetic species taxonomically must be decided for each case. Where no essential morphological or biological differences exist, such clones should be combined into collective species. Where a parthenogenetic line has originated from a bisexual species by an irreversible chromosomal event (for instance, polyploidy), it is usually advisable to consider it a separate (sibling) species, even though the morphological difference is slight. " (p. 411).

Schlinger and Doutt (1964) discuss the 3 indistinguishable forms of Prospaltella perniciosi in North America (1 biparental and 2 uniparental) which are distinct biologically and which were referred to as geographical species by Flanders (1950). They consider that these are sibling species, inferring that they should be described. Flanders (1953) advocates the use of biological characters in taxonomy to distinguish between "behavioral" species, and he gives examples of the use of behavioral characters in a key to 10 species of Coccophagus. But curiously, he does not use uniparentalism to separate species, rather apparently considering it representative of a non-specific character, as indicated by his statement "bisexuality and unisexuality may be purely phenotypic responses and of no value in taxonomy." Thus for the 45 species he lists as having been studied, no information on sexuality status is given.

The consideration by taxonomists of uniparental forms as species is common in diverse groups. All of the bdelloid Rotifera, for example, are uniparental species. Many unicellular organisms lack apparent sexuality but have been described as good species. Certain higher plants which reproduce either only vegetatively or parthenogenetically likewise have been described as species.

Again to take an example from Aphytis, the uniparental species we have collected and studied seem to form just as discrete, uniform and identifiable populations as do the biparental species. There are hundreds of specimens of uniparental Aphytis chilensis (Howard) and A. chrysomphali (Mercet) in our collection from various parts of the world, yet the uniformity is remarkable. One might expect that with uniparental species rapid subspecific evolution would be going on in diverse habitats to produce a host of variants. Such does not seem to be the case. Mayr (1963, p. 27) puts it another way: "If mutation and survival were random among the descendents of an asexual individual, one would expect a complete morphological (and genetic) continuum. Yet discontinuities have been found in most carefully studied groups of asexual organisms and this has made taxonomic subdivision possible. For this phenomenon I have advanced the explanation that the existing types are the survivors among a great number of produced forms, that the surviving types are clustered around a limited number of adaptive peaks, and that ecological factors have given the former continuum a taxonomic structure. Each adaptive peak is occupied by a different 'kind' of organism and if each 'kind' is sufficiently different from other kinds it will be legitimate to call such a cluster of genotypes a species."

In view of the aforementioned data and discussion, it would appear particularly desirable and apropos that uniparental forms of parasitic Hymenoptera be formally described as new species, even in those cases where biparental forms exist which have identical appearing females, i.e., where the uniparental species is also a sibling species. The latter is the most difficult case to handle from a practical taxonomic viewpoint. I propose an "ethological species concept" to cover all cases of uniparental species whether morphological or sibling species. In effect, this is already practiced in some cases. The old morphological species concept relying chiefly on morphological differences, as discussed by Mayr (1963), essentially rules out the recognition of sibling species; the biological species concept, involving interspecific reproductive isolation but intraspecific crossing, makes it difficult to include uniparental species, whereas the following ethological species concept should permit rational inclusion of such species.

The ethological species is based on ethological and biological characteristics whose sum total is equivalent to those similar characteristics found in recognized biological or morphological species. Briefly, any group of reproductively isolated organisms that behaves like a biological species (that is, plays a significantly different ethological or ecological role in the habitat) should be considered to be a valid species.

The following biological tests can be applied to help distinguish such species. Of course, if a uniparental population shows definite morphological differences from the related biparental and/or uniparental species, the case is even stronger and much more simple taxonomically.

Taxonomic Tests for Ethological Species

By comparison with the most closely related good morphological biparental species in the same genus (if there are any - if not, compare with other related groups), answer the following questions:

(1) Does the uniparental population show little or no greater amount of morphological variation between individuals?

(2) Are individuals within the uniparental population relatively uniform in their biology, ethology and ecology?

(3) Does the uniparental population differ significantly in

    (a) host (or food) specificity (including, for example, host stages or host organs attacked) or

    (b) habitat specificity (including either preferences between habitats or within a habitat)?

(4) Does the uniparental population show significant average differences in development, voltinism, diapause, fecundity, temperature tolerance, etc.?

If the answer is yes to all or most of these questions, especially 1, 2 and 3, it should be considered to be a valid species.

SIBLING SPECIES

This type of species has been defined as "morphologically similar or identical natural populations that are reproductively isolated". (Mayr 1963). It is generally accepted that the primary criterion of species rank of a natural population is reproductive isolation. Thus sibling species are good species but only can be recognized by biological differences, the best test of which is complete reproductive isolation. However, other biological difference such as host specificity, habitat specificity, fecundity, voltinism, diapause, longevity,

160

and temperature tolerance may be highly significant. Museum taxonomists **thus** rarely distinguish sibling species, whereas field biologists or ecologists are more likely to. It will be recalled that sibling species can be either biparental or uniparental.

The importance and significance of sibling species to biological control research has been emphasized before (Hafez and Doutt, 1954; DeBach, 1959, 1960; Schlinger and Doutt, 1964) and is well illustrated by the studies with Aphytis species. Suffice it to say that we now know that sibling species are common in Aphytis (about 25 per cent are siblings) and that any two such species can be importantly different biologically (see table 1). The adults of biparental Aphytis melinus DeBach and A. fisheri DeBach are indistinguishable. The former was imported from India–Pakistan, the latter from Burma, and both were colonized at the same time and in similar numbers against the California red scale in California. A. melinus has become an important part of the complex attacking the red scale, but A. fisheri did not persist.

It has been concluded on the basis of biological differences by Hafez and Doutt (1954) that there are at least 3 sibling species included under the name Aphytis maculicornis. These were imported into California and colonized against the olive scale but only one, the Persian–Indian form, be-came established and instrumental in successful biological control of the olive scale. These forms are currently undergoing taxonomic study but neither Dr. David Rosen nor I have yet found any morphological differences among them. One of them may be the true A. maculicornis, the others remain unnamed.

Somewhat the opposite happened with species of the aphid parasites, Trioxys. According to Hall, Schlinger and van den Bosch (1962), Dr. M. Mackauer in a 1959 revision of the European species of the genus Trioxys, placed most of them in species groups. To the pallidus group he assigned T. pallidus (Haliday), T. utilis Muesebeck, T. betulae Marshall, and T. pulcher Gautier and Bonnamour. On the basis of the morphological characters used to delimit the members of the pallidus group, Mackauer was unable to separate these four adequately. He later placed them all in synonymy with pallidus but suggested that biological studies might be essential to the proper identification of the individual species. Hall, Schlinger and van de Bosch conducted such studies on T. pallidus and utilis and found them to be distinct sibling species on the basis of reproductive isolation as well as on differences in host speci-ficity, host habitat and slight cryptic morphological differences. Inasmuch as each attacks different economically significant aphid species, the great impor-tance of recognizing and describing such species is evident.

There should be no reluctance on the part of a taxonomist to des-cribe a sibling species as new. The term is really quite relative, anyhow.

Many of today's morphologically distinguishable species were once included with other species under one name. They could have been called sibling species then, had the fact of reproductive isolation been known. Once a sibling species has been recognized as being distinct, it is likely to receive further study which may well reveal morphological differences not perceived by earlier workers.

A good case in point involves some current studies nearing completion at Riverside on species of the Muscidifurax-raptor complex which were imported into California from various parts of the world by Dr. Fred Legner. Studies of certain of these by McCoy (1967) and Legner (1969) indicated, on the basis of reproductive isolation and size variation, that several sibling species were involved but no reliable distinguishing morphological characters were confirmed. Drs. Marcos Kogan and Fred Legner are just completing an intensive study of these forms, utilizing both the phase microscope and the scanning electron microscope and can now separate them morphologically. Four new species will be described, all of which formerly were considered to be M. raptor (Kogan and Legner, 1969).

Biological control workers should never consider, a priori, that two similarly appearing populations in different geographical areas represent the same species, or at the very least they should maintain a reasonable doubt. It is better to err on the safe side, than it is to fail to import a natural enemy because it is considered to be already present. It was such lack of knowledge - understandable for the time - that precluded the importation of the most important parasites of the red scale into California for many years.

According to Compere (1961), during his trip to the Orient in 1932 an attempt was made to introduce into California all the parasites and predators found on California red scale with the exception of Aphytis species. This was because all the yellow species of Aphytis seen were thought to be A. chrysomphali, which already occurred in California. No attempt was made to introduce any of the Aphytis observed. It is now known that the species seen in India and elsewhere did not include chrysomphali. While returning with live material from India, by ship, Compere discovered in Hong Kong that a species of Aphytis was accidentally "contaminating" one of his scale cultures. It was believed to be A. chrysomphali and was destroyed. In the light of present knowledge, this species was doubtless either A. melinus DeBach or A. lingnanensis Compere, which are the two major species in biological control of red scale in California today and have virtually caused the extinction of chrysomphali there. This failure to recognize sibling species retarded the importation of A. lingnanensis into California by 16 years and of A. melinus by 25 years. A somewhat similar story involves the failure to recognize A. holoxanthus DeBach as distinct from A. lingnanensis for some 12 years (DeBach, 1960). Otherwise it would have been obviously available for importation into Israel against the Florida red scale much earlier than was ultimately done.

Sibling species of parasites or predators which are unsuccessful in biological control in one country should not be ignored as possibilities elsewhere. For example, A. fisheri should not be precluded from trials in Israel or other countries merely because it was unsuccessful in California. It is well established that in cases involving ecological homologs, such as A. melinus and A. fisheri, one species may win over the other in one habitat, whereas the reverse may occur in a different habitat (DeBach, 1966). This is illustrated in California today by the interactions between A. melinus and A. lingnanensis Compere, which also are ecological homologs. A. melinus displaced, and now excludes, A. lingnanensis from interior climatic areas where the latter once was dominant; whereas in coastal areas lingnanensis remains dominant and virtually excludes melinus.

It is important to recognize that in all probability most of the so-called races, strains, stocks or forms of many authors actually are either uniparental species or sibling species or both. However, Flanders (1945) considered uniparentalism as a racial character of some biparental species of Hymenoptera; again (1950), he wrote of races of apomictic (i.e., uniparental) parasites. Hafez and Doutt (1954) demonstrated and stated that they were dealing with 3 sibling species under the name Aphytis maculicornis, yet they referred to them as strains throughout the paper. Perhaps this was a semantic problem, deriving from the fact that they did not formally name the species.

Another case where sibling species were demonstrated and recognized, but not described, and still mentioned as strains in the paper, involved a biparental and a uniparental population of oleander scale, both known as Aspidiotus hederae (Vallot) (DeBach and Fisher, 1956).

It seems apropos to conclude this section with the following quotes: "There are many more references to sibling species in the literature but those cited show some types of physiological, ecological, and ethological differences that might be expected and looked for by future systematists working with 'similar' species which are often called races, strains or forms. That the discovery of sibling species in biological control work should be carefully investigated and terminated with a full, formal description of the species seems both practical and desirable to the authors." (Schlinger and Doutt, 1964, p. 259).

"Those who adhere to a purely morphological species concept usually refer to sibling species as 'biological races.' By far the majority of the so-called biological races of the literature are now acknowledged to be sibling species. In Thorpe's words, they are forms 'which on every biological ground should be classified as distinct species. .....there is no longer any reason why such cryptic species should be designated 'races'." (Mayr, 1963, pp. 56-57).

SEMI-SPECIES

This term has evolved to apply to conspecific populations which are partially reproductively isolated: perhaps to the extent of being thought of as incipient species (Mayr, 1963, p. 455). Obviously, such a term is not precise, hence it covers a broad range of reproductive isolation and genetic difference because the degree of isolation may range from very little to nearly complete. In biological control research, recognition and importation of a semi-species which is nearly completely isolated reproductively from the parental species, but has the same host preferences, may be essentially the equivalent to importation of a distinct species from a practical viewpoint. Sexual isolation might proceed rapidly to completion after the semi-species is colonized and one form would probably displace the other because they probably would be ecological homologs. According to competitive displacement theory, the winner should be more effective in population regulation (DeBach, 1966).

Another important possibility is illustrated by the two so-called strains or races of Comperiella bifasciata Howard, now established in California, which are morphologically indistinguishable. One, from China, develops in both the California red and yellow scales; the other, from Japan, does not develop on the red scale. These forms hybridize readily in the laboratory, so they must be considered as conspecific, but gene flow restriction is indicated in the field, hence they may be considered semi-species. Our field surveys and laboratory tests indicate that they apparently maintain their integrity as discrete "strains" in the field, even where sympatric. Parasites obtained from the yellow scale in the field are of the pure yellow scale strain; they do not develop on the red scale. We do not as yet understand how this may happen, especially since biological tests indicate that the red scale strain should be superior on both host scales, hence should displace the Japanese Comperiella. These results are still tentative but the possibility that semi-species can occur sympatrically, yet maintain their host-preference distinctness and genetic integrity in spite of some hybridization, is of considerable interest to biological control. It may also be illustrative of the possibility of sympatric speciation which Mayr (1963) argues against.

Semi-species can only be distinguished and evaluated by crossing tests between different population cultures. Our studies (Rao and DeBach, 1969) with the Lingnanensis group of Aphytis revealed a complex relationship between various species and semi-species obtained from different sources, which is of considerable significance both to taxonomy and to biological control. The results are depicted in Fig. 1.

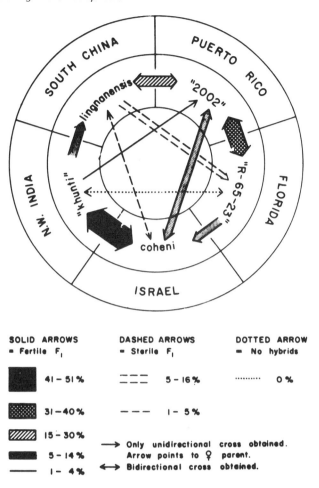

SOLID ARROWS   DASHED ARROWS   DOTTED ARROW
= Fertile F₁   = Sterile F₁   = No hybrids

[■] 41 – 51 %   ≡≡≡ 5 – 16 %   ········· 0 %

[▨] 31 – 40 %   — — — 1 – 5 %

[▧] 15 – 30 %   ⟶ Only unidirectional cross obtained.

[▬] 5 – 14 %   Arrow points to ♀ parent.

[—] 1 – 4 %   ⟷ Bidirectional cross obtained.

Fig. 1 - Crossing relations within the Lingnanensis group of <u>Aphytis</u>, showing
          per cent of F_1 progeny which are female and the nature of the F_1
          hybrids. Normal intra-species F_1 progeny production consists of
          60 – 75% females. (From Rao and DeBach, 1969).

      All Lingnanensis group species studied are siblings, virtually in-
distinguishable from one another. <u>A. coheni</u> (from Israel ex <u>Aonidiella aurantii</u>
(Mask.)) and <u>A.</u> "khunti" (from N.W. India ex <u>Aonidiella orientalis</u> Newst.)
hybridize readily in the laboratory, yielding fertile hybrids. However, the
hybrid sex-ratio and progeny production is somewhat lower than normal, and
the two show different crossing relations with <u>A.</u> "2002" (from Puerto Rico
ex <u>Aspidiotus destructor</u> Sign.), <u>A.</u> <u>lingnanensis</u> (from S. China ex <u>A.</u> <u>aurantii</u>)

and A. "R-65-23" (from Florida ex Unaspis citri (Comstock)), indicating that they are genetically rather distinct and should be considered as weak semi-species with respect to each other.

Lingnanensis and "2002" hybridize fairly readily (although considerably less so than coheni and "khunti"), but show great differences in their crossability with coheni and "R-65-23". They are considered to be semi-species.

The fact that lingnanensis produces only a few sterile hybrids with coheni confirms the genetical incompatibility between the two, and confirms their distinct species status.

When crossed with "khunti", lingnanensis produces very few hybrids, but they are fertile. However, the two show great differences in their crossability with coheni, "2002" and "R-65-23." Hence, "khunti" and lingnanensis are considered species with respect to each other.

Although "2002" produces fertile hybrids with coheni and "khunti," it does so rarely and only with laboratory manipulation. Therefore "2002" is considered a good species with respect to coheni and "khunti".

On the basis of limited information, "R-65-23" is considered a semi-species with resepct to "2002," with which it hybridizes rather readily. It produces sterile hybrids with lingnanensis and does not hybridize with "khunti" so is considered a distinct species with respect to these two. "R-65-23" and coheni appear to exchange genes to such a very limited extent that hybridization in nature is highly questionable, so they also are considered good species with respect to each other.

The simplest generalizations that can be drawn from this complex situation are that the five sibling forms. represent three biological species, A. coheni (with "khunti" as a semi-species), A. lingnanensis (with "2002" as a semi-species) and "R-65-23" (with "2002" as a semi-species). Thus, although A. lingnanensis and "R-65-23" are considered to be distinct biological species, they are linked through the mutual semi-species, "2002".

Aside from the fact that well developed semi-species may have significant biological differences important in biological control, the advantage in detecting and recognizing semi-species lies in the possibilities for genetic enrichment and manipulation of the species being used in biological control programs. The importance of genetics and of so-called races and strains (which may well be semi-species) in biological control research has been emphasized by several authors (Clausen, 1936; Smith, 1941; Flanders, 1950; DeBach, 1958; DeBach, 1964, pp. 449-52; Simmonds, 1963; and Force, 1967). The potential for exploratory research in genetic manipulation and in biological control importation appears great.

LITERATURE CITED

Clausen, C. P. 1936. Insect parasitism and biological control. Ann. Ent. Soc. Amer. 29: 201-23.

_____ 1962. Entomophagous Insects. Hafner Publish. Co., New York. 688 pp.

Compere, Harold. 1961 The red scale and its insect enemies. Hilgardia, 31(7): 173-278.

DeBach, Paul. 1958. Selective breeding to improve adaptations of parasitic insects. Proc. 10th Internatl. Congr. Entomol., 4:759-68, (1956).

_____ 1959. New species and strains of Aphytis (Hymenoptera; Eulophidae) parasitic on the California red scale, Aonidiella aurantii (Mask.), in the Orient. Ann. Ent. Soc. Amer., 52(4): 354-362.

_____ 1960. The importance of taxonomy to biological control as illustrated by the cryptic history of Aphytis holoxanthus n. sp. (Hymenoptera: Aphelinidae), a parasite of Chrysomphalus aonidum, and Aphytis coheni n. sp., a parasite of Aonidiella aurantii. Ann. Ent. Soc. Amer., 53(6): 701-705.

_____ (Editor). 1964a. Biological Control of Insect Pests and Weeds. Reinhold Publ. Corp., New York. 844 pp.

_____ 1964b. Some species of Aphytis Howard (Hymenoptera, Aphelinidae) in Greece. Ann. Inst. Phytopath. Benaki, N. S. 7(1): 5-18.

_____ 1966. The competitive displacement and coexistence principles. Ann. Rev. Ent., 11: 183-212.

DeBach, Paul, and T. W. Fisher, 1956. Experimental evidence for sibling species in the oleander scale, Aspidiotus hederae (Vallot). Ann. Ent. Soc. Amer., 49(3): 235-239.

Flanders, Stanley E. 1945. The bisexuality of uniparental Hymenoptera, a function of the environment. Amer. Natural., 79: 122-141.

_____ 1950. Races of apomicitic parasitic Hymenoptera introduced into California. Jour. Econ. Ent., 43: 719-720.

_____ 1953. Aphelinid biologies with implications for taxonomy. Ann. Ent. Soc. Amer., 46(1): 84-94.

Force, Don C. 1967. Genetics in the colonization of natural enemies for biological control. Ann. Ent. Soc. Amer., 60(4): 722-728.

Hafez. Mostafa, and Richard L. Doutt. 1954. Biological evidence of sibling species in Aphytis maculicornis (Masi) (Hymenoptera, Aphelinidae). Canad. Ent., 86(2): 90-96.

Hall, J. C., E. L Schlinger and R. van den Bosch. 1962. Evidence for the separation of the "sibling species" Trioxys utilis and Trioxys pallidus (Hymenoptera: Braconidae: Aphidiinae). Ann. Ent. Soc. Amer., 55(5): 566-568.

Kogan, Marcos and Fred Legner. 1969 (in press). A biosystematic revision of the genus Muscidifurax Girault and Sanders (Hymenoptera: Pteromalidae) with descriptions of four new species. Canad. Ent.

Legner, E. F. 1969. Reproductive isolation and size variation in the Muscidifurax raptor complex. Ann. Ent. Soc. Amer., 62(2): 382-385.

Mayr, Ernst. 1963. Animal Species and Evolution. Harvard Univ. Press, Cambridge, Mass. 797 pp.

McCoy, Clayton W. 1967. Biosystematic and Field Studies of Two Parasites of the Muscidifurax raptor complex (Hymenoptera: Pteromalidae) with particular reference to sex determination. Ph. D. dissertation. University of Calif., Riverside. 166 pp.

Phillips, W. J., and F. W. Poos. 1921. Life History studies of three joint worm parasites. Jour. Agric. Res., 21(6): 405-426.

Rao, Sudha V., and Paul DeBach, 1969. Experimental studies on hybridization and sexual isolation between some Aphytis species (Hymenoptera: Aphelinidae) II. Experiments on sexual isolation. Hilgardia, 39(19): 555-567.

Sabrosky, Curtis W. 1955. The Interrelations of biological control and taxonomy. Jour. Econ. Ent. 48(6): 710-714.

Schlinger, Evert L, and Richard L. Doutt. 1964. Systematics in relation to biological control. pp. 247-266. IN: Biological Control of Insect pests and Weeds, Paul DeBach, Editor. Reinhold Publ. Corp., N. Y. 844 pp.

Simmonds, F. J. 1963. Genetics and biological control. Canad. Ent., 95(6): 561-567.

Smith, H. S. 1941. Racial segregation in insect populations and its significance in applied entomology. Jour. Econ. Ent., 34: 1-13.

White, M. J. D. 1964. Cytogenetic mechanisms in insect reproduction. 1-12. IN: Insect Reproduction, Symposium No. 2, K. C. Highnam, Editor. Royal Ent. Soc., London, 120 pp.

Wilson, F., and L. T. Woodcock. 1960. Temperature determination of sex in a parthenogenetic parasite, Ooencyrtus submetallicus (Howard) (Hymenoptera: Encyrtidae), Australian Jour. Zool., 8(2): 153-169.

10

Reprinted from *The Species Problem,* E. Mayr (ed.), Am. Assoc. Adv. Sci. Publ. 50, 1957, pp. 125–153

THE SPECIES PROBLEM WITH
FOSSIL ANIMALS

JOHN IMBRIE: COLUMBIA UNIVERSITY, NEW YORK, N.Y.

In spite of the extended attention this problem has received, the nature of fossil species remains one of the most controversial topics in paleontology. That this should be so in a decade that has witnessed the publication of numerous synoptic studies on the origin of species may surprise some students unfamiliar with the materials and problems of paleontology. But two key questions are still being asked: What is a fossil species? How can fossil species be recognized?

In defining fossil species it would be possible to ignore living organisms completely and to frame definitions strictly in terms of fossils. In fact, such an unbiological approach to paleontological taxonomy is almost, but not quite, forced upon us in dealing with some groups such as the conodonts whose biological functions are obscure. But most attempts at a definition of fossil species begin with a review of species concepts held by students of living, sexual organisms, and from this foundation construct a theoretical model of fossil species. The concept of fossil species held by most paleontologists is largely an inference, an inference based both on the observed structure of living species and on a theoretical model of the evolutionary mechanism.

Paleontologists by no means agree on what a fossil species is. Burma (1954), for example, has given thoughtful expression to the thesis that species do not have an objective reality, a view that is rejected by Simpson (1951) and others. In a symposium on paleontological species, Eagar (1956) holds that for certain groups of fossil clams a workable species concept must be typological. Other students, including Newell (1956) and Sylvester-Bradley (1956), maintain that the concept of interbreeding populations is a necessary prerequisite for the definition and delineation of fossil species. Disagreement exists not only on the nature of species but also on the inevitable question of their proper scope. Thus Burma (1948) would distinguish as species the smallest statistically recognizable grouping of populations, whereas Imbrie (1956) argues that consistent application of such a criterion would lead to useless multiplication of species names.

Since all the problems alluded to in the preceding paragraph have their exact counterparts in neontology, it would be pointless to make of this paper a compendium of paleontological disagreement. Instead, we shall focus on those aspects of the species problem which are unique, or are at least uniquely developed, in dealing with fossil materials.

Species Concepts

In dealing with sexual organisms, whether fossil or living, two fundamentally different species concepts can be employed. The *typological* concept defines species as a group of individuals essentially indistinguishable from some specimen selected as a standard of reference. The *biological* species concept, on the other hand, considers the species to be made up of one or more variable, interbreeding populations. Both of these concepts serve as theoretical bases for taxonomic work in paleontology today.

Different criteria may be emphasized in delimiting biological species. For many students the criterion of interbreeding is decisive, and species so defined may be referred to as *genetic* species. In order to emphasize the fact that most modern and all fossil species are distinguished more on the basis of morphology than on breeding habits, some taxonomists recognize a *morphological* species concept as distinct from the genetical concept. But this is really a trivial distinction. Morphological data are never really considered by themselves; their interpretation is always colored to some degree by prevailing theories on population structure. Moreover, descriptions of species, like descriptions of molecules and genes, are inferences drawn from various sorts of data, including observations on geographic distribution and ecology as well as morphology and genetics.

It is widely recognized that many anomalies arise when the genetical definition of species as actually or potentially inter-breeding groups of organisms is strictly applied. Asexually reproducing organisms are left out of account, for example, as are the many instances on record in which local or temporary breakdowns occur in the genetical barrier between sympatric populations which on other evidence are classed as good species. Simpson (1951) argues that such inconsistencies occur only because the interbreeding criterion is taken as the final test of specific identity. He proposed that an *evolutionary* criterion be substituted for the genetical so that the species is defined as a segment of a phyletic lineage "evolving independently of others, with its own separate and unitary evolutionary role and tendencies." Clearly, this leaves wide latitude for judgment on the part of the taxonomist delineating a species; and when taken out of context Simpson's definition appears to be a different verbalization of the famous dictum that a species is "a community or number of related communities whose distinctive morphological characters are in the opinion of a competent systematist sufficiently definite to entitle it or them to a specific name" (Regan, 1926). Taken in context, however, Simpson's definition differs by insisting that a combination of morphological, biogeographical, associational, ecological, *and* genetical data be used to assess the evolutionary discreteness of a population or group of populations under study. By the nature of the evolutionary process we cannot eliminate arbitrary taxonomic judgments. Species-making will remain a practical art as well as a scientific discipline.

Typological Species in Paleontology. The typological concept of species is employed today either implicitly or explicitly by a considerable number of paleontologists. To illustrate this point we shall turn our attention to the work of a group of students who have contributed a great deal to our knowledge of British non-marine Carboniferous clams, notably Trueman, Weir, Leitch, and Eagar (for a good summary see Weir, 1950). Like their modern relatives the unionids, the shells described by these workers (*Anthraconaia, Carbonicola, etc.*) display an extraordinary amount of intrapopulation variation (Fig. 1). Now the mere fact of variation, however excessive, would not of course be used as a justification for a typological approach. But the difficulty in this case is enormously compounded by a combination of stratigraphic, biologic, and practical economic circumstances. In the first place, abundant collections of these shells have been obtained from widely distributed localities and very numerous

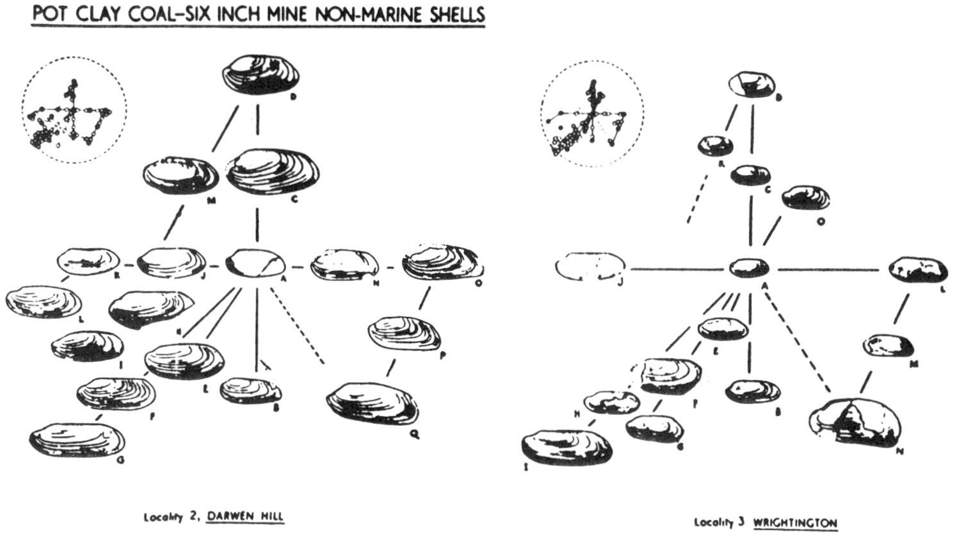

POT CLAY COAL–SIX INCH MINE NON-MARINE SHELLS

Locality 2, DARWEN HILL   Locality 3 WRIGHTINGTON

Fig. 1. Variation diagrams of two local populations of *Carbonicola* ? from a thin shell bed immediately above the Pot Clay and Six-Inch Mine Coals of Yorkshire and Lancashire. These shells are referred to *C. ? lenisulcata* Trueman and *C. ? aff. bellula* Bolton. Distribution diagrams, inset in the upper left-hand corner of each pictograph, show the numerical strength of variation trends. Black circles distinguish the figured variants, and white circles show the disposition of the remaining shells, the position of each one being controlled by its resemblance to one or more of the figured variants (Eagar, 1952b).

stratigraphic horizons in the British coal measures. The result is an embarrassment of riches. To make the problem more complex, many pairs of unit taxonomic characters vary independently, or at least show low total correlation. From this it follows that statistical characterization of populations by means of simple univariate or even bivariate distribution clusters will usually be unsatisfactory. By means of multivariate regression analyses Leitch (1940) has shown that it is possible objectively to identify variation norms and to place taxonomic discrimination on a quantitative basis. But such computations are far too laborious to enable the large number of population samples at hand to be processed. Another complicating factor is the labyrinthine course of evolution followed by these British clams: with one exception, rectilinear evolutionary trends have not been identified.

Faced with these complexities, Trueman and his co-workers have evolved an ingenious and workable taxonomic procedure. Each population sample is analyzed into variants which are illustrated and arranged in a systematic (and subjective) manner as in Fig. 1. Subsequent analyses of similar populations can then be abbreviated by means of appropriately placed dots on distribution diagrams. One or more modal or characteristic variants in any population may then be described as a species. As a consequence, an assemblage of shells from a single horizon and locality may be described as a group of species, even though there is every evidence that variation between the named species is continuous.

The students who employ the system described above recognize that their use of the term species violates the modern biological species concept, but the claim is made that this system of nomenclature has proved to be the only practical one for their peculiar biostratigraphic problems (Eagar, 1952a). Other workers have argued that the same practical results could be obtained within the framework of the biological species concept (Sylvester-Bradley, 1952) and without burdening international nomenclature with names of purely local application (Newell, 1956).

Biological Species in Paleontology. A majority of articulate paleontologists working today employ a biological species concept. Although this consensus reflects prevailing neontological views, the paleontologist's concept of species, which must take into account important segments of geological time, is inevitably more complex than the corresponding concept of zoologists. In order to clarify this point it will be helpful to examine the simplest possible phylogenetic model which includes the time dimension. Such a model, representing a small fragment of a phylogenetic tree, is shown in Fig. 2. The branches of this tree represent ancestral-descendent population sequences replacing one another through time as they undergo morphological and genetic divergence. For the sake of simplicity, it is assumed that the organisms involved are sexual, biparental, and that complications due to partial genetic barriers and *Rassenkreise* do not exist

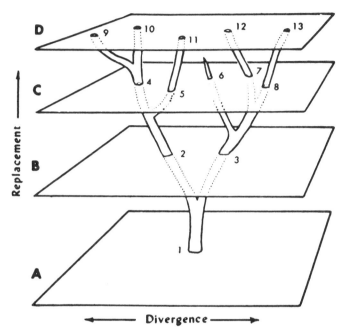

Fig. 2.   A simplified theoretical phylogeny. At the indicated stratigraphic horizons (A, B, C, D) transient species (1-13) are discrete evolutionary units with no morphological or genetic overlap. In rare instances, where the record of a line of descent is nearly continuous, segments of evolving lineages may be designated as successional species. (After Newell, 1956.)

at levels A, B, C, and D. All the individuals living at time A are capable of interbreeding. By time B speciation has occurred so that populations 2 and 3 are no longer capable of genetic interchange. Five similar branchings are recorded in the diagram.

Given the simplified conditions of this model, contemporaneous organisms are always distributed among discrete, reproductively isolated groups. For reasons discussed below, paleontological samples almost always consist of the remains of individuals who lived during a fraction of geologic time so short that evolutionary morphological change within the sampled time interval cannot be demonstrated. Thus species recognized on time planes A, B, and C by the paleontologist represent stages in an evolutionary continuum and are thus analogous to neontological species on plane D. In some rather rare instances the paleontologist can assemble material representing time planes so closely spaced that modal shifts in an evolving succession of populations can be demonstrated. Such circumstances are relatively rare, however, and the paleontologist usually deals with widely spaced cross sections of evolving lineages. The term *transient species* will be used in this paper to identify such cross sections, i.e., reproductively isolated groups of individuals living during a single instant of geological time. Normally the paleontologist's cross section is limited geographically, and when this is the case, the transient species of the paleontologist corresponds to the nondimensional species of the neontologist (Mayr *et al.*, 1953). In an increasing number of instances, however, paleontologists have been able to document taxonomically important infraspecific geographic differences, i.e., polytypic transient species.

For practical reasons the neontologist can rarely undertake the field sampling and breeding experiments required to document statistically significant seasonal shifts in gene frequencies. Hence the paleontologist of necessity and the neontologist by default describe transient species in the majority of cases now on record.

In favorable circumstances the paleontologist can obtain materials which enable him to document gradual morphological changes in a succession of fossil populations. In Fig. 2, for example, collections taken at a number of horizons might define the course of evolution between transient species 4 and 9. Quite naturally, paleontologists use the term species for such segments of phyletic lineages. Lineage segments of this sort can be called *successional species* to distinguish them from the static groupings referred to above as transient species. A number of theoretical taxonomic and nomenclatural problems which arise in defining the scope of successional species will be considered below in connection with a discussion of *Micraster*.

BASIS	TYPOLOGICAL SPECIES	BIOLOGICAL SPECIES		
	MORPHOTYPE	LIVING POPULATION	FOSSIL POPULATION	
DISTRIBUTION IN TIME	VARIOUS	CONTEMPORANEOUS	ESSENTIALLY CONTEMPORANEOUS	NON- CONTEMPORANEOUS
TYPE OF SPECIES	TYPOLOGICAL SPECIES	TRANSIENT SPECIES	TRANSIENT SPECIES	SUCCESSIONAL SPECIES
CRITERIA — GENETICAL	—	x	—	—
MORPHOLOGICAL	x	x	x	x
ASSOCIATIONAL	—	x	x	x
ECOLOGICAL	—	x	x	x
GEOGRAPHICAL	—	x	x	x
BIOSTRATIGRAPHICAL	—	—	—	x

Fig. 3.   Tabular summary of some characteristics of typological, biological, transient, and successional species. Operational taxonomic criteria associated with each of these concepts are indicated.

Figure 3 summarizes aspects of the species concept which have been emphasized in the preceding discussion.

Problems in Applying Biological Species Concepts to Fossils

Transient Species.   In the foregoing discussion attention has been focused on the theoretical model of the biological species in use today by a majority of paleontologists. We shall now examine some of the practical problems which arise when this model is applied to real paleontological data. Most of these problems arise from three sources: the inadequacy of morphological data, the prevalence of biased frequency distributions, and the incompleteness of the available fossil record.

1. *Inadequacy of morphological data.* The most obvious shortcoming of paleontological data is that fossils normally preserve only hard skeletal parts. To a student of soft-bodied living animals (say *Euglena*) this difficulty might appear insuperable. Indeed, some taxonomists assume for this reason alone that clas-

sifications of living and extinct species are on an entirely different level. For the vast majority of genera commonly found as
fossils, however, this judgment is exaggerated or untrue. There
can be, of course, no conflict between the classification of living
and extinct *Euglena:* like hosts of other soft-bodied forms this

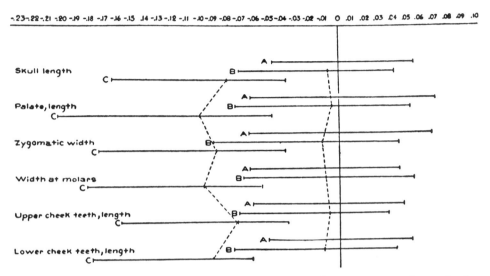

Fig. 4.   Ratio diagram showing comparisons of certain osteological characters in two species of the modern marten *Mustela* and two modern subspecies of *Mustela sibirica.* The latter show a strong overlap of measured
characters, whereas the two species show little overlap in the same characters. A, *Mustela sibirica fontanierii;* B, *M. s. davidiana;* C, *M. altaica ka-
thiah.* Abcissal scale represents for each character the difference between
the logarithm of any given value and the logarithm of the mean value of
the population selected as reference standard (in this case, population A).
Thus the horizontal distance between any two points represents the ratio
of either one to the other. Three points connected by a horizontal line are
plotted for a given character in each sample to represent the greatest, least,
and mean dimensions. The several means for each character in a population are connected by dashed or solid lines. For discussion of ratio diagrams, see Simpson (1941). Mammal data from Allen (1938) (Colbert
and Hooijer, 1953).

genus leaves essentially no fossil record. Furthermore, it is generally true that specific discrimination in groups of animals commonly found as fossils is (or can be) based on skeletal morphology. Consider, for example, the shell-bearing foraminifera, radio-
larians, corals, ectoproct bryozoans, brachiopods, snails, clams,

echinoids, and mammals. For such groups differences in the classification of fossil and living organisms at the species level are rarely attributable to the inadequacy of morphological data.

Students of some of the groups just listed may argue that many important specific taxonomic characters are not preserved in fossils—pelage characteristics in mammals, for example. This view, however, violates one of the basic tenets of taxonomy: that the *nature* of a unit biological character is not so important in

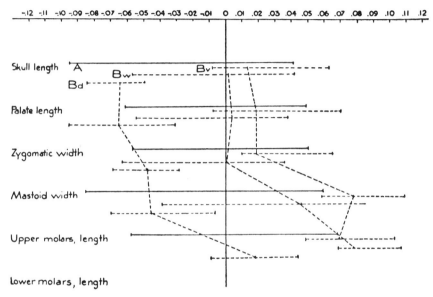

Fig. 5.   Ratio diagram comparing range of size variation in the fossil bamboo rat (*Rhizomys sinensis troglodytes*) and three modern subspecies of *R. sinensis*. A, *Rhizomys sinensis troglodytes*; Bd, *R. s. davidi*; Bv, *R. s. vestitus*; Bw, *R. s. wardi*. Diagram constructed in the same manner as Fig. 4 (Colbert and Hooijer, 1953).

taxonomy as its statistical *distribution* within and between populations (Simpson, 1943). This point is so fundamental to an understanding of the paleontologist's approach to classification on the species level that it will be illustrated with three examples drawn from diverse sorts of animals.

In a study of Chinese Pleistocene mammals, Colbert and Hooijer (1953) analyzed skeletal data on several species of modern Asiatic mammals and made comparisons with similar data on fossils. A ratio diagram (Fig. 4) based on skeletal meas-

urements of two species of the modern marten *Mustela* indicated
that the amount of morphological overlap between two subspecies is much greater than that between two species, showing
that osteological data alone reflect a classification (Allen, 1938)
based on geographic, ecologic, and pelage data. With this in

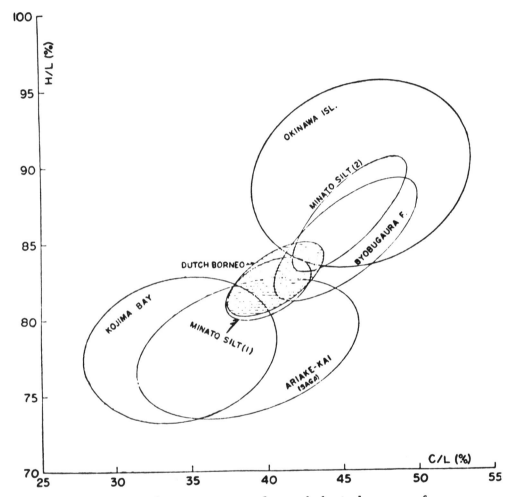

Fig. 6.   Diagram showing estimated morphological ranges of seven populations of the arcid pelecypod *Anadara*. H, maximum distance between
two lines parallel to the hinge; L, shell length; C, maximum depth of one
valve. Ellipses are statistical estimates of ranges to include 95% of the total
population ranges. Populations from Kojima Bay, Ariake Bay, and Dutch
Borneo are recent. Other populations are fossil. Samples from Dutch Borneo
and Minato silt (1) are assigned to *Anadara granosa granosa*; from Kojima
and Ariake Bays to *Anadara granosa bisenensis*; and those from the remaining areas to *Andara obessa* (Kotaka, 1953).

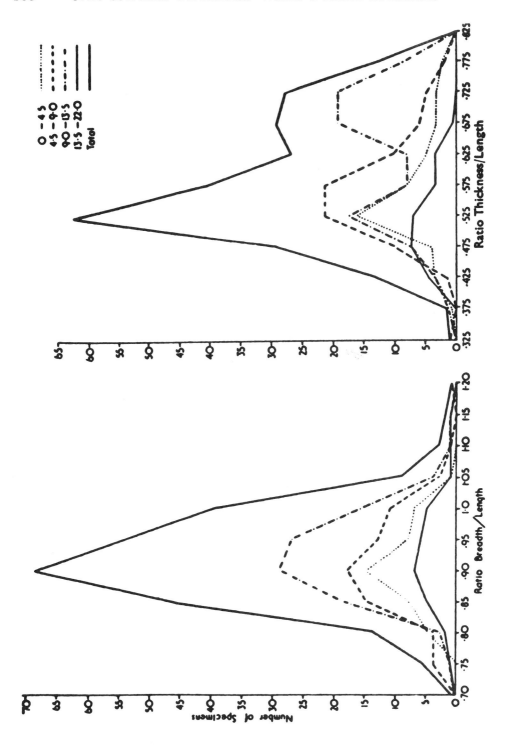

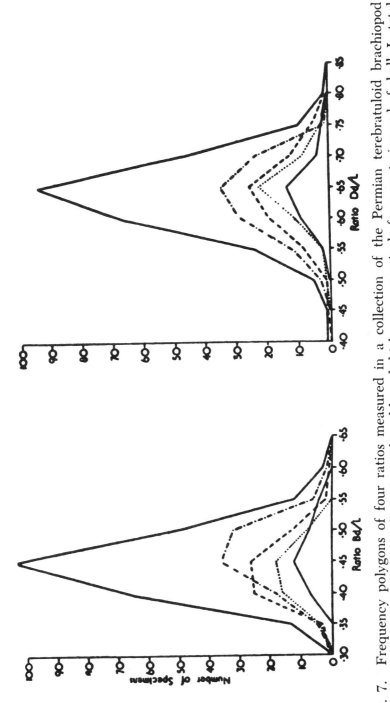

Fig. 7. Frequency polygons of four ratios measured in a collection of the Permian terebratuloid brachiopod *Dielasma elongata*. Bd, distance of maximum breadth and thickness respectively from posterior end of shell; L, total length of shell. Data analyzed into size groups based on total length (Westoll, 1950).

mind, data on a collection of the Pleistocene bamboo rat *Rhizomys* were compared with data on three subspecies of the modern *Rhizomys sinensis* (Fig. 5). The extensive mutual overlap among the four samples in the six measured skeletal features was then used as a basis for considering the fossil a subspecies, *R. sinensis troglodytes*.

A similar approach by Kotaka (1953) on recent and fossil populations of the arcid pelecypod *Anadara* is illustrated in Fig. 6. Having concluded that the population in question could best be distinguished on the basis of two shell indices (H/L and C/L), Kotaka calculated and graphed the 0.95 elliptical contour of each bivariate density distribution. Note that although four fossil and three recent populations are included in this study, each receives the same taxonomic treatment; and there is every reason to suppose that Kotaka's conclusions apply equally to fossil and modern forms.

An illustration of the taxonomic importance of intrapopulation variation patterns is furnished by Westoll's (1950) study of a large sample of the Permian terebratuloid brachiopod *Dielasma elongata* (Fig. 7). Frequency polygons of the thickness-length ratio reveal a distinct bimodality in larger size classes, although in all other respects shell characters display unimodal distribution patterns. This bimodality is interpreted as sexual dimorphism. Westoll's brachiopods and Kotaka's clams illustrate the same point: sound taxonomic inferences can be made solely on the basis of the distribution pattern displayed by shell features whose functional significance is incompletely known.

One troublesome limitation of paleontological data lies in the difficulty (usually the impossibility) of distinguishing phenotypic from genotypic variation. This problem is particularly evident to the taxonomist analyzing statistically significant morphological differences among a small number of samples whose stratigraphic relationships are poorly known. If suitable collections are available for study, however, the taxonomic (but not the genetic) problem may disappear. A case in point is McKerrow's (1953) detailed study of contemporaneous brachiopod communities sampled from many localities along the outcrop of a thin stratigraphic

unit known as the Fuller's Earth Rock. Although the genus
Ornithella displays a wide range of morphological variation at
each locality and a considerable overlap among geographically
separated populations, careful study reveals that certain modal
variants tend to characterize different localities, as indicated

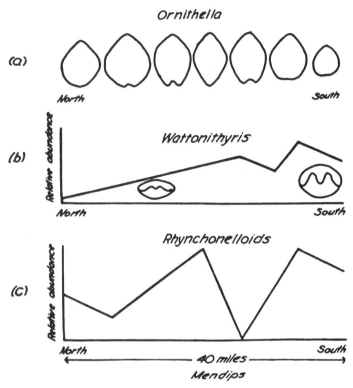

Fig. 8.   Diagram of some lateral changes in brachiopod communities in
the Jurassic Fuller's Earth Rock. (*a*) Changes in the outline of *Ornithella*,
simplified and somewhat exaggerated; (*b*) changes in the relative abundance and in the anterior commissure of *Wattonithyris*; (*c*) changes in the
relative abundance of the rhynchonelloids (McKerrow, 1953).

schematically in Fig. 8. Some morphological features in fact tend
to be symmetrically disposed about Mendips. Are we to interpret
these differences as the result primarily of genotypic or phenotypic variation? Even though this question must remain unanswered, the taxonomic expression of these data is in no way
affected. In either case the entire assemblage will be termed a
(transient) species.

Now suppose that McKerrow had had available only two geographically isolated but distinctive local populations. In this case, taxonomic disposition of these collections would be far more subjective. This serves to emphasize the point that the chief taxonomic difficulties which arise in dealing with paleontological

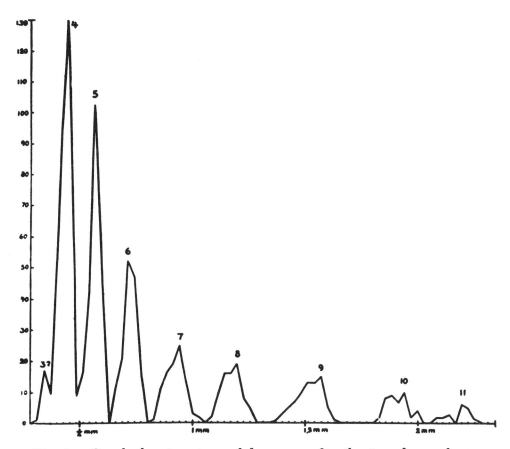

Fig. 9.   Graph showing size and frequency distribution of growth stages represented in a population of the Silurian ostracod *Beyrichia jonesi* from Gotland (Spjeldnaes, 1951).

materials are due not so much to the limitations inherent in post-mortem examination of skeletal anatomy, but rather to the incompleteness of the available fossil record.

2. *Biased frequency distribution.*   The size-frequency distribution of a few carefully studied paleontological samples seems to reflect fairly accurately the size distribution of the original living

population. For example, in a large collection of the Silurian ostracod *Beyrichia jonesi* analyzed by Spjeldnaes (1951) there is a progressive depletion in frequency at least from the fourth to the eleventh instars (Fig. 9). This pattern has been taken as evi-

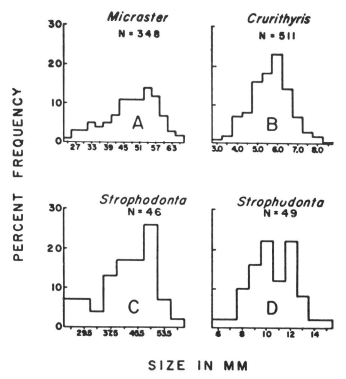

SIZE IN MM

Fig. 10.   Size-frequency distributions of four typical samples of fossil invertebrates. N, number of measured specimens; A, measurements of greatest width in a sample of the echinoid *Micraster coranguinum* from the Cretaceous of Northfleet, England. Data from Kermack (1954). B, measurements of maximum width in a sample of the brachiopod *Crurithyris plano-convexa* from the Dry Shale of Kansas. Data from Tasch (1953). C, measurements of maximum width of the brachiopod *Strophodonta* sp. from a single locality in the Gravel Point formation, Michigan. Original data. D, measurements of maximum length in a sample of *Strophodonta extenuata ferronensis* from a locality in the upper Ferron Point formation, Michigan. Original data.

dence that the collection approximates a random sample of the original population, and on this assumption Kurtén (1953) has calculated life tables giving mortality rates at each growth stage as well as other standard parameters of population dynamics.

Samples of the sort just described are by no means common, however. Four size-frequency distributions typical of fossil marine invertebrates are given in Fig. 10. Such distributions tend to be unimodal and either symmetrical or slightly skewed; many can be approximated by the normal distribution. In most instances, the observed distributions are strongly biased and reflect primarily a complex of ecologic, geologic, and operational factors which at best bear only obliquely on the taxonomic problem (Boucot, 1953; Kermack, 1954; Imbrie, 1955).

In dealing with groups of animals (mammals, for example) where practical and objective morphological criteria are available for the identification of definite growth stages, the existence of biased size distributions may cause little concern to the taxonomist. In dealing with fossil groups lacking criteria of this sort, however, particularly in groups displaying strongly allometric growth patterns, taxonomic judgments may be considerably affected. Once recognized, this problem can be quite easily solved by characterizing sampled populations in terms of growth patterns rather than growth stages (Kermack, 1954; Parkinson, 1954; Imbrie, 1956).

3. *Incompleteness of the available fossil record.* The most serious limitation of paleontological data is the sparsity of fossils. It is of course true that the total number of collecting localities which have yielded good fossils from every system younger than Precambrian is very large, and it is also true that future work will bring forth an unknown but certainly very large amount of new material from localities and horizons now unrepresented in existing collections. Nevertheless, from general theoretical considerations on the nature of sedimentation and diagenesis, and from practical experience in portions of the geological column which have been thoroughly examined for fossils, most paleontologists and stratigraphers would predict that no amount of future field work will ever fill a majority of existing phyletic gaps between transient species.

At least five factors are important in accounting for the incompleteness of the available fossil record, not including lack of ade-

quate field work: nondeposition, erosion, migration, nonpreservation, and inaccessibility. Together, these factors account for the
prevalence of transient species.

Since the publication of the classic paper by Barrell (1917),
stratigraphers have generally admitted that very few local sedi-

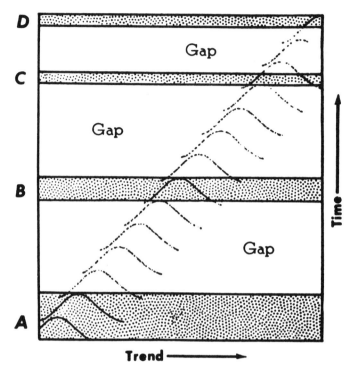

Fig. 11. Diagram to illustrate how gaps in the stratigraphic record result in a meager fossil record of a continuously evolving lineage. Gradual
evolution of a lineage is indicated by a series of shifting normal frequency
curves. Stippled areas represent preserved portions of the stratigraphic record. Solid frequency curves represent four transient species collected from
layers A-D. Gaps in the fossil record, indicated by dashed curves, cannot
be eliminated by collecting in this area. (After Newell, 1956.)

mentary sequences contain a direct, continuous record of the total
time span represented in a given stratigraphic sequence. This is
because many fossiliferous strata were formed in water so shallow
that the permanent accumulation of a sedimentary layer (with
entombed fossils) was a rare event, possible only when the surface of sedimentation was below the depth to which waves and

currents were effective in moving sediment. Figure 11 illustrates the formation of sedimentary and paleontological hiatuses according to this principle.

Mere deposition of sedimentary layers does not safeguard their preservation since large volumes of such rocks are destroyed by uplift and erosion. Even if the sediments escape this fate, it does not guarantee that even a small sample of skeleton-bearing organisms present in the original living community will become collectable fossils. In order to be preserved a skeleton must escape

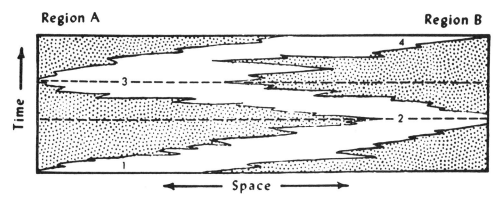

Fig. 12.   The effect of facies migration on the fossil record of evolving lineages. Well-defined transient species occur at horizons 1 and 3 in region A. Different transient species occur at horizons 2 and 4 in region B. Even if deposition and preservation have been continuous in this area, inaccessibility of the rocks lying between regions A and B makes the available record of this lineage incomplete. (After Newell, 1956.)

chemical, biochemical, and mechanical destruction by agencies acting before, during, and after burial.

Figure 12 illustrates the combined effect of migration and inaccessibility in reducing the number of collectable fossils. Stippled and unstippled areas on this diagram represent three contrasting environments (as well as the geologic record of those environments, or facies) which have continuously occupied the area. Three environments, each with its associated organic community, are represented at any given instant. Under normal circumstances geological conditions responsible for the localization of physical environments change, and the associated communities shift accordingly. Now consider the effect of this migration on the fossil record of an evolving succession of populations. Four transient species belonging to one lineage are symbolized by numbers 1 through 4. Under ideal conditions, fossils representing the entire lineage could be studied in outcrops of the appropriate facies. In practice, however, the geological column can be studied only in isolated, accessible areas. Hence a paleontologist examining fossils from region A records two transient species 1 and 3, while in region B his observations are limited to transients 2 and 4. If

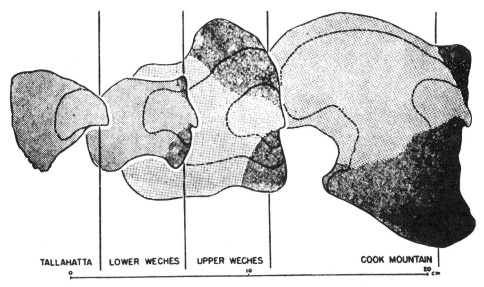

TALLAHATTA | LOWER WECHES | UPPER WECHES | COOK MOUNTAIN

Fig. 13.   Some of the characteristic features of four species of the Eocene oyster *Cubitostrea*. Heavy stippling represents auricles. Formation names indicate the stratigraphic position of individual species, as follows: Tallahatta, *C. perplicata;* Lower Weches, *C. lisbonensis;* Upper Weches, *C. smithvillensis;* Cook Mountain, *C. sellaeformis* (Stenzel, 1949).

morphological gaps between studied transients are too large, sound phylogenetic interpretations may be impossible.

One of the best documented examples of transient species recording portions of an evolving lineage is Stenzel's (1949) study of the oyster *Cubitostrea*. Four clear-cut species have been recognized, each restricted to a different stratigraphic level in the Eocene of the Gulf Coast. *C. perplicata*, the oldest known species in this line, is characterized by small size, strong ribbing, thin shell, absence of auricles, lack of arching, as well as other characters

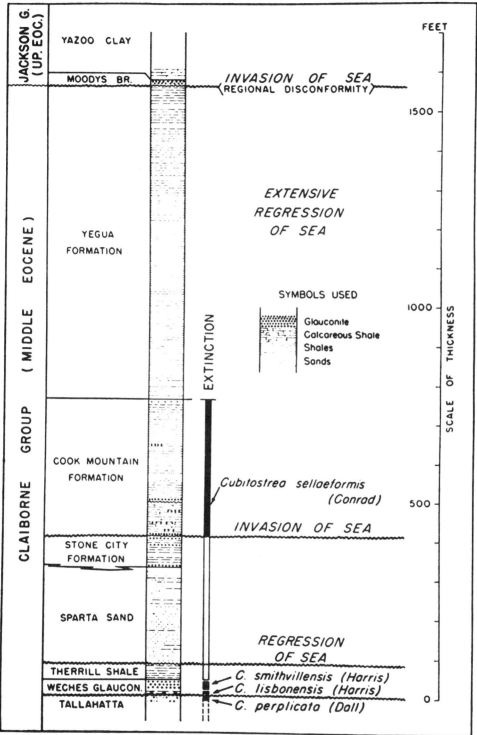

Fig. 14. Stratigraphic ranges of the chain of species comprising the *Cubitostrea sellaeformis* lineage in the Gulf Coastal Plain (Stenzel, 1949).

191

(Fig. 13). *C. sellaeformis*, the youngest known species, is characterized by large size, absence of ribs, thick shell, strongly developed auricles, and conspicuous arching. Gaps between these extremes are partly bridged by *C. lisbonensis* and *C. smithvillensis*.

This assemblage of species is viewed as the fossil record of a continuously evolving stock leading to *C. sellaeformis*. But the point to be emphasized here is that each of these species represents only a stage in this evolution and is a transient, not a successional, species. The stratigraphic range of each species is indicated in Fig. 14. Although *Cubitostrea* is represented almost continuously in beds ranging from the upper Tallahatta through the Weches formations, the morphological and stratigraphic ranges of the three species do not overlap. Similarly, transitional forms linking *C. smithvillensis* and *C. sellaeformis* are unknown. From independent stratigraphic evidence it is clear that the discontinuities just discussed are to be explained in terms of nondeposition, erosion, and migration associated with advances and retreats of the Gulf of Mexico.

Successional Species. All the difficulties discussed above in connection with transient species, with the single exception of the incompleteness of the fossil record, apply with equal force to successional species. In addition there is the theoretical taxonomic problem of selecting criteria for the subdivision of continuous lineages. From what has been said it will be clear that this problem is encountered far more often in the literature than in the laboratory. More extensive field work will undoubtedly bring forth more examples in the near future, but it is unlikely that the problem of successional species will ever be a burden to the student of fossils.[*]

One of the earliest and still the best example of successional speciation is the fossil spatangoid sea urchin *Micraster* originally described by Rowe (1899). A summary of *Micraster* evolution

---

[*] Successional species may, however, prove to be common in cores taken from deep ocean basins where deposition and preservation may be essentially continuous. Here lie fascinating and nearly untouched areas for taxonomic, evolutionary, and paleoecologic research.

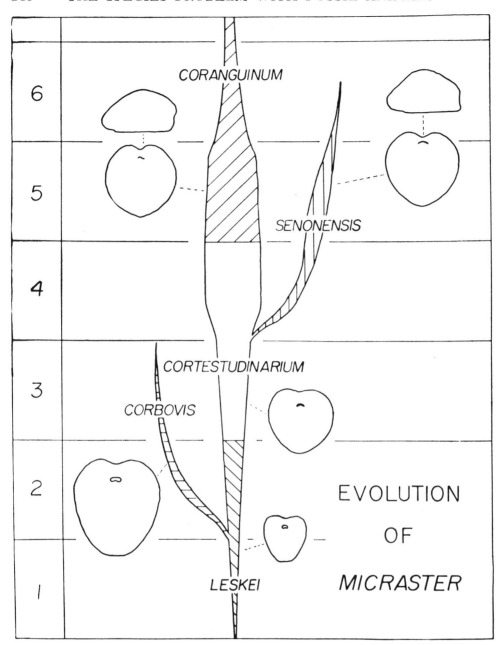

Fig. 15. Evolution of the spatangoid echinoid genus *Micraster* as recorded in six zones of the Cretaceous of southern England. Some of the characteristic features of the five designated successional species are indicated by ventral and lateral profiles. 1, Zone of *Cyclothyris cuvieri;* 2, Zone of *Terebratulina lata;* 3, Zone of *Holaster planus;* 4, Zone of *Micraster cortestudinarium;* 5, Zone of *Micraster coranguinum;* 6, Zone of *Marsupites testudinarius.* Constructed chiefly from data given by Kermack (1954).

will serve as a convenient focus for a theoretical discussion of the taxonomy of successional species. This review is based largely on Kermack's (1954) critical restudy of Rowe's materials.

From many horizons in the chalky limestones of the English Cretaceous large numbers of well-preserved *Micraster* have been collected. Most of the limestones are soft enough so that simple preparation techniques make it possible to free the tests from the enclosing matrix. Owing to the complexity of the echinoid test, a large number of unit taxonomic characters can be distinguished and interpreted functionally by analogy with living spatangoids. From many points of view, then, these fossils make ideal materials for evolutionary and taxonomic studies.

Some of the outstanding features of the fossil record of *Micraster*, as interpreted by Kermack, are shown in Fig. 15. The oldest known members of the genus (*M. leskei*) possess small tests with the widest portion of the test well ahead of midlength. The mouth, lacking a distinct labrum, is plainly visible in ventral aspect. The anterior ambital notch is shallow and the subanal fasciole small. Closely spaced collections of the main line of evolution from this form record a progressive shift in the average values of the skeletal characters just mentioned, and in other characters as well, giving rise to *M. coranguinum*. In this large species the widest portion of the test is approximately at midlength, the mouth is farther forward, and a strong labrum obscures the mouth opening in ventral aspect. The anterior ambital notch is deep and the subanal fasciole large. It should be emphasized that distinctions between successive population samples can be made only by comparison of the average values of overlapping frequency distributions.

Two side branches of the main *M. leskei-coranguinum* line can be distinguished. The first, *M. corbovis*, is a large form with a number of characteristic features not discussed here. The second branch, *M. senonensis*, differs from its contemporary *M. coranguinum* principally in its complete or nearly complete lack of a subanal fasciole. Frequency distributions of this character in a single population studied by Kermack show two nonoverlapping clusters. In addition, *M. senonensis* tends to be relatively taller than *M. coranguinum.*

Studies of living spatangoid echinoids make possible a reasonable interpretation of the data presented above in terms of environmental adaptations. According to Kermack's view, the evolution of the main *M. leskei-coranguinum* stock is to be interpreted as progressively better adaptation to a burrowing habit. This view is based primarily on known functions of the labrum and subanal fasciole. In burrowing urchins, the labrum increases the efficiency of the mouth as an organ of ingestion; and dense cilia associated with the subanal fasciole produce strong posteriorly directed water currents which aid in discharging water from the burrow.

The *M. senonensis* stock, on the other hand, seems to have evolved adaptations for living *on* rather than *in* the bottom. For this mode of life a subanal fasciole is unnecessary. The domelike form of the test, moreover, might facilitate cleaning of the surface; at least it would not hinder movement on the bottom.

We now come to the problem of expressing the facts and inferences about *Micraster* taxonomically. At least three possible criteria can be used for subdivision of such a continuum. First, boundaries between species (or subspecies) might be placed at those points in the phylogenetic tree where branching takes place. Assuming that the phylogeny has been adequately documented, this criterion has at least the merit of objectivity. But units so delineated may differ very greatly in scope. In the case of *Micraster*—assuming a relatively constant morphological evolutionary rate—the oldest lineage segment would be much smaller in morphological scope than the youngest.

Stratigraphic boundaries offer another possible basis for the delimitation of taxonomic units. *Micraster*, for example, might be split into eleven species with taxonomic boundaries placed at the limits of the six stratigraphic zones. Although to a biologist such a course might appear rather arbitrary, to a stratigrapher units so defined might be quite useful.

From a strictly biological point of view probably the most satisfactory basis for subdividing an unbranched lineage is morphology. For example, taxonomic boundaries can be placed in such a way that the total morphological difference between corresponding parts of successive species is of the same order as that between contemporary species. Application of this criterion of course involves a subjective evaluation of total morphological (and inferred genetical) differences.

The *Micraster* classification now in use and illustrated in Fig. 15 is based on a combination of the three criteria discussed above, with emphasis on the morphology. Note that the interpretation of the *M. leskei-coranguinum* lineage as the main line of *Micraster* evolution is reflected in the failure to subdivide *M. leskei* and *M. cortestudinarium*.

Summary

A review of recent literature in paleontology indicates that the nature of fossil species remains a controversial matter, although the biological species concept based on variable, interbreeding populations has largely replaced the typological concept based on morphotypes. Data on morphology, association, biogeography, paleoecology, and biostratigraphy are used by the paleontologist to delineate fossil species. Most species actually defined by neontologists and paleontologists are transient species, i.e., essentially contemporaneous aggregates of interbreeding populations. In rare instances paleontologists describe segments of phyletic lineages. Groupings of this sort are called successional species.

The principal source of difficulty in applying the biological species concept to fossils is the incompleteness of the available fossil record. This lack is attributed to a combination of factors, including nondeposition, erosion, migration, nonpreservation, and inaccessibility. Taxonomic problems also arise from the limitations inherent in morphological data and the prevalence of biased frequency distributions. In dealing with successional species the problem arises as to the selection of criteria for subdividing continuous lineages. Taxonomic boundaries may be designated on the basis of phyletic branching, stratigraphy, or morphology.

REFERENCES

Allen, G. M. 1938. The mammals of China and Mongolia. *Natural History of Central Asia*, Vol. 11, Pt. 1, American Museum of Natural History, New York, pp. 1-620.

Barrell, J. 1917. Rhythms and the measurement of geologic time. *Bull. Geol. Soc. Amer.*, **28**, 745-904.

Boucot, A. J. 1953. Life and death assemblages among fossils. *Am. J. Sci.*, **251**, 25-40.

Burma, B. H. 1948. Studies in quantitative paleontology: I. Some aspects of the theory and practice of quantitative invertebrate paleontology. *J. Paleontol.*, **12**, 725-61.

Burma, B. H. 1954. Reality, existence, and classification: a discussion of the species problem. *Madroño*, **12**, 193-224.

Colbert, E. H., and D. A. Hooijer. 1953. Pleistocene mammals from the limestone fissures of Szechwan, China. *Bull. Am. Museum Nat. Hist.*, **102**, 1-134.

Eagar, R. M. C. 1952a. Some problems in invertebrate paleontology. *Proc. Leeds Phil. Lit. Soc.*, **6**, Pt. 1, 50-53.

Eagar, R. M. C. 1952b. Variation with respect to petrological differences in a thin band of Upper Carboniferous non-marine lamellibranchs. *Liverpool and Manchester Geol. J.*, **1**, Pt. 2, 161-90.

Eagar, R. M. C. 1956. Naming carboniferous non-marine lamellibranchs. In P. C. Sylvester-Bradley (1956).

Imbrie, J. 1955. Biofacies analysis. *Geol. Soc. Amer., Spec. Papers*, No. 62, 449-64.

Imbrie, J. 1956. Biometrical methods in the study of invertebrate fossils. *Bull. Am. Museum Nat. Hist.*, **108**, 211-52.

Kermack, K. A. 1954. A biometrical study of *Micraster coranguinum* and *M.* (*Isomicraster*) *senonensis*. *Trans. Roy. Soc.* (*London*), **B237**, 375-428.

Kotaka, T. 1953. Variation of Japanese *Anadara granosa*. *Trans. Proc. Palaeontol. Soc. Japan*, n.s., No. 10, 31-36.

Kurtén, B. 1953. On the variation and population dynamics of fossil and recent mammal populations. *Acta Zool. Fennica*, **76**, 1-122.

Leitch, D. 1940. A statistical investigation of the *Anthracomyas* of the basal Similis-Pulchra Zone in Scotland. *Quart. J. Geol. Soc. London*, **96**, 13-37.

Mayr, E., E. G. Linsley, and R. L. Usinger. 1953. *Methods and Principles of Systematic Zoology*. McGraw-Hill Book Co., New York, pp. 1-328.

McKerrow, W. S. 1953. Variation in the Terebratulacea of the Fuller's Earth Rock. *Quart. J. Geol. Soc. London*, **91**, 97-122.

Newell, N. D. 1956. Fossil populations. In P. C. Sylvester-Bradley (1956).

Parkinson, D. 1954. Quantitative studies of brachiopods from the Lower Carboniferous reef limestones of England. I. *Schizophoria resupinata* (Martin). *J. Paleontol.*, **28**, 367-81.

Regan, C. T. 1926. Organic evolution. *Rept. Brit. Assoc. Southampton*, 1925.

Rowe, A. W. 1899. An analysis of the genus *Micraster*, as determined by rigid zonal collecting from the Zone of *Rhynchonella Cuvieri* to that of *Micraster coranguinum*. *Quart. J. Geol. Soc. London*, **55**, 494-546.

Simpson, G. G. 1941. Large Pleistocene felines of North America. *Am. Museum Nat. Hist.*, **No. 1136**, 1-27.

Simpson, G. G. 1943. Criteria for genera, species, and subspecies in zoology and paleozoology. *Ann. N.Y. Acad. Sci,*. **44**, 145-78.

Simpson, G. G. 1951. The species concept. *Evolution*, **5**, 285-98.

Spjeldnaes, N. 1951. Ontogeny of *Beyrichia jonesi* Boll. *J. Paleontol.*, **25**, 745-55.

Stenzel, H. B. 1949. Successional speciation in paleontology: the case of the oysters of the *sellaeformis* stock. *Evolution*, **3**, 34-50.

Sylvester-Bradley, P. C. 1952. In R. M. C. Eagar (1952a, pp. 52-53).

Sylvester-Bradley, P. C., ed. 1956. The species concept in paleontology. *Systematics Assoc. Publ. No. 2*.

Tasch, P. 1953. Causes and paleoecological significance of dwarfed fossil marine invertebrates. *J. Paleontol.*, **27**, 356-444.

Weir, J. 1950. Recent studies of shells of the coal measures, *Sci. Progress*, **38**, 445-58.

Westoll, T. S. 1950. Some aspects of growth studies in fossils. *Proc. Roy. Soc. (London)*, **B137**, 490-509.

Part IV

SPECIES IN HIGHER PLANTS
AND ANIMALS

Editor's Comments
on Papers 11 Through 17

The most generally accepted definition of species for higher plants and animals is the biological species one. Grant (Paper 11) defines the biological species as "the reproductively isolated system of breeding populations." Mayr (Paper 15) defines the biological species as "groups of interbreeding natural populations that are reproductively isolated from other such groups." The first four papers (11 through 14) in this section deal with species concepts in higher plants, the next (Paper 15) deals with species concepts in animals, and the last two (Papers 16 and 17) present challenges to the biological species concept.

Both Grant (Paper 11) and Löve (Paper 12) express their views on the applicability of the biological species definition to plant groups. Grant also points out the difficulties involved with sibling species. Since sibling species do not interbreed, yet are almost indistinguishable morphologically, such species create problems for taxonomic identification. Grant suggests that groups of noninterbreeding populations be considered biological species, while groups of morphologically distinct populations be considered taxonomic species, regardless of their breeding relationships. The taxonomic species, according to this definition, is a unit of convenience for the purpose of identification. Löve expresses the view that the biological species definition is applicable to all organisms, even those that reproduce asexually.

Like domestic animals, cultivated plants offer a number of possibilities for studying the theoretical limits of species. The biological species concept as applied to cultivated plants is explored by Baker (Paper 13). As Baker points out, cultivated plant species have all too often been defined on some basis other than a reproductive one. Yet cultivated species have numerous advantages not shared by noncultivated species. Cultivated species have been grown under different environmental conditions, and they have been exposed to breeding experiments and hybridization. Also, there are economic incentives for discovering interbreeding relationships between groups of populations of cultivated plants.

A similar concept to Grant's taxonomic species is the "aggregate species" described by Heywood (Paper 14). In the "aggregate species" concept, an aggregate is made up of a number of morphologically closely related species that are difficult to distinguish and are reproductively isolated from one another. This is one way to bring together theoretical systematics and practical considerations of taxonomy into some form of workable system.

Species concepts in animals are discussed by Mayr (Paper 15). In this paper Mayr provides his definition of the biological species, and his views on the utility of this species concept in solving some of the questions of ecological and evolutionary biology.

Papers 16 and 17 present some serious criticisms of the biological species concept. Sokal and Crovello (Paper 16) point out that much of the analysis involved in attempting to discover reproductive relationships is of a phenetic nature. They also point out that, in their opinion, the biological species definition is extremely difficult, and often impossible, to apply to natural groups, and that it is the local population rather than the species that has any value for studying evolutionary and ecological processes. Sokal and Crovello conclude that the most useful species concept is a phenetic one. In practice, many of the phenetic data are morphological in nature and are analyzed by computers through the methodology of numerical taxonomy (see Sokal and Sneath, 1963; Sneath and Sokal, 1973).

Ehrlich and Raven (Paper 17), on the other hand, point out that the exchange of genetic material, or gene flow, in sexually reproducing organisms may be considerably more limited than has been suspected. They suggest that although a species may have some form of common gene pool, it is selection rather than gene flow that maintains the general phenetic nature of the species. They present some data from both plants and animals demonstrating that even within a population, actual gene exchange or gene flow may be very limited. However, it must be kept in mind that we have almost no knowledge of how much gene flow, particularly in the context of the time dimension, is necessary to maintain the integrity of a species, and to what extent low levels of gene flow can counteract low levels of selection.

The biological species definition must also be criticized on the grounds of both hybridization and ethological isolation. Some populations belonging to different animal species and a number of populations belonging to different plant species are able to hybridize and produce fully or partially fertile offspring. Yet such populations are distinct enough to be called species by taxonomists. Similarly, some distinct groups of populations that are presently called species are behaviorally isolated under natural conditions and do not interbreed, although they are capable of producing fertile offspring under laboratory conditions. In this respect, the biological species definition suffers from assigning an arbitrary cutoff point to a continuum of reproductive relationships which might be predicted from the gradual nature of speciation and evolution.

11

Reprinted from V. Grant, *Plant Speciation*, Columbia University Press, 1971, pp. 19-36

THE BIOLOGICAL SPECIES

V. Grant

Introduction · An Example · The Biological Species as a Corollary of Sexual Reproduction in a Biotic Community · Sibling Species · Biological Species vs. Taxonomic Species

Introduction

The biological species is a fundamental unit of organization in biparental organisms. It is the reproductively isolated system of breeding populations. In other words, the biological species is the sum total of interbreeding individuals and, hence, the most inclusive unit of normal biparental reproduction. The biological species concept is reached in several ways.

It was reached originally by the early naturalists from direct observation of nature. It was apparent to these observers, as it has been to their modern followers in population biology, that living organisms do not form a continuum, but fall into a series of more or less discrete clusters of interbreeding individuals. Thus the members of the cat family are seen to fall into distinct groups such as lions, tigers, bobcats, and domestic cats. Each group breeds true to type or, in the language of the early naturalists, begets its own like, and hybrids between the groups are either nonexistent or so rare as to call for special attention. This discontinuous pattern of relationship and of variation is found in many animal families and among some higher plants. The discrete breeding groups were the species.

As regards species in the plant kingdom we can do no better than quote the views of Cesalpino in *De plantis libri* (1583), of John Ray in *Historia plantarum* (1686), and of Linnaeus in *Critica botanica* (1737) and *Philosophia botanica* (1751).

Cesalpino stated, with reference to species, that like always produces like (cf. Sachs, 1906). John Ray went on to state that plants which spring from the same seed and produce their kind again through seed belong to the same species (Sachs, 1906). "No more certain criterion of a species exists," he said, "than that it breeds true from seed within its own limits" (Darlington, 1937b).

And Linnaeus followed with statements contrasting species with varieties. "The Author of Nature, when He created species, imposed on his Creations an eternal law of reproduction and multiplication within the limits of their proper kinds. He did indeed in many instances allow them the power of sporting in their outward appearance, but never that of passing from one species to another." (*Critica botanica*; cf. Ramsbottom, 1938.) But varieties are a different matter. "There are as many varieties as there are different plants produced from the seed of the same species." (*Philosophia botanica*; Ramsbottom, 1938.)

It would take us too far afield to trace the subsequent history of the species concept in any detail here (but see Mayr, 1957, and Grant, 1963, pp. 336 ff.). Suffice it to say that the species concept of the early naturalists has been retained in principle but developed and clarified by modern population biologists. That concept in its modern form is known as the biological species concept and, by extension, the inclusive breeding groups themselves are designated biological species.

If biological species are distinct reproductive groups, barriers to hybridization should exist between them, and the finding of such barriers would constitute a second argument for the biological species concept. The postulated barriers, or reproductive isolating mechanisms, have indeed been found to exist. The sterility of the mule is legendary, and the early plant hybridizers sometimes referred to their sterile hybrids as plant mules or mule plants. Buffon in 1749, followed by Kant in 1775 and by many later students, was to use sterility of progeny as the main objective criterion for distinguishing between separate species. However, the situation is not quite this simple.

Interbreeding between biological species is prevented by many kinds of isolating mechanisms. Some pairs of species form sterile hybrids, to be sure, but other combinations can be made to produce fertile hybrids artificially, yet do not normally hybridize naturally owing to various external barriers such as aversions to mating or mechanical difficulties in crossing.

An Example

Gilia capitata and *G. tricolor* are related species belonging to the same section of the genus Gilia (Polemoniaceae). They are herbaceous plants with an annual life cycle, diploid chromosome condition ($2n = 18$), and predominantly cross-fertilizing breeding system.

Gilia tricolor occurs in the valleys and foothills of central and northern California. *Gilia capitata* occurs in the same areas and also ranges farther north, farther south, and farther west to the coast line (Figure 2). In many localities, individual plants of the two species grow side by side or close together. The two species, in other words, are sympatric.

The morphological characteristics of representative specimens of the two species are shown in Figures 3 and 4. The plants are large and tall in *Gilia capitata* and relatively small in *G. tricolor*. The inflorescence is a dense head in *G. capitata* and a loose cyme in *G. tricolor*. The sepals of the calyx have narrow midribs in *G. capitata* and broad, green bands in *G. tricolor*. The corolla shape is different in the two species. And in *G. capitata* the corolla is of one color, blue-violet, while in *G. tricolor* it is three-colored, with purple spots and an orange tube contrasting with a blue-violet background.

This is not to say that either species is uniform. In fact, much geographical variation exists within *Gilia capitata*. The characteristics of the flowers, capsules, and seeds vary racially as shown in Figure 5

205

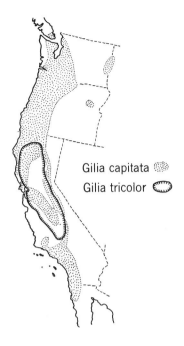

Gilia capitata

Gilia tricolor

Figure 2 Distribution areas of *Gilia capitata* and *G. tricolor* on the Pacific slope of North America.

along a transect from coastal sand dunes to interior mountains in the San Francisco Bay area. There is complete intergradation between these and other racial forms in *G. capitata* (Figure 6). Geographical variation occurs in *G. tricolor* also but is less developed here. But the variations are circumscribed within each species. No intermediate forms between *Gilia capitata* and *G. tricolor* are known. No hybrids between these two species have ever been found.

Experimental hybridizations have been carried out within each species and between them. Seven strains belonging to five geographical races of *Gilia capitata* were intercrossed. The races cross with one another in all combinations and, in most combinations, cross with ease. The interracial F_1 hybrids are highly fertile or semifertile with 50% to 90% good pollen and abundant seeds. These give rise to F_2 generations which are generally viable but include a small proportion of subvital plants (Grant, 1950a, 1952a). A northern and a southern race of *G. tricolor* also proved to be interfertile (Grant, 1952b).

Repeated attempts to cross *Gilia capitata* with *G. tricolor*, on the other hand, have always failed. The interspecific cross-pollinations lead

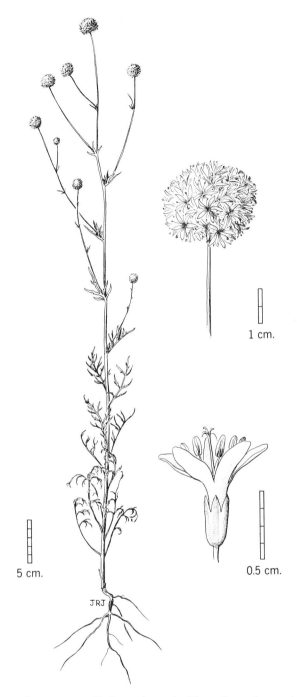

1 cm.

5 cm.

0.5 cm.

JRJ

Figure 3 *Gilia capitata* (Polemoniaceae). The plant shown belongs to subspecies *G. c. capitata*.

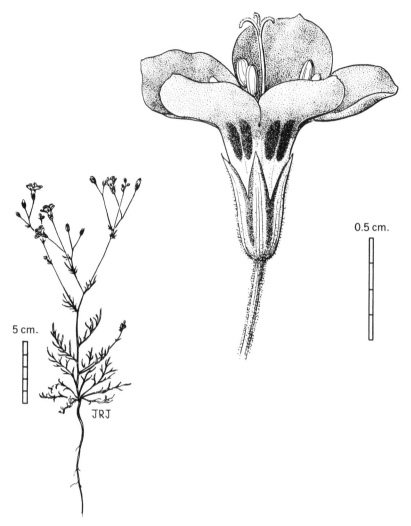

0.5 cm.

5 cm.

JRJ

Figure 4 *Gilia tricolor.*

to the formation of abortive seeds, but no sound seeds and no F_1 hybrids are produced. In addition it is known that *G. tricolor* will not cross with any other related species of Gilia. *Gilia capitata* crosses artificially with difficulty with some other related species, but then the hybrids are highly sterile (Grant, 1952b, 1954b).

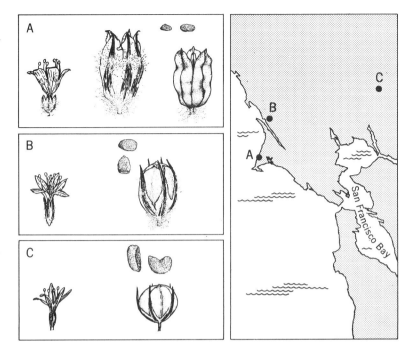

Figure 5 Flowers, capsules, and seeds of three races of *Gilia capitata* on a transect from the coast to the interior mountains north of San Francisco Bay, California. (A) *Gilia capitata chamissonis.* (B) *G. c. tomentosa.* (C) *G. c. capitata.*

Thus *Gilia tricolor* and *G. capitata* are separate biological species. Sexual reproduction takes place between members of *G. tricolor* and leads to intergrading variations. Interbreeding takes place in a similar way and has similar effects in *G. capitata.* But *G. tricolor* and *G. capitata* cannot and do not interbreed with one another owing to the operation of strong, reproductive isolating mechanisms.

The Biological Species as a Corollary of Sexual Reproduction in a Biotic Community

The biological species concept can be reached by a third line of reasoning. It can be shown that the organization of breeding populations

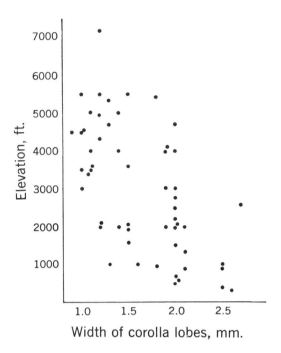

Figure 6 Geographical variation in width of corolla lobes in a series of populations of *Gilia capitata* ranging from the San Joaquin Valley to middle elevations in the Sierra Nevada, California. (Grant, 1950a.)

into separate biological species is a necessary accompaniment of the sexual process in a heterogeneous environment. The premise has been laid down by Dobzhansky (1937a) and Cain (1954). As Cain has put it (1954, p. 130):

> One has only to imagine the consequences of unrestrained hybridization between all living animals to appreciate the extreme importance of the process of speciation. If all specific barriers were suddenly and miraculously removed, the result would be an appalling welter of hybrids with every possible combination of characters. No single individual would be properly adapted to any one mode of life, and many of the characters of each might be adapted for well-nigh incompatible purposes.

And Dobzhansky (1937a) has stated that the "maintenance of life is possible only if the gene patterns whose coherence is tested by natural selection are prevented from disintegration due to unlimited hybridization." Let us now develop an argument based on this premise.

Any inhabitable local area on the earth's surface normally contains diverse ecological niches which are occupied by different sympatric populations of organisms. Each population is adapted for its particular niche in the biotic community by a combination of physiological and morphological characteristics. Each character combination is based in turn on a combination of genes.

Now sexual reproduction is a mechanism for bringing about gene recombination. This is not an absolute good. Gene recombination has advantageous effects in some situations and disadvantageous effects in others. The adaptive properties of different possible gene combinations vary widely according to the particular genes involved and their interactions.

The individuals belonging to a given breeding population may vary in several hereditary characters, yet they can intercross to produce viable and fertile progeny. The population is polymorphic for an array of coadapted genes. In terms of a simple example, the gene A is present in two allelic forms, A_1 and A_2, and a separate gene B is likewise present in two forms, B_1 and B_2. The nine diploid genotypes which can be produced by the sexual process from these two polymorphic genes ($A_1A_1 \, B_1B_1, A_1A_1 \, B_1B_2, \ldots, A_2A_2 \, B_2B_2$) exhibit individual differences; nevertheless they are all normal representatives of their population. They are all adapted for living and reproducing more or less successfully in their population's ecological zone. The good adaptive characteristics of the several recombination types are not a fortunate coincidence, moreover, but result from natural selection having acted through past generations in this breeding population to preserve the alleles with good combining ability.

A second population living in a different ecological niche in the same community has, like the first population, an adaptive character combination which is subject to variation within circumscribed limits. But it is polymorphic for a different array of coadapted genes. Let us say that it contains the alleles A_8 and A_9 and B_8 and B_9, which combine to form the nine diploid genotypes, $A_8A_8 \, B_8B_8, A_8A_8 \, B_8B_9, \ldots, A_9A_9 \, B_9B_9$. These genotypes, despite individual differences, are all fitted for life in their population's niche.

211

The consequences of crossing between members of the two populations are very different as regards the adaptedness of the offspring. Consider, for example, the nine types of F_2 progeny resulting from the cross of $A_1A_1 \, B_1B_1 \times A_8A_8 \, B_8B_8$. The two parental types reappearing in the F_2 generation are certainly viable, and the F_1 type may be viable. The remaining six genotypes, representing untested recombinations of the parental genes, are likely to be poorly adapted for either parental environment or for any other available environment. If the genes A and B are unlinked, these inviable or subvital recombination types can be expected to constitute 10/16 of the F_2 zygotes.

For other combinations of parents from the two populations, i.e., $A_1A_1 \, B_2B_2 \times A_8A_8 \, B_9B_9$, etc., the Mendelian proportion of recombination types in F_2, defined here as non-P and non-F_1 types, is the same, namely, 62.5%. In general, therefore, the progeny resulting from hybridization between two populations differing with respect to a simple adaptive gene combination are preponderantly recombination types of reduced fitness.

The proportion of subvital recombination types rises rapidly as the number of gene differences between the parental populations increases. Suppose that two populations differ allelically in five unlinked genes, A to E, which determine different adaptive modes in each population. Then the cross of $A_1A_1 \cdots E_1E_1 \times A_8A_8 \cdots E_8E_8$ produces F_2 zygotes, only 3.3% of which are genotypically like the parents or F_1s. The remaining 96.7% of the F_2 zygotes are recombination types which are expected to be more or less subvital. If the parental populations differ with respect to an adaptive gene combination based on ten independent genes, 99.9% of their F_2 zygotes are subvital recombinations.

In other terms, 966,797 of every million F_2 zygotes derived from hybridization between populations differing in an adaptive gene combination composed of five independent genes will possess an ill-adapted genetic constitution. And 999,022 per million F_2 zygotes derived from hybridization between populations differing in an adaptive character combination determined by ten independent genes will be likely to fail in any available environment.

Actual populations will, of course, deviate from these simplified models in various ways. Some factors like linkage will act to lessen the burden of hybridization. Other factors, such as the great complexity of the genetical differences between sympatric species, increase that burden. The latter factors probably outweigh the former. Therefore our numerical examples probably do not give an exaggerated estimate of the potential burden of hybridization between physiologically differentiated, sympatric populations.

The enormous loss of reproductive potential resulting from interbreeding between differentiated sympatric populations stands in marked contrast to the generally beneficial results of interbreeding within populations. Those individuals which cross with other members of the same population will usually leave vastly greater numbers of descendants than the individuals which hybridize with foreign populations. Under these conditions any hereditary aversions or blocks to hybridization will be favored by natural selection and will spread through each sympatric population.

We thus arrive at the conclusion that sexual reproduction, if not confined within the limits of separate populations in a biotic community, would lead to the breaking up of the adaptive gene combinations within each population. The continued existence of the sympatric populations is threatened in proportion to the freedom of interbreeding between them. Conversely, the stable biotic communities are those composed of reproductively isolated breeding populations or, in other words, of biological species.

Sibling Species

The essential characteristic of biological species, as we have seen, lies in their breeding relationships. The ability of individuals to exchange genes successfully, that is, to cross freely and produce fertile and viable progeny, characterizes them as members of the same biological species, whereas the inability to exchange genes freely and successfully is the mark of separate biological species. All else, including morphological difference, is superstructure.

Related biological species usually do differ in external morphological characters, as well as in underlying physiological traits, for many morphological features are components of the adaptive character combinations of the respective species. Traditional taxonomic methods of classification and identification rest on this common association of external morphological characters with physiogenetic traits.

213

But the correlation does not always hold. We find cases of good biological species which are virtually indistinguishable morphologically. Such cryptic species are termed sibling species.

A classical example is that of *Drosophila pseudoobscura* and *D. persimilis*. These morphologically similar flies were originally considered to be members of a single species, *D. pseudoobscura*, until certain "intraspecific" crosses revealed the existence of hybrid sterility barriers. The intersterile entities were then found to form sympatric populations over a vast area in western North America without hybridizing, and were accordingly recognized as separate species (Dobzhansky and Epling, 1944; Dobzhansky, 1951).

A search by several workers resulted eventually in the finding of minor morphological differences in the male genitalia and wings, as well as some behavioral, physiological, and cytological differences (see review by Mayr, 1963, pp. 34–35). The character differences are very slight, and the flies are difficult to identify by ordinary taxonomic procedures.

However, the flies readily recognize one another. When males and females of *Drosophila pseudoobscura* and *D. persimilis* are intermixed in a population cage in the laboratory, they mate exclusively or predominantly in intraspecific combinations; and only rarely do species-foreign females and males copulate under ordinary laboratory conditions (review in Grant, 1963, pp. 362–63). Likewise in nature, where the opportunities for hybridization are widespread, interspecific copulations are extremely rare and species hybrids are unknown (Dobzhansky, see Grant, 1963, p. 390). Obviously Drosophilas can discriminate between *D. pseudoobscura* and *D. persimilis* whether taxonomists can or not.

Sibling species are found in other species complexes in Drosophila, and in many other groups of animals (review in Mayr, 1963, pp. 33 ff.). Sibling species also occur in many genera of higher plants (Grant, 1957). Here the phenomenon is often associated with polyploidy.

A tetraploid species with the genomic constitution *AABB* will resemble morphologically, and may intergrade with, the ancestral diploid species *AA* for two reasons. First and foremost, the *A* genome is in the tetraploid species. Second, the tetraploid is likely to segregate some individuals like the *A* parental type, especially if it is a segmental allotetraploid. The tetraploid will resemble its other diploid parent, species *BB*, for the same reasons. The diploid species *AA* and *BB* will produce more or less sterile F₁ hybrids because of their chromosomal differentiation; and the hybrids between the tetraploid species *AABB* and either diploid, being triploid, will also be sterile. What appears to be a continuously intergrading population system on external morphology, and may be treated as a single species by the taxonomist, is thus a group of three intersterile sibling species (Grant, 1964a).

By way of illustration we consider a case in the *Gilia transmontana* group, which has been carefully analyzed by Day (1965). The plants are small annual herbs of the Mojave Desert and adjacent areas in western North America. They are predominantly autogamous but are cross-pollinated by insects to a small but biologically significant extent. Their general appearance is shown in Figures 7 and 8.

The *Gilia transmontana* group consists of not three but five interrelated diploid and tetraploid species. One of the tetraploid species, *G. transmontana*, is derived from the two diploids, *G. minor* and *G. clokeyi;* the other tetraploid, *G. malior*, stems from the diploids, *G. minor* and *G. aliquanta* (Day, 1965). It will be noted that the two tetraploid species have one diploid ancestor (*G. minor*) in common. All five species were regarded as variant forms of a single species in the earlier taxonomic treatments.

Artificial hybridizations show that the five species, although fertile themselves, are highly intersterile in all combinations. In nature they grow sympatrically in various combinations without interbreeding (V. and A. Grant, 1960; Grant, 1964a; Day, 1965).

Day (1965) has grown and compared a series of strains representing the known range of variation of each species under uniform environmental conditions in the greenhouse. She finds that the species do differ slightly but consistently in almost every plant part (see Figures 7, 8, and 9). Thus *Gilia aliquanta* is distinguished by its slightly larger flowers (Figure 8E); but the other four species have flowers of a similar small size (Figure 8, A–D). *Gilia minor* has smaller seeds than the other species (Figure 9). The leaves, the corolla colors, the capsules, and other features also show small interspecific differences.

But these external phenotypic differences are not such as to permit identification in every instance. Consider seed size again. The seeds range in weight from 10–20 mg in *Gilia minor*, 20–30 mg in *G. transmontana*, and 30–85 mg in *G. clokeyi*. These three species differ in

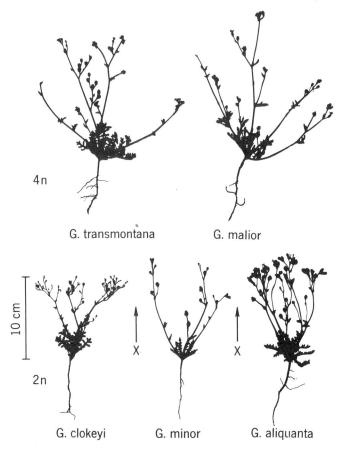

Figure 7 Form of the plant body in a group of sibling species in Gilia. (Day, 1965.)

average seed size (Figure 9, A–C) but form a continuum when the range of variation within the several species is considered (Day, 1965).

In general, *Gilia transmontana* bridges the morphological gap between its diploid ancestors, *G. minor* and *G. clokeyi*, so that clear-cut distinctions between the three species are hard to find. Similarly, *G. malior* exhibits apparent intergradation with *G. minor* and *G. aliquanta*. And, since the *G. minor* genome is present in both *G. transmontana* and *G. malior*, these two tetraploid species have many morphological features in common.

216

Figure 8 Flowers of the five sibling species of Gilia shown in Figure 7. (A) *Gilia clokeyi* (2x). (B) *G. transmontana* (4x). (C) *G. minor* (2x). (D) *G. malior* (4x). (E) *G. aliquanta* (2x). (Day, 1965.)

The problems of taxonomic identification in the *Gilia transmontana* group are, however, irrelevant to the question of the biological composition of this group. *Gilia transmontana, malior, minor, clokeyi,* and *aliquanta* form five separate breeding groups, and thus are good biological species whether we can always identify them by their external morphological characters or not.

Biological Species vs. Taxonomic Species

The early naturalists studied chiefly the higher animals and plants within a local fauna and flora. Hence they were dealing with sympatric populations of sexually reproducing organisms distinguished by prominent morphological differences. The species which they recognized could be defined equally well by breeding relationships or by morphological discontinuities. The inclusive unit of biparental reproduction and the basic unit of taxonomic classification were synonymous for them. In other words, no distinction was made, and no distinction was needed, between biological species and taxonomic species.

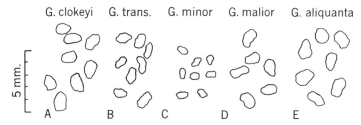

Figure 9 Seeds of the same five sibling species of Gilia. (Day, 1965.)

Similarly, in many groups of organisms which have been well studied by modern methods, there is good agreement between the criterion of breeding relationships and the criterion of morphological discontinuity. In such groups also, as they are currently understood, the biological species and the taxonomic species are synonymous.

It should be noted, however, that the criteria of breeding relationships and of morphological distinction do not necessarily always coincide. Inevitably, therefore, with the extension of biological research since the period of the early naturalists, numerous cases have come to light in which the two criteria do not coincide. Which criterion then should be given priority? On the answer to this question there has been no satisfactory general agreement among biologists. Instead, the question has been answered in terms of divergent practices carried out by divergent schools of workers.

One situation in which the breeding and the morphological criteria come into conflict is that involving sibling species. These entities are real biological species, but they are not readily identifiable by their morphological character differences and hence are not good taxonomic species.

This is not to say that related sibling species cannot be distinguished by their phenotypic features. In fact they can in every group of sibling species that has been analyzed thoroughly. But the amount of effort required to make identifications in such groups is much greater than the norm in routine taxonomic practice.

Let us reconsider the common pattern in higher plants of related diploid and tetraploid species introduced in the preceding section. External morphological characters alone are likely to provide unreliable criteria for distinguishing between three species with the genomic constitutions: *AA*, *BB*, and *AABB*. But a knowledge of the chromosome number when added to the morphological evidence is usually sufficient for purposes of identification. The two diploid species, *AA* and *BB*, are the morphological extremes within the group, and ordinarily they can be distinguished from one another by external characters. The morphologically intermediate species, *AABB*, can be distinguished reliably from either diploid by chromosome number alone.

Thus *AA*, *BB*, and *AABB* can be identified by a combination of external and internal phenotypic features. But the first step in identification is the determination of the chromosome number. This step, however, by requiring a microscopic examination of living plant material, goes well beyond the procedures which are standard for routine identification in the higher plants.

Another situation which has brought the morphological and the breeding criteria of species into conflict has resulted from the extension of a universal system of classification and nomenclature to all organisms. It is axiomatic according to the International Code of Botanical Nomenclature that every plant belongs to a species. Not every plant, however, is sexual, and not every plant group consists of individuals linked by mating bonds into breeding populations.

The association between morphological resemblances or differences and breeding relationships may break down in uniparental organisms as it does in sibling species groups. In the latter we found separate breeding populations with closely similar morphologies. In uniparental organisms prominent morphological differences may exist between classes of individuals without indicating their membership in different breeding groups.

In summary, the history of the species concept involves branching lines of thought. From a common starting point in the period of the early naturalists, the species concept has developed along two partially independent lines. One line has led to the modern biological species concept. The other main line has been the development of a concept of species which is useful in taxonomy. As a result, different meanings have become attached to the term species as it is used in population biology and in museum taxonomy. Many discussions of species fail to make the distinction between the two usages. It is commonplace to criticize the biological species concept from the viewpoint of the taxonomic species concept without recognizing the difference in viewpoints. Needless to say, such discussions perpetuate confusion of thinking.

Attempts have also been made to clarify the issue by restricting the technical term species to only one of its traditional usages. Gilmour and

Heslop-Harrison (1954) and Sonneborn (1957) would keep the term species for formal taxonomy and propose new terms (hologamodeme, syngen) to designate the inclusive breeding group in nature. I once made the opposite suggestion that we use the word species in its biological sense exclusively and employ a different term (binom) for the unit of formal classification (Grant, 1957). These proposals are logical but unhistorical. Undoubtedly they would clarify discussions of the species problem, if they were widely adopted. But they stand little chance of becoming widely adopted because, in each case, they ignore long-standing historical claims on the term species by one or another large school of workers.

A way out of the semantic impasse which achieves the desired end of clarifying discussions, yet avoids the pitfall of going against long-established usages, is to recognize, and distinguish between, *biological species* and *taxonomic species* (Cain, 1954, Ch. 7; Grant, 1963, p. 342). The distinction between the two types of species has proved its usefulness in the presentation and discussion of the problem in this section.

Consider again the case of sibling species—so often disputed by taxonomists—in the light of this distinction. The individual sibling species are good biological species and can be recognized as such by workers interested in their genetical or ecological behavior. At the same time, the whole sibling species group can be treated as a single taxonomic species for purposes of routine identification.

We are confronted here with a new form of the old dichotomy between natural and artificial systems of classification. The former reflects genetic relationships but may not be convenient to use; the latter is useful in practical taxonomic work but may not express biological relationships. The dichotomy between these approaches to classification has usually involved the higher categories. But we find it repeated again at the species level wherever the taxonomic species recognized in ordinary practice are not equivalent to the biological species (Grant, 1964a).

The distinction between biological and taxonomic species goes far toward resolving differences in approach between different schools of workers. But this distinction also leaves some important problems unresolved. A third species concept, that of the so-called evolutionary species, is necessary in order to deal with these remaining problems, as we shall see in the next chapter.

REFERENCES

Cain, A. J. 1954. Animal Species and Their Evolution. Hutchinson and Co., Ltd., London; and Harper and Row, New York.

Cesalpino, A. 1583. De plantis libri.

Darlington, C. D. 1937b. The early hybridisers and the origins of genetics. *Herbetia* 4:63–69.

Day, A. 1965. The evolution of a pair of sibling allotetraploid species of Cobwebby Gilias (Polemoniaceae). *Aliso* 6:25–75.

Dobzhansky, Th. 1937a. Genetic nature of species differences. *Amer. Nat.* 71:404–20.

Dobzhansky, Th. 1951. Genetics and the Origin of Species. 3rd ed. Columbia University Press, New York.

Dobzhansky, Th., and C. Eplin. 1944. Contributions to the genetics, taxonomy, and ecology of *Drosophila pseudoobscura* and its relatives. *Carnegie Inst. Washington Publ. 554.*

Gilmour, J. S. L., and J. Heslop-Harrison. 1954. The deme terminology and the units of micro-evolutionary change. *Genetica* 27:147–61.

Grant, V. 1950a. Genetic and taxonomic studies in Gilia. I. *Gilia capitata. Aliso* 2:239–316.

Grant, V. 1952a. Genetic and taxonomic studies in Gilia. II. *Gilia capitata abrotanifolia. Aliso* 2:361–73.

Grant, V. 1952b. Genetic and taxonomic studies in Gilia. III. The *Gilia tricolor* complex. *Aliso* 2:375–88.

Grant, V. 1954b. Genetic and taxonomic studies in Gilia. VI. Interspecific relationships in the Leafy-stemmed Gilias. *Aliso* 3:35–49.

Grant, V. 1957. The plant species in theory and practice. In: The Species Problem. Ed. by E. Mayr. *Amer. Assoc. Adv. Sci. Publ. 50,* pp. 39–80.

Grant, V. 1963. The origin of Adaptations. Columbia University Press, New York.

Grant, V. 1964a. The biological composition of a taxonomic species in Gilia. *Advances in Genetics* 12:281–328.

Grant, V., and A. Grant. 1960. Genetic and taxonomic studies in Gilia. XI. Fertility relationships of the diploid Cobwebby Gilias. *Aliso* 4:435–81.

Linnaeus, C. 1737. Critica botanica.

Linnaeus, C. 1751. Philosophia botanica.

Mayr, E. 1957. Species concepts and definitions. In: The Species Problem. Ed. by E. Mayr. *Amer. Assoc. Adv. Sci. Publ. 50,* pp. 1–22.

Mayr, E. 1963. Animal Species and Evolution. Harvard University Press, Cambridge, Mass.

Ramsbottom, J. 1938. Linnaeus and the species concept. *Proc. Linnean Soc. London* 150:192–219.

Ray, J. 1686. Historia plantarum. London.

Sachs, J. 1906. History of botany. Translation. Oxford University Press, Oxford.

Sonneborn, T. M. 1957. Breeding systems, reproductive methods, and species problems in Protozoa. In: The Species Problem. Ed By. E. Mayr. *Amer. Assoc. Adv. Sci. Publ. 50,* pp. 155–324.

12

Reprinted from *Taxon*, 13(2), 33–45 (1964)

THE BIOLOGICAL SPECIES CONCEPT
AND ITS EVOLUTIONARY STRUCTURE

Askell Löve (Montreal)

Biology started as taxonomy, and it may well be said to be as old as human thought. In a sense taxonomy may perhaps be regarded as having originated with reacting organisms, since even the lowest of biota respond differently to a varied environment and effectively order their own world. It is but reasonable to expect that such an ancient and universal activity, vital to the most primitive tribes and the most advanced scientists alike, should have developed into a precise and undisputed technique. It may, therefore, be astonishing that it still is not uncommon for different students of the same material to arrive at altogether different classifications, and these may at times seem to be evaluated more by the reputations of their authors than on their approximation to reality. One of the reasons for this is probably the fact that even truly observational science has not yet reached more than a fraction of the biota of the world, and very many of those who work in the field of taxonomy are still confined to the basic ideas of pre-Darwinian thinking. Because of several seemingly unsurmountable difficulties, empirical studies still predominate with their inevitable tendency towards authoritarianism.

It must necessarily be realized that the method of approach to any scientific problem is of marked importance, and will have great effects on the type of discovery made. Or, to put the matter the other way round, the method of approach is itself largely ruled by the kind of answer one anticipates; it is, actually, also a kind of a question. In addition, time and the advance of knowledge in each particular field are likely to change the question in such a way that, when one method has provided the main crop of answers that it could be expected to yield, then it is time to ask another kind of question by adopting a new approach.

This is just what has happened in the field of taxonomy, where the original and basic approach is inevitably descriptive, because biologists set out to describe as fully and accurately as possible the variety of organisms and the phenomena which they display. This approach is designed to answer the question about what are the facts; though it needs categories as do all kinds of studies, these are arbitrarily chosen and hardly need to be more closely defined. This long-lasting phase of biological science was initiated by the ancient Greeks; it was but natural that they based their classification of all objects on a single philosophical system, because they did not realize the difference in origin and development of living beings and dead materia. All natural objects were grouped by the distinctions of their morphological characters, which were regarded as unalterable entities distinguishable by complete and equally important discontinuities and characterized by qualities of similar significance, as are chemicals and stones. This concept was, thus, purely typological.

The descriptive approach must inevitably be supplemented by the comparative. This is first centered around the question of more advanced grouping or classification, because we need to know what pattern an aggregate of biota has in common, and what distinct types there are at various levels of characterization. This leads to classification of organisms in a hierarchical system of categories which have to be more or less clearly defined, although some degree of arbitrariness can easily be tolerated. The result of this approach in the field of biology was the acceptance of the so-called rational classifications, or systems closely connected with the object to be classified.

The basic categories to be used were, however, vaguely conceived and their circumscription was clearly based on the acceptance of the typological concept, or perhaps rather of its variant, the morphological concept, as is obvious in the works of Linnaeus and his successors. Nevertheless, it was the important work based on this approach and these concepts that lead to the discovery and later acceptance of the theory of evolution.

Implicit in such a system is the idea of biological relationship. With the acceptance of the theory of evolution, this implicit postulate becomes explicit, and the question asked by the comparative method must become similarly altered, because behind common resemblances we must reach for common ancestry. The result of this is a phylogenetic classification, or a grouping intended to express evolutionary descent and relationships, and for this classification the definition and delimination of at least the main categories is evidently important. When the great evolutionary significance of the category of species at last had been established, the replacement of the typological concept, which in the living world had become a misconception, and also of its variant, the purely morphological concept, might seem to have become a necessity, because an evolutionary approach requires an evolutionary concept. As a matter of fact, such a concept had already been defined by De Candolle (1813) when he claimed that a species is "la collection de tous les individus que se ressemblent plus entr'eux qu'ils ne ressemblent à d'autres; qui peuvent, par une fécondation reciproque, produire des individus fertiles; et qui se reproduisent par la génération, de telle sorte qu'on peut par analogie les supposer tous sortis originairement d'un seul individu". Though this is a definition considering basic properties of the species in an evolutionary system, it has several disadvantages that are perhaps nowhere more evident than in the fact that it and numerous genetical species concepts proposed since have still not been able to extirpate the purely morphological idea as the basic concept of most taxonomists concerned with species description *per se*. Also, it is a confusion of the vaguely defined morphological concept and the theory of evolution that resulted in the absurd splitting of natural species into geographically defined taxa regarded to belong to this level by the followers of Wettstein and Komarov (cf. Juzepczuk, 1958), an idea which, if applied to the human species, would result in the splitting of mankind into even more "species" than the major races now recognized.

The comparative method in conjunction with the theory of evolution requires a new procedure, an approach which is best termed differential analysis. This seeks to clarify the major question about the causes of differences between the members of a related group and also between the related groups themselves. This, in fact, is the modern method of cytogenetics, making analyses after hybridization and studying the mechanism of cell division, and it forms one of the main pillars of what we term biosystematics. It is firmly associated with studies of the interrelationships and total pattern of each system of detectable components and the history of evolutionary divergence and its causes. It goes without saying that this treatment requires exact definition of its basic categories, since it sees in them important evolutionary steps that are repeated endlessly by all kinds of organisms. It is from this approach that we have been able to conclude not only that the category of species is a biological phenomenon of utmost significance, but also that the ability of this category to be sympatric to other related taxa of the same group without mixing coincides with the stage of evolution when a major genetical system becomes closed and loses its ability to interbreed and fuse with other such systems. It is true that good species are sometimes able to hybridize, but, if they are biologically sound, then their inherent reproductive barriers are likely to disturb the processes of interbreeding so radically that they effectively prevent miscibility. It is miscibility, not crossability, which is evolutionarily important. These genetical observations have added strength to the evolutionary ideas of classification below the generic level. As a result the idea of the species as the most important step in the evolution of barriers to genetical miscibility has been much clarified. However, by what looks like the irony of fate, at the same time the hope for a cytogenetical background for a phylogenetic system of plant classification including higher levels has faded away, because even cytological observations seem to be of a secondary and insecure value above the level of genus (cf. Constance, 1963; Löve, 1963); the scanty paleological evidence is still the only safe basis for general phylogenetic considerations. The idea of species, on the contrary, has been transformed into what we prefer to term the biological species concept. It emerged gradually and has been defined and redefined by many, whereas the most simple and clear definition was proposed by Mayr (1940) who regarded this species as "groups of actually or potentially interbreeding natural populations which are reproductively isolated from other such groups". The avoidance of all reference to morphological characters is significant.

It is an almost general claim by taxonomists who work on the basis of morphological or other quasi-typological concepts, and also by cytogeneticists reluctant to escape the dominance of their education, which was based on these concepts, that species are of so many kinds that several definitions would not suffice (cf. Davis and Heywood, 1963). This is a misconception that proves the necessity of the biological species concept, and it seems to be caused by disregard of the fact that "to be a different species is not a matter of difference but of distinctness" (Mayr, 1963). The biological species concept is the only such definition that is universal and equally applicable to all biota, be they human, fishes or birds, mosses or angiosperms, or even bacteria, and, by proper inference from characters other than reproduction, even for taxa the sexuality of which has been replaced by apomixis (cf. Löve, 1960).

Another important discovery made by the aid of the cytogenetical approach is that races within a species — be they classified as subspecies, varieties, ecotypes, demes, or something else — are genetically open population systems with at least a potential ability for effective interbreeding that will certainly remove their distinctive identity by mixing whenever they can hybridize freely. They are Mendelian populations, which may differ in as little as a single gene, though more frequently they deviate in a number of hereditary traits, either visible and thus useful to the taxonomist, or invisible and determining physiological characters that can only be studied experimentally. Studies on numerous animals and plants have revealed that the differential traits of subspecific units are connected with all kinds of genetical distinctions, like a number of single gene mutations, multiple alleles and, perhaps most frequently, polygenes. The development of these subspecific or intraspecific traits has been shown to have progressed through the three basic processes of neo-Darwinian evolution: gene mutations, genetic recombination and natural selection. This discovery may seem to explain the futility of using morphological characters as a basis for definitions of species; but when such traits have become fixed by reproductive isolation and changed or added to by further evolution, they become most useful tools in distinguishing the genetically closed species systems.

It has been emphasized by Stebbins (1959) that gene mutations do not direct the course of evolution, nor do they provide the immediate source of variation on which natural selection acts. They rather replenish the gene pool, substitute for genes that are being lost by natural selection, and then become reshuffled into adaptive gene blocks by means of the processes of recombination.

The dynamism of the processes of subspeciation varies widely. They are thought to be highly effective in subtropical areas and especially in arid regions in the south (Stebbins, 1949). The so-called polymorphism in the more or less xeromorphic plants of New Zealand seems to be an example of wide subspeciation which may be breaking down again through hybridization, perhaps affected by ecological changes induced by human activities, as recently emphasized by Rattenbury (1962). The variations of the Mediterranean and southern North American taxa of *Platanus* and *Quercus* are apparently mainly subspecific, though jealous taxonomists have often split them into narrowly limited so-called species. These subspecific processes may also be responsible for the unwieldy variation in some groups of plants in tropical regions, particularly in the Pacific islands where geographical isolation and an equitable climate seem to favour vivid subspeciation, and they must inevitably aid in fixing certain traits within each isolate, especially in these climatically agreable regions where diploidy is likely to be predominant among herbs. In the cold deserts of the northlands, however, subspeciation appears to be extremely limited and slow and, thus, even old and isolated islands here are not characterized by a high degree of endemic morphological traits. It is possible that this slowness of subspeciation in the Arctic may be caused by the fact that the effects of the genetical processes of evolution are markedly slowed down in perennial polyploids, in which these floras are particularly rich.

In some laboratory animals, and plants studied experimentally, distinct subspecific changes are observed after some generations of selective treatment. Cultivated plants and domesticated animals are good examples of relatively fast and drastic subspeciation. The human species itself, with its endless multitude of geographically more or less distinct variations at different subspecific and varietal levels, is also one of the best examples we know of rapid stabilization of various genetical traits by the aid of selection, isolation, and repeated hybridization. One of the many recently studied examples of rapid evolution in plants is an exception to the rule of the rarity of this kind of process in polyploid perennials of the northlands, since it comes from the Scandinavian-Icelandic species *Papaver nordhagenianum*, a decaploid and perennial alpine-arctic poppy with distinct morphological variations, studied mainly by Knaben (1959a, b) and somewhat by Löve (1955, 1962a, b). Within this species there are at least two distinct levels of subspeciation, one of which, classified as subspecies by the present writer, seems to have been formed not later than during the last Interglacial and possibly earlier, whereas within these taxa occur a number of different races, classified as varieties, which may have evolved in small isolates in the Scandinavian and Icelandic mountains during the perhaps 10,000 years that have elapsed since the last Pleistocene glaciers retreated.

Other species have evolved their morphological subspecific traits more slowly. There is a gentle gradation from the examples above to cases of no observable changes at all for 80 million years, as in the American *Opossum* (cf. Dobzhansky, 1951). Biogeographers know of numerous cases in plants, populations of which have been geographically isolated for perhaps millions of generations on islands, or even continents, without a conceivable morphological divergence. An example of this is the rare moss species *Bryoxiphium norvegicum* (Löve and Löve 1953; Löve, 1964) known from scattered localities in high-arctic northeastern Greenland, Iceland, a limited unglaciated area mainly south of the Great Lakes in North America, Mexico, a locality on Mt. Rainier, and two places in Alaska. In all these localities it shows so little variation

225

that specialists cannot distinguish specimens with certainty without information about their origin, whereas Asiatic and Madeiran material differs somewhat at the subspecific level. In Iceland this species may even be a relic from the Tertiary-mesophytic flora which reached that region from the west about 60 million years ago (cf. Löve, 1963b, 1964). Another good example of a somewhat more recent isolation without any trace of subspeciation is *Carex scirpoidea*, which is widespread in North America but known only from a single locality in northern Norway where it has survived at least the last Pleistocene glaciation (Gjærevoll, 1963); and as a third one may quote the arctic circumpolar and very disjunct populations of the octoploid *Acetosella graminifolia* (Löve, 1943). One of the most significant cases of slow subspeciation seems to be the section *Cerastes* of the genus *Ceanothus*, recently studied by Nobs (1963), who showed that the taxa of this section usually classified as species on the basis of their morphological distinctness are in fact biological ecotypes, or races at some subspecific levels, which have been unable to create a reproductive barrier since the Miocene, or during at least 25 million years. To the same group of slowly evolving taxa without detectable reproductive barriers, other than geographical isolation, belong the two taxa of *Platanus* classified as species by Linnaeus and others, several of the European and American so-called species of some Amentiferae, and a number of other groups on both sides of the North Atlantic the distribution and close relationships of which seem strongly to support the hypothesis of continental drift.

The processes of subspeciation have been thoroughly studied in laboratories and experiments by geneticists, as amply reviewed in the classical works by Dobzhansky (1951) and Clausen (1951, 1959). From these studies "it cannot be emphasized too strongly that the population is ultimately the key to every evolutionary problem" (Mayr, 1963), since even the evolutionary opportunities of incipient species and taxa that later become isolated from older groups are based on the gene pool which was first combined and tried out in small populations. However, little has been done so far to find an explanation of the different speed and efficacy of subspecific processess. None of the explanations so far ventured seems to be biogeographically fully convincing. Since the methods of genecology used by Turesson, Gregor, Clausen, Keck and Hiesey, and others, and also the methods of population genetics as applied by Fisher and Sewall Wright and their schools, have satisfactorily clarified many of the problems of the rapidly evolving races, it is likely that concentrated efforts using similar methods will also solve the riddle of the apparently almost unbelievably slow morphological evolution of the extremely rigid species.

According to a still generally accepted view, the same processes as cause subspecific and morphological variability also lead to speciation and the evolution of genera and families. This would mean that subspecies are incipient species, as believed by Darwin, who postulated the gradual change of one species into another by aid of additive changes of populations into geographical varieties, through major geographical races up to the species level. Certainly, morphological differences between species have been formed by the same processes as produce subspecific variations, since gene mutations, genetic recombination, and natural selection continue to act within taxa at all levels. However, there seem to be ample reasons to believe with Goldschmidt (1940) that the genically determined processes causing intraspecific variability do not necessarily lead to speciation, or to the reproductive isolation of the genetically closed systems we name species. They seem rather to be a kind of a blind alley carrying the species no further than to subspecific development and increased adaptation to diverse ecological conditions that ultimately may lead to extinction, though at the same time they form the paramount gene pool which determines the success of species and higher categories, if or when these are formed. As repeatedly pointed out by geneticists, most recently by Dobzhansky (1963) and Mayr (1963), a subspecies is an incipient species only insofar as an emergence of reproductive isolation between such genetic systems may give it a specific status, since reproductive isolation alone constitutes the effective closing of the breeding system at this level, actually or potentially. Our present knowledge does not exclude the possibility that such a barrier to reproduction could be formed by genetic changes of a similar kind and occurring parallel to those causing microevolution or subspeciation, if it affects some kinds of sterility genes, though we know of no safe example indicating that such genes have accumulated into a distinct and unsurmountable reproductive isolation. Even the case of the South American *Drosophila paulistorum* of the superhumid tropical forests, recently studied by Ehrman (1960, 1962), that Dobzhansky (1963) suggests may be "the missing link" in this chain, is still too obscure to be convincing, because it is still not impossible that the sterility genes observed in certain races of this species may prove to be comparable to the S-genes in plants and certain kinds of maternal effects resulting only in partial sterility of limited significance though perhaps subspecifically important. In all other cases so far studied there seems to be no observable correlation whatsoever between the processes of subspeciation, or the genetic changes which make races and species visibly and physiologically different, and the mechanisms which produce distinct reproductive isolation by means of hybrid sterility. This was originally demonstrated by Müntzing (1930) for *Galeopsis* and has later been substantiated by several others studying various genera of plants and animals (cf. Vickery, 1959). It is another matter that certain of the processes of speciation, like chromosomal rearrangements that result in partial sterility, begin already within the species and may proceed parallel to the subspeciation processes and even further them by the aid of partial sterility and the formation of irreversible gene blocks.

The processes leading to reproductive isolation are the processes of speciation in the strict sense. As defined by geneticists and especially by Mayr (1942, 1963), this term includes all those differences which prevent two populations from exchanging genes through the formation of fertile or, perhaps, partially sterile hybrids, actually or potentially. This kind of isolation ought not to be confused with isolation caused by marked differences in occurrence in space, in ecological preferences, in seasons of flowering, or in pollination mechanisms, since the latter are of a different nature and comparable to spatial or social isolation between human beings. Extensive cytotaxonomical research has shown that reproductive isolation is brought into being either by changes in the genetical arrangement within the chromosomes, or simply by changes in their number. The former process has fittingly been named gradual speciation by Huxley (1942) and Valentine (1949, 1963), whereas the latter has been termed abrupt speciation.

The processes of gradual speciation are complex and wear many guises, but they are always due to a variety of changes that lead to hybrid inviability, sterility and, finally, incompatibility, without affecting the chromosome number. As far as is known, they are caused by a number of inversions, segmental interchanges, and other chromosomal rearrangements, which prevent or interrupt chromosome pairing in hybrids. It is apparent from the extensive studies by Dobzhansky and his collaborators working with various species of *Drosophila* — the only organism which has so far been thoroughly studied from this point of view — that these changes tend to be additive. Inversions occur within every plant and animal species so far closely studied, sometimes even in considerable number, as has been reported though not yet thoroughly verified in *Paris quadrifolia* by Geitler (1937, 1938), and it looks, at least in some plants, as if many of these soon will be rejected because of selective inferiority. But if they survive and show a selective superiority or neutrality then they are slowly joined by aid of hybridization, whereas new alterations within the same chromosomes add to their effect on chromosome pairing until this has reached the degree of an effective barrier to genetic exchange. These changes are, naturally, irreversible at all stages. As pointed out by Dobzhansky (1963) for *Drosophila* and also clearly manifested in the diploid races of *Rumex* and dioecious *Acetosa* studied by the present writer (unpublished), natural selection seems to perfect the reproductive isolation of karyotype races more quickly in sympatric populations where hybridization is frequent than in allopatric races where exchange of chromosomes is prevented by geographical isolation. This seems also to have been the case in the evolution of *Clarkia franciscana* and some related species studied by Lewis and Raven (1958), who suggested that they may have originated "as a consequence of rapid reorganization of the chromosomes due to the presence, at some time, of a genotype conducive to extensive chromosome breakage". If these observations can be further substantiated from other organisms, they perhaps indicate that, though the effects of geographical isolation on the processes of subspeciation are considerable, its effects on the processes of speciation may be negligible, contrary to common belief. It goes without saying that geographical isolation, preventing genetic exchange and collecting and keeping independently produced chromosomal rearrangements, must inevitably, in the long run, result in speciation, as indicated by the floras of many islands that have been isolated for a long period of time. But the speed of this kind of evolution seems to be considerably slower than often surmised (cf. Skottsberg, 1938), and extinction of intermediates may be more effective in producing apparent distinction than the development of the real reproductive barriers themselves.

It is obvious that morphologically indistinguishable populations harbouring successful homozygotic combinations of a number of chromosomal recombinations of selective value may, in fact, have a better claim to be regarded as incipient species than have morphologically distinct subspecies without such chromosomal rearrangements. The limit between that kind of intraspecific sterility which is caused by chromosome changes and effective reproductive isolation is not sharp, and is often difficult to define; in some groups a few effective chromosomal rearrangements may result in a complete barrier to gene exchange, whereas in other groups, like the Onagraceae and *Paris*, many translocations and numerous inversions can apparently be tolerated without putting such a barrier into effect. Without going further into details of our still much too great ignorance of the development of this kind of isolation in plants, we can conclude that gradual and additive chromosomal rearrangements supported by hybridization and guided by natural selection seem to form by far the most important process by which reproductive isolation is being built up in most plant groups. Taxonomists have recognized this kind of isolation by means of morphological discontinuities, which are soon created by the ordinary processes of subspeciation and extinction of intermediates in such groups, and also by the fact that taxa having reached reproductive isolation are able to occur sympatrically without mixing, even when they do not reproduce by apomixis or autogamy. Nevertheless, it ought to be emphasized that gradual speciation is a slow and erratic process with irregular manifestation; it is in great need of considerably more attention by plant biosystematists having the ingenuity, patience and facilities to design and carry out suitable experiments with appropriate material.

The other process of speciation is the abrupt and instantaneous creation of a very effective barrier to reproductive miscibility by means of changes in the number of chromosomes. This may happen by alterations in the basic number through certain kinds of segmental interchanges or by a loss of a chromosome pair. In the families Cyperaceae and Juncaceae and in certain lower plants and insects this can also happen by the very special and still too little understood process of agmatoploidy, in which an increase in chromosome number occurs without an increase in chromosome matter, because the chromosomes are polycentric and can be broken into several pieces that still function. Most frequently, however, the abrupt creation of a reproductive barrier is connected with polyploidy, or the duplication of an entire chromosome set of an individual. This process is considerably less complex than gradual speciation and so it has been observed intensely and in greater detail.

Studies on chromosome numbers of at least the higher plants indicate that polyploidy is one of the major trends of evolution, though its frequency and importance varies considerably in different groups. It may even be claimed to be *the* major factor of evolution, if we consider that the protokaryotype is likely to have been based on a single chromosome pair and that even the higher plants started with only two chromosomes, as recently argued by Satô (1962). For practical considerations, however, it is convenient to limit the term to the cases in which differences in the chromosome numbers within a genus or a related group indicate that some of the species have been abruptly formed from the others. Recent estimates indicate that polyploidy occurs in about 30% of the dicotyledons, 50% of the monocotyledons, and more than 90% of the pteridophytes that now cover the earth, whereas some groups, like the Selaginellaceae, the gymnosperms, and the Annonaceae, have hardly any polyploids.

In this connection it may be appropriate to add a few words about the frequency of polyploids in different regions, since it has long been known that polyploids are more frequent in northern or alpine locations than they are in more moderate climates. When this was first pointed out, by Hagerup (1932), it was supposed to be caused by a higher frequency of formation of polyploids under extreme conditions. Phytogeographical observations, however, proved this to be a fallacy, since the distribution of most species of northern polyploids indicates that they are ancient and may have been well-established long before the formation of the climatical conditions under which they live at present. Several explanations of the increased frequency of polyploids with an increase in latitude or in the extremes of climate have been ventured in recent decades. An opinion expressed by Stebbins (1950) and supported by Reese (1961) and others, suggests that the increased frequency of polyploids towards the north is caused by the supposedly greater ability of polyploids than of diploids to invade areas newly laid bare, in this case the regions of northern Europe from which glaciers retreated some 10,000 years ago. This explanation seems, however, to be amply contradicted by the fact that the time since the ice retreated from northernmost Scandinavia is more than sufficient for the dispersal to that region and later stabilization of every species of higher plants met with in the unglaciated parts of Central Europe. It is also in conflict with the detailed studies of weeds recently made by Mulligan (1960), since he was unable to demonstrate any superiority of polyploids in invading open areas frequented by such plants. Above all, it is refuted by the fact that the frequency of polyploids in the northlands is highest on subarctic and arctic islands with a high percentage of glacial survivors, whereas recent invaders to these countries show a distinctly lower frequency of polyploids (cf. Löve and Löve, 1949, 1957, 1964; Löve, 1953, 1959). The only geobotanically and evolutionarily explanation of this phenomenon seems to be that of the selective superiority of polyploids based on their greater genetical variability, as proposed by Melchers (1946) and supported by Löve and Löve (1949) in connection with their critical review of the geobotanical significance of polyploidy. That explanation easily accounts for the apparently greater resistance to the environment shown in the occurrence of many polyploids in old floras that have had to survive the extreme conditions of the Pleistocene glaciations in the northlands, where only the selectively strongest could persist. It also explains the high frequency of polyploids among the now relic pteridophytes of which the diploids and lower polyploids seem to have been selectively weakest. And, finally, this is also the most plausible explanation of the recent finding by Mangenot and Mangenot (1962) that the tropical African flora is characterized by a very high frequency of ancient polyploids, with $n = 11$ and 12, the diploid ancestors of which have long since succumbed to the rigid selection in these regions, where the species number is extremely high at the same time as each species is extremely infrequent (cf. Dobzhansky, 1950).

It has been understood for a long time that the abruptly formed barriers create a very effective reproductive isolation. In many cases a complete incompatibility is met with between diploids and tetraploids, whereas this barrier is usually weakened between higher levels of polyploidy and, thus, increases again the possibility of crossability (cf.

Bernström, 1953). Since even such hybrids are more or less unable to give rise to strong and constant offspring, this kind of increased crossability does not impair the argument of polyploidy differences as a highly effective preventive to genetical miscibility.

It has been implied that abrupt speciation is the continuation of hybridization, since by far the highest number of successful polyploids undoubtedly have originated from hybrids. However, this is an argument to be taken with a grain of salt, because polyploids are most frequently formed by a duplication of the chromosome number of non-hybrid individuals of a normal population. Since such polyploids are, however, rarely successful, this does not invalidate the claim of the effect of hybridization on the survival ability of polyploids.

When polyploidy first became recognized as a speciation process, scientists were of the opinion that it in fact involved two typical and very different patterns, which were termed autopolyploidy and allopolyploidy by Kihara and Ono (1926). In the first instance, a single diploid population is visualized as giving rise to a taxon with the doubled chromosome number. This taxon is supposed to be very similar to the original population, though it is isolated from it reproductively and may have different adaptive properties caused by the difference in chromosome number alone. Formation of multivalents at meiosis was, and still is, regarded as a good indication of autoploidy, and even old and well established polyploids seem to be able to stand this disadvantage and compete successfully with other plants. Though the original poliploid was supposed to be morphologically very close to its diploid parental strain, further evolutionary divergence by aid of the subspeciation processess of gene mutations, recombination, and natural selection was assumed to take place to create morphological distinctions for the new species.

The alternative type of pattern is that of the rare and difficult hybridization between two species which are so widely distinct that their chromosomes are almost completely non-homologous and cannot pair, so that the hybrid is completely sterile. Its polyploid product, then, is a constant alloploid, combining the morphological and physiological characters of the parent species, and with essentially the meiotic properties of a diploid, no multivalent formation, and no sterility.

Studies of polyploids in the past two or three decades have revealed that situations intermediate between the two classical type patterns are considerably more frequent among successful natural polyploids. Therefore, polyploidy is certainly best understood as a single process more or less strongly connected with hybridization of taxa which are at different stages of gradual differentiation of their chromosome complements, and their success seems to be closely connected with how far this differentiation has advanced. Nevertheless it has been found practical to continue to speak about autoploids and alloploids, and even to divide each into two subgroups based on their origins (Löve and Löve, 1949). Typical alloploids, as described above, are then termed panalloploids, and typical autoploids are called panautoploids. In between these, without any distinct limit, are the hemialloploids, which are formed from not fully sterile species hybrids, and the hemiautoploids, which are produced either from more or less fertile intraspecific hybrids or by differentiation of the chromosome set of successful panautoploids. These two intermediate groups constitute the majority of known natural cases, of which the present writer has preliminarily scrutinized some 300 complexes that are reasonably well known (unpublished).

Panalloploids are extremely rare, wheras panautoploids have been observed in the frequency of 1—5 per thousand in most populations cytologically studied on a suffently large scale, even in species of *Picea* and *Pinus* and some other genera in which natural polyploidy is completely absent (cf. Löve and Löve, 1961). Because of their genetical and cytological handicaps, such panautoploids rarely survive more than a generation or two and become successful only in the extremely rare cases when they manage to produce seeds and adapt their chromosome homologies very rapidly towards those of the hemiautoploids. This they will probably do most easily if formed in populations with some structural hybridity so they will already at the start be on the limit to hemiautoploidy.

Because of the widespread confusion that still exists between the morphological and the biological species concepts, much ink has been wasted on discussions on the classification of polyploids, mainly by followers of the morphological concept. This hardly involves panalloploids, since they are almost invariably visibly distinct and, thus, recognized by all taxonomists as species of the same quality as good species of the gradually evolving group. The same is true for many hemialloploids, though some are morphologically less distinct, either because the parental species are closely related or, more frequently, because the polyploid may resemble one of its putative parents more closely than the other in characters regarded as taxonomically important from the morphological point of view.

The morphologically most critical group of natural polyploids are the hemiautoploids. Many cases are known in which classical taxonomists have recognized their discontinuities as compared to their diploid ancestors and, consequently, named them as species, whereas in other cases such taxa have been acknowledged as subspecies or varieties only. This acceptance is, however, not universal among morphological taxonomists, and it is not rare to see such taxa reduced to lower ranks or even ignored because of their close resemblance to the parental species in characters deemed more important than those in which they differ.

Hemiautoploids and hemialloploids are certainly as good biological species as are panalloploids. Therefore, their few differences rather than their perhaps many similarities ought to be strongly stressed, even or especially in cases when the perhaps most decisive character for the determination of some individuals or populations may still be their chromosome number. This was recently stated by Raven (1963) in a discussion of the critical species of western North American *Achillea*, and it has been repeatedly claimed by Löve and Löve, jointly and separately, during the past 20-odd years, in connection with studies of numerous species and genera of boreal plants. It is, indeed, difficult to comprehend how this taxonomical conclusion can be logically avoided except by rejecting the biological species concept. However, the reluctance to accept this without reservation, even by some prominent biosystematists, manifests the difficulty of emancipating from the classical procedures found even among those who know that such a rejection is not a slight but a very serious misconception of the basic principles of evolutionary biology.

In the case of the panautoploids the condition is different. As mentioned earlier, they are usually ephemeral phenomena of no evolutionary significance; thus, it is pointless to give them any taxonomic recognition. In the extremely rare cases when such polyploids manage to survive, they are, however, to be regarded as incipient or cryptic species which will require attention similar to that of hemiautoploids as soon as they have demonstrated their ability to reproduce and form an area of their own.

This carries us to a conclusion.

As implied at the beginning, taxonomy is the science of affinities, and its object is to invent a scheme of classification which mirrors not only the phylogenetic relations that unite different groups of organisms, but also the phylogenetic similarities at each taxonomical level. The system created by the classical method does this up to a certain degree, though its failure to define clearly the basic categories is inherent in its lack of appreciation of fundamental evolutionary processes. This has led to the constantly repeated statement that species are of so many kinds that several definitions would not suffice, an argument based on morphological observations but ignoring the discontinuities already observed by Ray and applied as a basis of species distinction by Linnaeus and De Candolle and their followers.

Biosystematists have shown that the real species, or perhaps rather the biological species as contrasted to the more or less artistic species of the ancient typologists and some more recent morphologists, is a natural and non-arbitrary unit of a genetically closed population system that has lost its ability to interbreed with other such systems. It usually coincides with the Linnaean species selected by aid of the reproductive gap. The genetical barrier has been found to be caused by cytological differences, and so it can be discovered and defined by aid of cytological methods. It cannot be emphasized too strongly that the biological species concept, even in the numerous cases where it has to be based on inference, usually permits the delimitation of a sounder and far more meaningful taxonomical species than does the often random aggregation of individuals based on the groping concepts of the classical avoidance of such a singular definition. Its general acceptance would soon change the ancient art of classification into the modern science of critical taxonomy.

When classifying subspecific taxa, we must realize that each species is a reproductive community, which interacts as an ecological unit with other such communities. It consists of populations, each of which is an expression of an integrated gene pool. Since their variations are formed by aid of the subspeciation processes of gene mutations, recombination, and natural selection, but without participation of the speciation processes of reproductive isolation, evolution below the species level is characterized by a continuum of variations and not by a succession of distinct types, except when affected by some kind of successively formed geographical or other similar isolations. Subspecific variations may be very distinct due to geographical or other isolation; since they lack an internal barrier to gene exchange they are, however, only temporary advances that at any time can be reversed into the general gene pool of the main population of the species.

The biological species concept is the basic idea of biosystematics. It is perhaps likely that the classical ideas will long have to coexist with this concept, because the material requiring taxonomical studies still stretches over a complete range, in a gentle gradient, from the purely empirical art of classifying a single specimen representing the only knowledge of the living beings of a remote land, to the exact scientific evaluation of data and measurements from modern experiments with populations of well-known organisms. To require the same exactness of all taxonomical work is, thus, not possible and indeed illogical. But if all taxonomists aiming at an evolutionary classification would realize that the biological species concept is also applicable even at the levels of rudimentary knowledge because certain morphological character combinations may often be relatively safe indicators of reproductive principle, then this may perhaps shorten the way towards a universal and standard understanding of the biological species, which should be familiar to all scientists, steadily looked to, stubbornly struggled for and, even though perhaps never perfectly achieved for all groups of organisms, constantly approximated to, and thereby persistingly spreading and deepening its influence and augmenting our understanding of evolution in general and of speciation in particular. The only absolute demand that ought to be made of those working towards this goal of natural classification is that, whenever more advanced stages of information are reached for an animal or plant, then less exact classifications ought to be replaced by more advanced definitions and systems. This is the simple principle of progressive science. Only by adopting this ideal can we continue the successful improvement of our understanding of the phenomenon of the multiplicity of life and its endless variations that have interested mankind from time immemorial.

References

BERNSTRÖM, P. 1953. – Increased crossability in *Lamium* after chromosome doubling. Hereditas 39: 241-256.

CLAUSEN, J. 1951. – Stages in the evolution of plant species. – Ithaca, N.Y.

–– 1959: Gene systems regulating characters of ecological races and subspecies. Proc. X. Intern. Congr. Genet. I: 434-443.

CONSTANCE, L. 1963. – Chromosome numbers and classification in Hydrophyllaceae. Brittonia 15: 273-285.

DAVIS, P. H. & HEYWOOD, V. H. 1963. – Principles of angiosperm taxonomy. Edinburgh.

DE CANDOLLE, A. P. 1813. – Théorie élémentaire de la botanique. Paris.

DOBZHANSKY, T. 1950. – Evolution in the Tropics. Amer. Scientist 38: 209-221.

–– 1951: Genetics and the origin of species. Third edition, revised. New York.

–– 1963: Species in *Drosophila*. Proc. Linn. Soc. London, 174: 1-12.

EHRMAN, L. 1960. – The genetics of hybrid sterility in *Drosophila paulistorum*. Evolution 14: 212-223.

–– 1962: The transitional races of *Drosophila paulistorum:* A study of hybrid sterility. Proc. Natl. Acad. Sci. 48: 157-159.

GEITLER, L. 1937. – Cytogenetische Untersuchungen an natürlichen Populationen von *Paris quadrifolia*. Zeitschr. Vererb. 73: 182-197.

–– 1938: Weitere cytogenetische Untersuchungen an natürlichen Populationen von *Paris qua-drifolia*. Zeitschr. Vererb. 75: 161-190.

GJAEREVOLL, O. 1963. – Survival of plants on nunataks in Norway during the Pleistocene glacia-tion. In: LÖVE, Á & LÖVE, D. (ed.): North Atlantic Biota and their History: 261-283.

GOLDSCHMIDT, R. 1940. – The material basis of evolution. New Haven, Connecticut.

HAGERUP, O. 1932. – Über Polyploidie in Beziehung zu Klima, Ökologie und Phylogenie. Hereditas 16: 19-40.

HUXLEY, J. 1942. – Evolution. The modern synthesis. London.

JUZEPCZUK, S. V. 1958. – Komarovskaya kontseptsiya vida yeyo istoricheskoye razvitiye i otrazheniye vo "Flora SSSR". Problema vida v botanika 1: 130-204.

KIHARA, H. & ONO, T. 1926 – Chromosomenzahlen und systematische Gruppierung der *Rumex*-Arten. Zeitschr. Zellf. mikrosk. Anat. 4: 475-481.

KNABEN, G. 1959a. – On the evolution of the *radicatum*-group of the *Scapiflora* Papavers as studied in 70 and 56 chromosome species. Part. A. Cytotaxonomic aspects. Opera Botanica 2, 3: 1-74.

–– 1959b. – On the evolution of the *radicatum*-group of the *Scapiflora* Papavers as studied in 70 and 56 chromosome species. Part. B. Experimental studies. Opera Botanica 3, 3: 1-96.

LEWIS, H. & RAVEN, P. 1958. – Rapid evolution in *Clarkia*. Evolution 12: 319-336.

LÖVE, Á. 1943. – Cytogenetic studies in *Rumex* subgenus *Acetosella*. Hereditas 30: 1-136.

–– 1953. – Subarctic polyploidy. Hereditas 39: 113-124.

–– 1955. – Cytotaxonomical remarks on the Icelandic *Papaver*. Nytt Mag. Bot. 4: 5-18.

–– 1959. – Origin of the arctic flora. Publ. McGill Univ. Mus. 1: 82-95.

–– 1960. – Biosystematics and classification of apomicts. Feddes Repert. 62: 136-148.

–– 1962a. – Typification of *Papaver radicatum* – a nomenclatural detective story. Bot. Not. 115: 113-136.

–– 1962b. – Nomenclature of North Atlantic *Papaver*. Taxon 11: 132-138.

–– 1963a. – Cytotaxonomy and generic delimitation. Regnum Vegetabile 27: 45.

–– 1963b. – Conclusion. In: LÖVE, Á. & LÖVE, D. (ed.): North Atlantic Biota and Their History: 391-397.

–– 1964. – Sverdmosinn. Náttúrufr. 33: 113-122.

LÖVE, Á. & LÖVE, D. 1949. – Geobotanical significance of polyploidy. I. Polyploidy and latitude. Portug. Acta Biol. (A), R. B. Goldschmidt. Vol.: 273-352.

–– & –– 1953. – Studies on *Bryoxiphium*. Bryol. 56: 73-94, 183-203.

–– & –– 1957. – Arctic polyploidy. Proc. Genet. Soc. Canada 2: 23-27.

–– & –– 1961. – Chromosome numbers of Central and Northwest European plant species. Opera Botanica 5: I-VIII, 1-581.

–– & –– 1963. – Útbreidsla og fjöllitni. Distribution and polyploidy. Flóra: Journ. of Icel. Bot. 1: 135-139.

MANGENOT, S. & MANGENOT, G. 1962. — Enquête sur les nombres chromosomiques dans une collection d'espèces tropicales. Revue Cytol. Biol. Végét. 25: 411-447.

MAYR, E. 1940. — Speciation phenomena in birds. Amer. Nat. 74: 249-278.

—— 1942. — Systematics and the origin of species. New York.

—— 1963. — Animal species and evolution. Cambridge, Mass.

MELCHERS, G. 1946. — Die Ursachen für die bessere Anpassungsfähigkeit der Polyploiden. Zeitschr. f. Naturforsch. 1: 160-165.

MULLIGAN, G. A. 1960. — Polyploidy in Canadian weeds. Canad. Journ. Genet. Cytol. 2: 150-161.

MÜNTZING, A. 1930. — Outlines to a genetic monograph of the genus *Galeopsis*. Hereditas 13: 185-341.

NOBS, M. A. 1963. — Experimental studies on species relationships in *Ceanothus*. Carnegie Inst. Wash. Publ. 623: 1-94.

RATTENBURY, J. A. 1962. — Cyclic hybridization as a survival mechanism in the New Zealand forest flora. Evolution 16: 348-363.

RAVEN, P. 1963. — A flora of San Clemente Island, California. Aliso 5: 289-347.

REESE, G. 1961. — Karyotype and plant geography. Rec. Adv. Bot.: 895-900.

SATÔ, D. 1962. — Law of karyotype evolution with special reference to the protokaryotype. Sci. Papers Coll. Gen. Educ. Univ. Tokyo, 12: 173-210.

SKOTTSBERG, C. 1938. — Geographical isolation as a factor in species formation, and its relation to certain insular floras. Proc. Linn. Soc. London 150: 286-293.

STEBBINS, G. L. 1949. — Rates of evolution in plants. — In: JEPSEN, G. L., MAYR & SIMPSON, G. L. (ed.): Genetics, paleontology and evolution: 229-242.

—— 1950. — Variation and evolution in plants. New York.

—— 1959. — Genes, chromosomes, and evolution. Vistas in Botany 1: 258-290.

VALENTINE, D. H. 1949. — The units of experimental taxonomy. — Acta Biotheoretica 9: 75-88.

VICKERY, R. K. 1959. — Barriers to gene exchange within *Mimulus guttatus* (Scrophulariaceae). Evolution 13: 300-310.

13

Reprinted from *Genetic Resources in Plants—Their Exploration and Conservation*,
O. H. Frankel and E. Bennett (eds.), IBP Handbook 11, 1970, pp. 49–68

TAXONOMY AND THE BIOLOGICAL SPECIES CONCEPT IN CULTIVATED PLANTS

H. G. BAKER

University of California, Berkeley,
California, U.S.A.

INTRODUCTION

There are very few 'classical' taxonomists left now. By this I mean that very few present-day workers are content to judge the taxonomic disposition of a plant simply on the basis of its external morphology, let alone its morphology when dead, dried and stuck down on a herbarium sheet. Almost everyone is agreed that whenever possible information about the physiology, the ecology, the geographical distribution, the cytology, the genetics (and particularly the population genetics and the breeding behavior) of the plants should be considered along with their morphology. Even herbarium botanists are supplementing their hand lenses with compound microscopes and paying attention to microscopic features of the plants—most notably pollen grain size and morphology—and they are accepting the evidence from internal structure, sometimes even from fine-structure studies and, to an increasing extent, from biochemistry.

But it is no news to the reader that there is considerable disagreement among taxonomists as to the most desirable methods of dealing with this abundance of information. Which kind of information, if any, is to be considered more important when attempts are made to draw taxonomic conclusions?

On the surface it seems reasonable that the classification which is based upon the greatest number of attributes will be the most natural and will mirror most accurately the evolutionary events which have produced the contemporary flora. No problems would arise if all the data to come from all the attributes of the plants pointed in the same direction. If this should be the case, any kind of attribute would be as suitable as any other and the sum total of the data would leave no doubt as to the taxonomic decisions to be made. But often there are what appear to be conflicting trends and decision-making is required. Nowhere has this been more evident than when cytological and genetical data have had to be integrated with the morphological. Obviously this is a matter to which we must give serious attention in a book whose concern is with the utilization and conservation of gene pools.

There are those—the numerical taxonomists—who insist (like their patron saint Michel Adanson) that all characters used in assessing the similarity and, therefore, the taxonomic relationship of organisms should be given equal weight, whether they be morphological, physiological, ecological or cytological. Their extreme position is almost matched by that of those more conventional taxonomists who agree to accept cytological and genetical information into their basically morphological–chorological classificatory schemes but who insist that chromosome number, chromosome size and chromosome shape are morphological characters just like petal number, petal size and petal shape—and should be given comparable weight in making taxonomic decisions.

We are surely justified in expostulating, like Löve (1960), that 'we must remember that chromosomes are *not* just another character comparable with the superficial morphological characters taxonomists are forced to use for the indentification of herbarium material. The chromosomes determine the characters, whereas the characters do not determine the chromosomes'. Fortunately, possibly with a slight change in wording, most contemporary taxonomists would agree with this statement and they do give special attention to cytological features and those genetical features which reveal most about genomic constitutions.

However, it is true that the numerical taxonomists and, too often, other synthetic taxonomists, have usually not the time to grow their plants and, even more important, to attempt to make crosses between them. This is particularly unfortunate because it has taken an experimental approach to find a key to taxonomy at the species level—i.e., reproductive isolation.

THE 'BIOLOGICAL SPECIES' CONCEPT

When attempts are made to cross distinct species, or when hybrids between them are sought in natural populations, it is usually found that there are reproductive barriers which reduce gene-flow (miscibility) between the populations of the two species without, at the same time, reducing it within each one (cf. Mayr, 1957). This is the feature of the taxonomic species which seems to be of primary importance. Morphological and physiological differences between species become fixed because of reproductive isolation; sometimes they are direct results of the evolutionary processes which bring reproductive isolation into existence.

The barriers to miscibility may show up as barriers to interpollination or as impediments to normal growth and to fertility in the hybrids (Clausen, 1951). It is to be emphasized that they are taxonomically significant only when they separate populations; sporadic occurrences of a mutant of a teratological nature do not qualify the individuals concerned for new latin binomials. The most widely accepted definition of a species on a miscibility basis is that by Mayr (1942) 'Species are groups of actually or potentially interbreeding natural populations, which are reproductively isolated from other such groups'. This has been referred to by its author as a 'biological species' concept (in contrast to 'typological' and other concepts) and a history of the concept has been published by Löve (1962), and discussed by Bennett (1964).

Despite the nearly universal recognition of the evolutionary importance of reproductive isolation and the concession that it is almost always there between species, still the 'biological species' concept with its basic connection with gene pools, their maintenance and restriction, is not universally applied by botanical taxonomists. I think it is worthwhile for us to examine why this is the case because I want to use the arguments which have been made against its application as arguments in *favor* of adopting it for the taxonomic treatment of cultivated plants and their close wild relatives.

Arguments against using a 'biological species' concept fall into two classes; (*a*) those opposed to the concept itself; and (*b*) those opposed to its application on practical grounds.

THEORETICAL ARGUMENTS AGAINST THE 'BIOLOGICAL SPECIES' CONCEPT

Defenders of those classificatory systems which give greater weight to morphological and distributional criteria than they accord to evidences of reproductive isolation sometimes justify their attitude by the argument that morphological differentiation may be expected to provide a good guide to the amount of evolutionary divergence which has taken place in the descent of any two taxa from a common ancestor, whereas a barrier to gene exchange merely indicates that evolutionary divergence is likely to occur in the future. They maintain that it is the duty of taxonomy to record the former whereas speculation as to the future is outside the scope of the discipline.

It is further argued, often by the same taxonomists, that barriers to gene flow, such as those between taxa which are at different ploidy levels or which, although having the same chromosome number differ by a limited number of chromosomal rearrangements, are real but are no greater than those between spatially separated populations of an undeniable species. Consequently, it is argued that unless morphological differentiation warrants the distinction it should not be made on the basis of an internal barrier to gene flow (cf. Lewis, 1967).

Additionally, there is the Adansonian objection to giving any degree of weighting to any character whatever its nature.

PRACTICAL ARGUMENTS AGAINST THE 'BIOLOGICAL SPECIES' CONCEPT

Only a very tiny fraction of the world's flora can be brought into cultivation even if all the botanical gardens and experiment stations in all countries should be given over to this purpose. Even for those putative taxa which can be brought into experimental gardens where they can be hybridized the problem arises as to how many specimens are needed to represent adequately the natural intraspecific variation. The number of hybridization attempts which must be made, the number of plants which must be raised in the first hybrid generation and the number of subsequent generations which must be grown to see whether fertility is maintained and whether segregation occurs, all place limitations upon the comprehensiveness of the experiments. And, theoretically, attempts should be made to cross each specimen with each other one. The total task, for naturally occurring plants, is beyond human capacity for achievement.

Of course, some of the difficulties can be overcome by allowing nature to make the experiments and observing the results. However, the fact that two adjacent (rather than sympatric) taxa do not show obvious miscibility may be due to environmental influence (e.g., lack of a suitable intermediate habitat for the hybrids or even a habitat for seedling establishment at all) and the populations concerned may be differentiated only at the ecotype level with no inherent barriers to crossing at all (Baker, 1951, 1952). In addition, nature is not always making the experiments now, even though she may have done so in the past; many closely related taxa may no longer come into contact with each other.

A second major difficulty in applying the 'biological species' concept to naturally occurring plants is that it cannot be applied to those cases in which sexual reproduction has been completely (or nearly completely) set aside and replaced by asexual reproduction (either as agamospermy or substitutive vegetative reproduction). As Mayr (1957, p. 379) pointed out, 'The essence of the biological species concept is discontinuity due to reproductive isolation. Without sexuality this concept cannot be applied. In truly asexual organisms there are no "populations" in the sense in which this term exists in sexual species nor can "reproductive isolation" be tested'.

Morphological differences between 'biological species' are sometimes very slight and, in a number of cases, require microscopy, most notably where polyploidy is involved (and differences in pollen grain volume or guard cell size may be the only adequate characters for use in separating plants at different levels of ploidy). In such cases as the populations of *Holocarpha obconica* (Compositae) in the Inner Coast Ranges of California, there is full interfertility within any local population (which may contain millions of individuals) but each such population may be a breeding unit by itself and sharply separated from its neighbors (to the extent of forming only sterile hybrids) (Clausen, 1952). In gross morphology there are only slight differences between the populations and it is only by careful cytological study that the reproductive barriers can be traced to repatterning of the chromosomes.

ARGUMENT IN FAVOR OF A 'BIOLOGICAL SPECIES' CONCEPT FOR CULTIVATED PLANTS

All of the objections to the consistent application of a 'biological species' concept to naturally occurring taxa are more or less valid. I wish to state, however, that I believe their validity is greatly reduced when cultivated plants are the object of attention. Our needs are different; if we have an evolutionary interest (or a conservational interest) in any group, we must consider the possible futures of the taxa contained in it and not merely be concerned with their pasts.

Each of the objections described above can be answered when our concern is with cultivated plants and their close wild relatives. For example, instead of a seemingly infinite array of wild taxa we are dealing with a circumscribed number of cultivated taxa, most of which are already in cultivation and which have proven themselves amenable to it.

Furthermore, much of the ground work for an experimental investigation has been laid already; these plants have been grown under environmentally controlled conditions and differences which have no genetic basis will have been noted and can be avoided. In addition, plant breeders already have recorded much of the data on fertility in the hybrid generations and the potentialities for transfer of genetic material.

An important practical consideration concerns the availability of financial support for the controlled environment experiments and crossing experiments. Often this is hard to obtain where the objects of research are wild species of no known economic value; for taxa whose value to man is demonstrable the situation may be quite different. Not only may the facilities of government agricultural departments be available but also those of international agencies (and international biological programs!).

In this book we are concerned with the conservation of gene pools; for this we must have information about the genetics of the organisms involved, meaning that the crossings have to be made in any case. Also, as I have said, being concerned with gene pools, we must be more concerned than the general taxonomists are with the potentialities of the taxa; the degree of reproductive isolation between taxa becomes a matter of more than merely academic interest.

For each of these reasons, I believe that the time has come when we should insist on the *biosystematic* treatment of cultivated plants and their wild relatives. A biosystematic treatment of a taxonomic problem is one which is based upon experimentation with plants, not merely observation of them (Table 5.1). Cultivation under controlled conditions, investigation of breeding systems, cytological studies, investigation of crossing relationships and the fertility of hybrids, physiological and biochemical studies, all of these have their places in biosystematics. Artificial crossings should be attempted as well as the planting together of the test plants in 'isolation plots' where the possibilities of crossing by natural pollination agencies can be investigated. It is obvious that the latter test will be most meaningful if it is carried out in the geographical area in which the populations normally grow and more than one plant from each population should always be involved. Finally, the judgement as to whether there is reproductive isolation between the populations should be made on the basis of *all* the experimental and observational evidence taken together.

An example of the improvement in understanding which can be brought about when biosystematic methods are used and a 'biological species' concept is invoked is provided by the study of the species-complex which includes *Vicia sativa*. This has been in confusion as various morphological-distributional treatments from those of Seringe (1825) to Fiori and Paoletti (1925) have variously assigned and distributed taxa (with a range of one to fourteen recognized species). Mettin and Hanelt (1964) and Hanelt and Mettin (1966) have studied

TABLE 5.1 Bases of 'biological species' determination in cultivated plants

Observational	Full description of morphological variation.
	Physiological and biochemical information.
	Chromosome number and karyotype analyses.
	Evidences of natural hybridization.
Experimental	Cultivation of population samples in uniform and varied environments (using experimental gardens or controlled environmental chambers)—observing evidences of race-formation, ranges of environmental tolerance, plasticity, etc.
	Attempts at hybridization (artificially) and by setting test plants in 'isolation plots' exposed to appropriate pollinating insects.
	Estimation of vigor of F_1 hybrids, F_2, etc.
	Estimation of fertility of F_1 hybrids, F_2, etc.
	Chromosome constitution of F_1 hybrids, F_2, etc.
	Analysis of meiosis in F_1 and subsequent generations.

the complex intensively using biosystematic methods and recognize as separate species *Vicia cordata* ($2n = 10$), *V.angustifolia*, *V.macrocarpa* and *V.sativa* (all with $2n = 12$), and *V.amphicarpa*, *V.incisa*, and *V.pilosa* (all with $2n = 14$). *V.angustifolia* contains two subspecies; *angustifolia*, a distinct wild form, and *segetalis*, a weedy plant associated with cereal crops. *V.sativa* is divided into a variety *cosentini* (which contains weedy as well as probably primitive cultivated forms) as well as the cultivated variety *sativa*. This degree of appreciation of the history and contemporary relationships of a complex of wild, weedy and cultivated plants would have been quite impossible without biosystematics.

241

In the case of a large genus which contains only a few species of economic importance, it is likely that for a long time only a part of the genus (containing the economic plants) will receive biosystematic treatment while the remainder does not. Such genera as *Ipomoea*, *Trifolium* and *Cocos* may suffer this fate. This need not be very serious as long as a complete infra-generic group such as the subgenus, section or species-complex containing the cultivated species can be treated at one time.

SPECIAL FEATURES OF 'BIOLOGICAL SPECIES' IN CULTIVATED PLANTS

The monographer of a genus which contains cultivated as well as wild taxa may reasonably carve out species in the former with roughly the same morphological range as for those in the latter. Subsequent biosystematic investigation, however, sometimes shows that the assumption of similar morphological ranges is incorrect and it may be worth our while to examine some of the reasons why this can be the case.

In the first place, the circumstances of cultivation, particularly of the more advanced kinds where crop plants are kept weed-free, and are optimally spaced, fertilized and irrigated, may permit the survival and reproduction of biotypes which would have been strongly selected against in nature. In cultivation there may even be positive artificial selection for some of the very characteristics which would be deleterious in nature. Mangelsdorf (1965) has presented evidence that the major part of the leaf area of a 'wild maize' which he and his colleagues have reconstructed serves to nourish an extensive root system. By contrast, artificial selection through many centuries in cultivated material has increasingly shifted the photosynthetic support to the nourishment of ever larger quantities of grain. The cumulative effects of changes in a number of such characters may make a profound difference in the morphology and physiology of the plants being studied.

In the case of maize, as Mangelsdorf (1965, p. 48) has pointed out, 'Four evolutionary forces: mutation, genetic drift, selection and hybridization interacting to a degree seldom encountered in nature and accelerated and intensified by the activities of man have produced in the maize plant evolutionary changes so profound and in so short a time that a paleontologist seeing the species only at the beginning and the end might well suspect that evolution under domestication is cataclysmic and the product of violent saltation'. And yet is is probable that there has been no speciation.

In nature, those characters of the plant which are directly concerned with its reproduction tend to be conservative. Successful seed dispersal systems, in particular, involve the coordination of a number of characters of the flower and fruit and only certain combinations are so appropriately balanced that they are successful (cf. Zohary, 1965, for *Triticum*). In cultivation where man can take care of such seed-dispersal as is called for (and seed dispersal by other means may even be disadvantageous if it is a seed-crop which is to be harvested), floral and inflorescence features may be selected which would be disastrous in nature. The classic case here is the stout, laterally borne cob of maize carrying firmly affixed grain and sheathed in an envelope of leaves, a combination of characters which renders seed-dispersal impossible.

So different is a modern maize from the probable wild ancestor of the species and from the weedy species which is called teosinte that before the experimentalists demonstrated that they are unquestionably congeneric (and have influenced each other significantly through hybridization) they were usually treated as species of the separate genera *Zea* and *Euchlaena*, respectively. It might even be argued that both of these taxa could be included in the same genus with the species of *Tripsacum* (which genus appears to have been involved in hybridization with *Zea mays* to produce *Zea (Euchlaena) mexicana*). The maize story is summarized in Mangelsdorf, MacNeish and Galinat (1964), and a modern treatment of *Euchlaena* is provided by Wilkes (1967).

Another example of the selection by man of a mutant form which would be suicidal in nature is to be seen in the kapok tree (*Ceiba pentandra*) of the tropics. I have shown (Baker, 1965) by experimental crossings and cultivation that the kapok tree of commerce is most probably derived from the hybridization of two kinds of native trees growing in West Africa but that an extra character has been added—that of the permanently closed fruit which retains both the seed and the kapok fibers around it so that they may be harvested. Presumably this closed-pod character arose by mutation and was taken advantage of by West African cultivators. Neither of the parents possesses this character (nor could they survive in the wild if they did). Prior to my experimental study the taxonomy of the trees in the *Ceiba pentandra* complex was in a very confused state with some names having been awarded on the mistaken belief that the closed or dehiscent nature of the fruit could be used as a primary division of the species (e.g., Ulbrich, 1913).

In the cases just cited, dramatic differences in floral or inflorescence characters of a magnitude sometimes associated with generic distinction when they occur in nature prove to be inadequate even to indicate specific distinction in the cultivated plants.

Artificial selection with striking morphological consequences may affect other parts of the plant than the inflorescence : the production of tubers in *Ipomoea*, a switch from a perennial to an effectively annual habit in *Gossypium*; these and other changes are apt to mislead the taxonomist whose morphological species concept is derived from experience with wild species. They should be less upsetting to a bio-systematic investigation.

In a number of cases there have been significant changes in breeding systems at the time when potential economic plants have been taken into cultivation or subsequently. The switch from cross-pollination to selfing in *Lycopersicon* (Rick, 1950) is well known. Hutchinson (1965) has pointed out that in all crop plants the flower structure is such that cross pollination must have occurred in some ancestors ; the switch to selfing and its utilization by man to preserve desired characteristics in the crop plants means that in many of them the taxa have either become mixtures of virtually pure lines or at any rate mixtures of lines homozygous for particular marker genes. In such a case the experimental approach is needed to counteract any tendency to be over-impressed by the clarity of the distinctions between these lines and to give them exaggerated taxonomic status.

More extreme examples of the same phenomenon can be seen where the switch has been from outcrossing sexuality to apomixis or to habitual vegetative reproduction. The taxonomic difficulties presented by clones in such genera as *Rubus* and *Musa* are well known. Occasional cross-pollination between different biotypes followed by the perpetuation of the resulting new biotypes by apomixis or vegetative reproduction can produce a network of phenotypes with which it is beyond the capacity of conventional taxonomic methods to deal. The perennial meadowgrasses of the genus *Poa*, so many of which have risen in artificial situations, provide a striking example (cf. Clausen, 1952). If sexual reproduction (amphimixis) never occurs in the plants of a taxon, the status of that taxon vis-a-vis another taxon on a 'biological species' basis is untestable. Among facultative apomicts, on the other hand, even the products of wide crosses may be reproductively successful by producing seed through agamospermy and thereby avoiding the meiotic sieve. This makes the plotting of the boundaries of 'biological species' a very difficult and time-consuming matter (although it has been carried out successfully in such a case as the forage grass genus *Dichanthium* by Harlan and de Wet, 1963, where it has been valuable in indicating the evolutionary history of the complex). One of the chief advantages of establishing 'biological species' boundaries in amphimictic groups is the information about combining power which is provided for plant breeders; if, in an apomictic complex, this reward is not available, the expenditure of effort in establishing the boundaries may not seem worthwhile. In such circumstances, it may be adequate to circumscribe 'species' in the apomictic group in such a fashion that the range of morphological variation included corresponds to the amount found in the closest related amphimictic species. Discussion of this problem can be found in Davis and Heywood (1963, pp. 381–6).

If it does nothing else, the experimental investigation of cases such as these will reveal the nature of the problems and prevent false optimism and subsequent disappointment for the investigator. I am haunted by the memory of the late W.C.R. Watson's lifetime of devotion to the attempted classification on a purely morphological basis of the British blackberries (*Rubus*) without understanding of the implications of their apomixis (Watson, 1958).

HYBRIDIZATION AND THE TAXONOMY OF CULTIVATED PLANTS

A special taxonomic problem posed by cultivated plants is the origin of some of them by hybridization between taxa which would never have come together naturally. Little difficulty is caused by such a hybrid as the London Plane tree (*Platanus × hybrida*) derived from the hybridization of an Old World species (*P.orientalis*) and a New World one (*P.occidentalis*) without change in chromosome number. Slightly more difficult is the case of the pink flowered horse-chestnut (*Aesculus × carnea*) which is the amphidiploid derivative of an artificial hybrid between Old World *A.hippocastanum* and New World *A.pavia* (Skovsted, 1929). The origin of *A.carnea* is biologically equivalent to that of any natural allopolyploid species but, because it is unknown outside cultivation, it has to be considered an 'interspecific hybrid' according to the International Code of Botanical Nomenclature and the corresponding International Code of Nomenclature for Cultivated Plants (and bear the cross in front of its specific name). Only because it is not technically a species are we saved from embarrassment by the fact that it cannot be fitted into either the Section Aesculus or the Section Pavia which house *A.hippocastanum* and *A.pavia*, respectively.

However, without biosystematic study it might have been very difficult to interpret the history and determine the taxonomic status of such a species as *Sorghum almum* which appears to have arisen from the hybridization of a member of the Section Arundinacea of *Sorghum* with a member of the Section Halepensia after *both* had been introduced from the Old World to South America. The Halepensia are tetraploid while the Arundinacea are diploid and the origin of *S.almum* must have involved the union of an unreduced gamete from the diploid with a normal gamete from the tetraploid (Doggett, 1965). Again the problem of sectional affiliation arises. It may be suggested that biosystematics is dealing death blows to most of the formal infra-generic *sections* which so delight the morphologically minded monographers (cf. arguments put forward by Bowden (1959) in dealing with the wheat genus *Triticum*).

Genetic barriers between taxa which are not separated by them in nature may arise under the conditions of cultivation. Pickersgill (1967) advances some evidence for the evolution of such a reproductive barrier through cryptic structural hybridity which has developed in the chromosomes of the South American peppers *Capsicum chinense* and *C.pendulum* since these previously allopatric species have come into contact during cultivation in rather primitive agricultural systems. Hybrids between *C.chinense* and wild forms of *C.pendulum* are less abnormal than hybrids made from cultivated forms of *pendulum*.

An apparently opposite situation occurs in the genus *Raphanus* (Panetsos and Baker, 1968) but it, too, would never have been discovered without experimentation, nor could it have been properly dealt with taxonomically without a biosystematic investigation. *Raphanus sativus*, the cultivated radish, differs chromosomally from *R. raphanistrum* (a weed of cultivated fields) by a single rather large translocation. In some European and Californian populations of *R.sativus* which have escaped from cultivation into a life of weediness, hybridization with *R.raphanistrum* has taken place and progeny have been formed which are homozygous for the *raphanistrum* state of the translocation. When further hybridization occurs between these plants (which, in most cases, could pass as *R.sativus*) and *R.raphanistrum* there is no longer any reduction in fertility in the offspring.

246

These examples from *Capsicum* and *Raphanus* emphasize the point that an adequate taxonomic treatment of a group of cultivated plants must also take account of their wild relatives, whether these be primitively wild or feral.

Hybridization between taxonomically distinct individuals whether deliberately controlled or accidentally (naturally) occurring creates, of course, enormous opportunities for the evolution of new taxa as well as for the increase of genetical variation within taxa. The effects may be expressed in two ways, in introgression or in allopolyploidy. It may be worth while to spend a little time considering these evolutionary mechanisms and their taxonomical consequences.

INTROGRESSION

Introgression, or introgressive hybridization, the subtle introduction of genetic material from one taxon into another through hybridization followed by backcrossing had to fight for scientific respectability in the early years of Edgar Anderson's development of the theory (cf. Anderson, 1949, etc.). Now, it may be that we are too ready to offer an explanation on this basis for any case where two extreme forms are connected by intermediates. In some of these cases we may be witnessing the differentiation of extreme forms out of a heterogeneous collection of biotypes rather than the fusion of distinct forms through hybridization. Such differentiation (or purification into 'lines') may be especially likely to occur under human selective pressure and especially in those cultivated taxa where self-pollination is the rule.

Even when hybridization is actually occurring the breeding systems of the plants are of extreme importance in determining the probable outcome. Grant (1958) and Baker (1959) have discussed various aspects of this. Among self-compatible annuals hybridization is most likely to lead to allopolyploidy through the functioning of unreduced gametes; in perennials strong vegetative reproduction also facilitates polyploidization through somatic doubling. By contrast, introgressive hybridization is facilitated by self-incompatibility (because of the importance of back-crossing between hybrids and parental species in producing the subtle infiltration of genes).

A few apparent exceptions to this exist, notably in the evolution of cultivated barley (Section Cerealia of the genus *Hordeum*), where Zohary (1959) has produced evidence of considerable hybridization which apparently produced introgressive effects. Very recently, Grant (1967) has suggested an explanation of what looks like introgression in these predominantly self-pollinating (autogamous) plants, depending upon a linkage between genes which control certain morphological characters and others which affect growth and vigor in early developmental stages of the sporophyte or gametophyte. After a rare hybridization, self-pollination would produce an F_2 and subsequent generations; however, because of the linkage only plants more or less resembling the parent types will survive in the progeny. Recombination of the unlinked genes, together with the linkage of the others, will simulate the subtle infiltration of genes that characterizes introgression without any backcrossing actually taking place.

In cases of introgression, substitution of alleles may occur on an individual gene basis or there may be substitution of entire blocks of alleles from one taxon into another. When these blocks contain a number of genes concerned with various aspects of the same character, as, for example, the 'speltoid' character of the inflorescence in hexaploid wheat (Frankel and Munday, 1962) or the stamen and style morphology and physiology of a heterostylous flowering plant (Baker, 1966) the block may be called a 'super-gene' or 'complex gene'. Evidence is accumulating that super-genes are not uncommon.

Even characters affecting functionally unrelated characters of the species may be inherited *en bloc*. Thus, it has been pointed out already that the only obvious chromosomal difference between *Raphanus sativus* and *R.raphanistrum* is in respect of a single translocation (Panetsos and Baker, 1968). In crosses between the species, the interspecific differences in root-structure and flowering time are inherited as a unit, suggesting that the major genes determining them may be located on the translocated portion of one chromosome. As a special example of the inheritance of super-genes, Grant (1966) has reviewed the block inheritance of viability genes in plant species, giving attention to several genera of economic importance, e.g., *Gossypium*, *Phaseolus*, *Zea* and *Triticum*. Ting (1967) has demonstrated cytologically the existence of a chromosome inversion common to maize and to teosinte and produced evidence that it (and the genes which it must carry) has introgressed from teosinte into maize.

As a consequence of these various demonstrations of block inheritance of characters and of linkages between the blocks and viability determiners, we can no longer take seriously the contention of the taxonomists, numerical and otherwise, who believe that characters for their use can be chosen without prior experiment and that all which can be useful are of equal value.

POLYPLOIDY

Introgression involves the replacement of genetic material from one taxon with material from another; in cases of allopolyploidy (or alloploidy) whole genomes are added together. This kind of speciation with its origin in the hybridization of well-differentiated species followed by doubling of the chromosome number is so well known as to need little comment here except, perhaps, the suggestion that it takes experimentation to prove allopolyploidy—either by re-synthesis of a polyploid from its putative parents or by crossing the polyploid with each of its putative parents and observing the pairing of the chromosomes at meiosis in the resulting hybrids. The number of cases which have been completely authenticated in such a manner is still limited.

However, between the unambiguous allopolyploid and the strict autopolyploid (formed by doubling the chromosome complement of a plant which is not any kind of a hybrid) there is a large area of intermediate conditions. Löve (1964) has suggested a classification based on the taxonomic status of the diploids which contribute the genomes to the polyploids. In between typical allopolyploids (called 'panalloploids' by Löve) and strict autopolyploids (called 'panautoploids') are 'hemialloploids' which are formed from not fully sterile species hybrids and 'hemiautoploids' which are derived from intraspecific hybrids or by the differentiation of the chromosome sets of successful panautoploids. According to Löve (*op. cit.* p. 41) the two intermediate groups constitute the majority of known cases.

Panautoploids are likely to be sporadic in occurrence and, because of infertility resulting from multivalent formation at meiosis followed by uneven disjunction, are relatively unlikely to persist. All workers agree that, for wild plants, sporadic autopolyploid plants of this sort do not merit taxonomic recognition. If we accept the criterion that species 'must exist as independent differentiated populations' (Davis and Heywood, 1963, p. 217), these occasional plants clearly do not qualify. Even if autopolyploids occur (or are created, for example, by colchicine treatment) in cultivation and are perpetuated as clones by vegetative propagation, they still constitute individuals rather than populations. However, in the latter circumstances there may be real merit to the acknowledgement of the polyploidy by giving the clones taxonomic recognition at the cultivar level.

With the hemiautopolyploids and hemiallopolyploids (which usually do form independent populations in nature), an appropriate taxonomic treatment is harder to recommend. The contention that allopolyploids are worthy of specific recognition but that autopolyploids, by reason of diminished fertility (as well as inadequate morphological differentiation), should have, at best, some infraspecific designation can no longer be upheld, particularly for cultivated plants. The demonstration by Riley and Chapman (1958) of genic control of pairing between homeologous (rather than completely homologous) chromosomes in wheat (see the general account in Riley, 1965) which also appears to apply to cotton and tobacco (Kimber, 1960) means that full fertility may be found in hemiautopolyploids as well as in allopolyploids.

The paucity of morphological distinctions may prevent full species recognition of the hemiautopolyploids in wild plants and in cultivated plants in primitive agriculture, where pure lines or clones are not maintained (cf. Dodds, 1965, for some potatoes). On the other hand, with the taxa involved in more sophisticated agriculture the case for giving fertile hemiautopolyploids taxonomic recognition may be as strong as for allopolyploids. In such cultivated material it will be known, or should be capable of determination, that a particular population is diploid or at some level of polyploidy, and, being identifiable, the polyploid should be given recognition.

The question of the appropriate taxonomic treatment of polyploids has excited more discussion than almost any other subject in biosystematics. Opinions have ranged from those of Löve (1951, etc.)who maintains that all polyploids which form populations of their own should be recognized as specifically distinct from their diploid relatives to the much greater number of authors who advocate only subspecific or varietal naming for those polyploids which can be distinguished morphologically without microscopy (unless they are clear allopolyploids).

The reproductive isolation between a polyploid population and the populations at lower levels of ploidy from which it is derived is the biological basis of advocating the specific recognition of polyploids. However, the extent of this isolation varies all the way from slight to complete, depending upon the structure and behaviour of the chromosomes. In addition, Marks (1966a, b) has produced some results to show that in tuberous *Solanum* triploids are rarely produced even when crosses are made between diploids (as pistillate parents) and tetraploids. The predominance of tetraploids in the offspring results from the functioning of unreduced female gametes. Marks points out that the avoidance of the production of sterile triploids means that 'polyploidy may not always be such an efficient isolating mechanism as is generally supposed' (Marks, 1966a, p. 556). Despite the difficulty of producing triploids in many taxa by artificial crossing and their rarity in many natural cases, triploid cultivars of bananas, watermelons, sugar-beet, cassava and apples give superior yields (Marks, 1966b) and therefore cannot be ignored. Thus, for practical purposes, with cultivated plants, there seems little doubt that recognition of the existence of polyploidy is important; the decision as to the level at which that recognition is given must be made by well-informed students of the particular genera concerned.

AGMATOPLOIDY

Fortunately, neither the *Juncaceae* nor the *Cyperaceae* contain many economically important plants. Consequently, we are saved from the difficulty of having to discuss the taxonomic treatment of agmatoploidy (Davis and Heywood, 1963, p. 226) that results from the chromosome fragmentation which is facilitated in these families by the diffuse (or multiple) kinetochores (or centromeres) in those chromosomes. Certainly differences in chromosome number in these cases have no intrinsic taxonomic significance.

EFFECTS OF USING A 'BIOLOGICAL SPECIES' CONCEPT

The overall effect of substituting biosystematics and a 'biological species' concept for a taxonomy which does not make basic use of genetical data in the treatment of cultivated plants and their wild relatives is likely to be a narrowing of species limits in some cases due to the revelation of polyploidy and other barriers to miscibility in what had previously been treated as a single species. However, where a cultigen consists of a number of cultivars, each of which is preserved through time in relatively pure populations (possibly with the aid of regular self-fertilization), there has always been a temptation for the 'classical' taxonomist to give these varieties exaggerated status. In this case, as in the classification of the wheats by Bowden (1959), the application of a 'biological species' concept has an opposite effect by discounting the significance of certain morphological characters for species distinction. Most often at the generic level there is likely to be a broadening of the limits rather than narrowing as intercompatibilities are demonstrated

—and *Aegilops* is fused into *Triticum* on this basis by Bowden (op. cit.) (although Chennaveeraiah, 1960, does not agree entirely with this treatment). In all cases, it may be expected that the taxonomic system will be improved by the change.

A classification system which emphasizes genetical relationships and discontinuities has advantages for breeders, pathologists and others who work with cultivated plants and their wild relatives. By enlarging genera on a basis of miscibility (probably keeping the old genera as subgenera) it can be made clear to these workers where gene-exchange is possible (for breeding new forms). When two species are separated by being placed in different genera, they are less likely to be tried as sources of genetic material. Also, of course, if the most important gene pools are to be conserved they must first be recognized.

REFERENCES

ANDERSON E. (1949) *Introgressive Hybridization*. Wiley and Sons, New York.

BAKER H.G. (1951) Hybridization and natural gene-flow between higher plants. *Biol. Rev.* **26,** 302–337.

BAKER H.G. (1952) The ecospecies—prelude to discussion. *Evolution* **6,** 61–68.

BAKER H.G. (1959) Reproductive methods as factors in speciation in flowering plants. *Cold Spring Harb. Symp. quant. Biol.* **24,** 177–191.

BAKER H.G. (1965) Characteristics and modes of origin of weeds. In *The Genetics of Colonizing Species* (Eds. Baker H.G. and Stebbins G.L.), 147–168. Academic Press, New York.

BAKER H.G. (1966) The evolution, functioning and breakdown of heteromorphic incompatibility systems. I. The Plumbaginaceae. *Evolution* **20,** 349–368.

BOWDEN W.M. (1959) The taxonomy and nomenclature of the wheats, barleys and ryes and their wild relatives. *Can. J. Bot.* **37,** 657–684.

CHENNAVEERAIAH M.S. (1960) Karyomorphologic and cytotaxonomic studies in *Aegilops*. *Acta Horti gothoburg.* **23,** 85–178.

CLAUSEN J. (1951) *Stages in the Evolution of Plant Species*. Cornell University Press, Ithaca.

CLAUSEN J. (1952) New bluegrasses by combining and rearranging genomes of contrasting *Poa* species. *Proc. 6th Int. Grassl. Congr.* **1,** 216 seq.

DAVIS P.H. & HEYWOOD V.H. (1963) *Principles of Angiosperm Taxonomy*. D. van Nostrand Co, London and Princeton.

DODDS K.S. (1965) The history and relationship of cultivated potatoes. In *Essays on Crop Plant Evolution* (Ed. Hutchinson J.B.), Cambridge University Press, Cambridge.

DOGGETT H. (1965) The development of the cultivated sorghums. In *Essays on Crop Plant Evolution* (Ed. Hutchinson J.B.), Cambridge University Press, Cambridge.

FIORI A. & PAOLETTI G. (1925) *Nuova Flora Analitica d'Italia*, Firenze.

FRANKEL O.H. & MUNDAY ANNE (1962) The evolution of wheat. In *The Evolution of Living Organisms*, 173–180. Melbourne University Press, Melbourne.

GRANT V.E. (1958) The regulation of recombination in plants. *Cold Spring Harb. Symp. quant. Biol.* **23**, 337–363.

GRANT V.E. (1966) Block inheritance of viability genes in plant species. *Am. Nat.* **100**, 591–601.

GRANT V.E. (1967) Linkage between morphology and viability in plant species. *Am. Nat.* **101**, 125–140.

HANELT P. & METTIN D. (1966) Cytosystematische Untersuchungen in der Artengruppe um *Vicia sativa* L. II. *Kulturpflanze* **14**, 137–161.

HARLAN J.R. & DE WET J.M.J. (1963) Role of apomixis in the evolution of the *Bothriochloa-Dichanthium* complex. *Crop Science* **3**, 314–316.

HUTCHINSON J.B. (1965) Crop plant evolution: a general discussion. In *Essays on Crop Plant Evolution* (Ed. Hutchinson J.B.), Cambridge University Press, Cambridge.

KIMBER G. (1960) The association of chromosomes in haploid cotton. *Heredity* **15**, 453.

LEWIS H. (1967) The taxonomic significance of autopolyploidy. *Taxon* **16**, 267–271.

LÖVE A. (1951) Taxonomical evaluation of polyploids. *Caryologia* **3**, 263–284.

LÖVE A. (1960) Taxonomy and chromosomes—a reiteration. *Feddes Rep.* **62**, 192–202.

LÖVE A. (1962) The biosystematic species concept. *Preslia* **34**, 127–139.

LÖVE A. (1964) The biological species concept and its evolutionary structure. *Taxon* **13**, 33–45.

MANGELSDORF P.C. (1965) The evolution of maize. In *Essays on Crop Plant Evolution* (Ed. Hutchinson J.B.), Cambridge University Press, Cambridge.

MANGELSDORF P.C., MACNEISH R.S. & GALINAT W.C. (1964) Domestication of corn. *Science,* **143**, 538–545.

MARKS G.E. (1966a) The origin and significance of intraspecific polyploidy: experimental evidence from *Solanum chacoense. Evolution* **20**, 552–557.

MARKS G.E. (1966b) The enigma of triploid potatoes. *Euphytica* **15**, 285–290.

MAYR E. (1942) *Systematics and the Origin of Species.* Columbia University Press, New York.

MAYR E. (1957) *The Species Problem. Publs. Am. Ass. Advmt. Sc.* **50**.

METTIN D. & HANELT P. (1964) Cytosystematische Untersuchungen in der Artengruppe um *Vicia sativa* I. *Kulturpflanze* **12**, 163–225.

PANETOS C. & BAKER H.G. (1968) The origin of variation in ' wild' *Raphanus sativus* (Cruciferae) in California. *Genetica* **38**, 243–274.

PICKERSGILL BARBARA (1967) Interspecific isolating mechanisms in some South American chili peppers. *Am. J. Bot.* **54**, 654.

RICK C.M. (1950) Pollination relations of *Lycopersicon esculentum* in native and foreign regions. *Evolution* **4**, 110–122.

RILEY R. (1965) Cytogenetics and the evolution of wheat. In *Essays on Crop Plant Evolution* (Ed. Hutchinson J.B.), Cambridge University Press, Cambridge.

RILEY R. & CHAPMAN V. (1958) Genetic control of the cytologically diploid behaviour of hexaploid wheat. *Nature, Lond.* **182**, 713–715.

SERINGE N.C. (1825) *Vicia*. In *Prodromus Systematis Naturalis Regni Vegetabilis*, Vol. II. (Ed. A. P. de Candolle), Paris.

SKOVSTED A. (1929) Cytological investigations of the genus *Aesculus* L. *Hereditas* **12,** 64–70.

TING Y.C. (1967) Common inversion in maize and teosinte. *Am. Nat.* **101,** 87–89.

ULBRICH, E. (1913) Die Kapok liefernden Baumwollbäume der deutschen Kolonien im tropischen Afrika. *Notizbl. des Königl. botan. Gartens und Museums zu Dahlem bei Stieglitz* (Berlin), **6,** 1–37.

WATSON W.C.R. (1958) *Handbook of the Rubi of Great Britain and Ireland*. Cambridge University Press, Cambridge.

WILKES H.G. (1967) *Teosinte: the closest relative of maize*. Bussey Inst., Harvard University.

ZOHARY D. (1959) Is *Hordeum agriocrithon* the ancestor of six-rowed cultivated barley? *Evolution* **13,** 279–280.

ZOHARY D. (1965) Colonizer species in the wheat group. In *The Genetics of Colonizing Species* (Eds. Baker H.G. and Stebbins G.L.), Academic Press, New York.

14

Reprinted from *Regnum Veg.*, **27**, 26–37 (Mar. 1963)

THE 'SPECIES AGGREGATE' IN THEORY AND PRACTICE

V. H. Heywood (Liverpool)

I. INTRODUCTION

One of the prime functions of formal taxonomy is to provide information or a means to obtaining information about organisms. It is essential, therefore, that the taxonomic categories and groups should be unambiguously employed and understood. Strict definition is not of course possible or even desirable and the International Code of Nomenclature has never attempted to do so; but the general application of the terms of nomenclatorial taxonomy must be clearly appreciated, both by taxonomists themselves and by the users of taxonomy.

Recently a device has been gaining currency in taxonomic practice, which is aimed largely at the general botanist—this is the so-called aggregate concept. The concept is not a new one and has been employed under various names for over half a century, but like most taxonomic ideas today is being subjected to a dualistic interpretation—by orthodox taxonomists on the one hand by "experimental" taxonomists or "biosystematists" on the other. (Heywood 1958a; Manton 1958; Mayr 1958).

The use of the term aggregate is necessarily linked with the term species so that it is impossible to discuss the problem without indicating in what sense the latter is employed.

The view adopted here is straightforward. The species is an empty category, and as

Mason (1959) says, "is definable universally only in the language of formal relations and not by the property of organisms". We therefore have to decide with what kind of biological situations or groups it is best filled. In other words, taxonomists have the task of deciding "what variational units among all those they encounter can be fitted with least violence into (the species category)" (Heslop-Harrison 1962). This approach, which I believe is essential if we are to avoid confusion and misunderstanding, distinguishes between the species as a category, i.e. a level in the hierarchy, and species as groups of individual organisms (see discussion in Blackwelder, 1962).

The discontinuities of variation that may be perceived in nature are not of one kind only, but depend upon what the observer chooses to perceive. Morphological discontinuities will be perceived and recognized as significant by the traditional taxonomist, while discontinuities in breeding pattern may be sought by the experimentalist. Both may be used as the basis for the recognition of species and both are equally valid. The biological significance of species so defined will be different as will be their degree of arbitrariness and practical value (Davis & Heywood, 1963).

The species is, however, a taxonomist's unit and he has prior claim on it if it should be subjected to two or more widely discordant interpretations. Long-standing usage and practical considerations alone demand that the species be retained in the traditional taxonomic sense of "assemblages of individuals with morphological features in common and separable from other such assemblages by correlated morphological discontinuities in a number of features". (Davis & Heywood, 1963). The species defined in this way will represent different kinds of evolutionary situations and will be equivalent only by designation, and not by virtue of the nature or extent of their evolutionary differentiation (Heywood, 1958b: 20).

Any definition of the species which is phrased in terms of Mendelian populations. gene-pools and reproductive isolation is rejected quite simply on the grounds that is attempting to describe a different kind of unit—a breeding population, a hologamodeme, syngen, a "biological" species, etc. It is now generally agreed that taxonomic species and ecospecies are based on quite differently conceived abstractions, although they may coincide *in practice* and frequently do (cf. Gilmour & Heslop-Harrison, 1954; Walters, 1962). Attempts to redefine species genetically and replace the basic taxonomic unit by such a word as binom are unrealistic and shortsighted. The statement of Grant (1957) that "Biologists who reserve the category of species for morphologically similar groupings of individuals, on the other hand, have not left any alternative designation for the reproductively isolated system of breeding populations" indicates very clearly the prestige value of the term species for the experimentalist but fails, in my view, to recognize the chaos which using it for the experimentally defined unit would lead to (Keck, 1957).

My reasons for rejecting any take-over bids for the term "species" by biosystematists are as follows.

Although Sirks (1952) may perhaps exaggerate in saying that on theoretical and practical grounds "the interest of nearly every right-minded biologist is still focussed on the concept of species", it is nevertheless true that more than any other unit, it is the daily concern not only of taxonomists but of non-systematist biologists. The species concept must therefore be manageable by those who have to work with it. How far does an experimentally defined species meet this vital requirement? Firstly, leaving aside questions of objectivity, it is theoretically applicable in only a limited number of cases. It is, for example, inapplicable in asexually reproducing organisms, and in persistent inbreeders. In practical terms, it is inapplicable in many kinds of sexual organisms—in allopatric forms, etc. Sonneborn (1957) estimates that the biological species concept is applicable to only a minority of all organisms.

Secondly, biologically defined species would result in the recognition, in some groups, of units which would be "to an appalling degree unrecognizable and unidentifiable by routine taxonomic procedures" (Sonneborn, 1957). This objection is directed, of course, mainly at the formal recognition of morphologically undistinguishable (or virtually so) cytodemes, although there are other reasons for not recognizing these. Taxonomists are often accused of regarding nomenclatorial taxonomy as an end in itself rather than as a means to an end. But surely in demanding nomenclatorial recognition of morphologically indiscriminable forms, some cytotaxonomists, etc. are guilty of just this (cf. Bell, 1954; Lewis, 1957).

Thirdly, in flowering plants (of which there are probably some 250,000 species) experimental and cytological data are available for only a minute proportion, mostly in the Northern Hemisphere where genotypic diversity and taxonomic complexity are often much less marked than in other regions, such as, for example, the Mediterranean. The case against the utilization of the species concept for biologically-defined units is neatly summed up by Sonneborn (l.c.), who says (p. 200) ". . . its value is very narrowly limited, in the first place to outbreeding organisms in principle and in the second place to the very small proportion of them that will in the foreseeable future be studied sufficiently".

So far, the intrinsic value of a biological species concept has not been challenged, but it is perhaps misleading to pass this aspect over. In theory, biological species are less arbitrary (though not more objective, cf. Mayr, 1957, p. 15) than taxonomic species in that fewer criteria are applicable to which a "yes or no" answer can be given. The biological species is defined in terms of breeding populations, common gene-pools, re· productive isolation and breeding behaviour. The task of defining a population is fraught with difficulties: although a local breeding population occupying a compact area (topogamodeme) normally presents no problem, the task of delimiting populations or population series of approximately specific scope, in ecotypically diverse groups, etc. may be extremely difficult.

If considered in terms of potentially common gene-pools the problem is no less intractible. And how is one to relate gene-pools to morphological units to which one eventually has to have recourse if one's units are to be at all recognizable. Only an infinitesimal proportion of the genotypes which constitute a gene-pool of specific scope can be tested. It is *assumed* that the majority will conform to the general behaviour of the tested minority and the prediction is based on morphological similarity. It is *assumed* that the members of a population will be, or are potentially capable of, exchanging genes, although in only a very small number of individuals of a population numbering, say, tens of thousands, can this be shown, and even then usually in artificial conditions in the experimental garden. There may be indirect morphological evidence, but this is not always reliable.

The factual, non-arbitrary and so-colled objective biological species is, on analysis, shown to be based on criteria which are difficult to apply in practice however theoretically sound they may be, and primarily recognizable only by morphological reference.

Several conclusions seem inescapable. No matter what the theoretical definition of the biological unit (syngen, common gene-pool, hologamodeme, biospecies, etc.), the initial evidence or recognition of membership must be primarily morphological. But morphological evidence is not necessarily correlated with the genetic criteria of the definition, therefore the morphological unit will be in some cases larger than the biological unit.

Species should therefore be recognized as morphologically definable units, the containers and expression of one or more gene-pools.

To abandon the practical universal use of the term species in a primarily taxonomic

257

sense in favour of a restricted usage in a limited, unpracticable, theoretical sense is, I believe, short-sighted and unrealistic.

The biospecific principles have already had to be modified, if not abandoned by biosystematists in apomicts, inbreeders, etc. (Valentine & Löve, 1958): I am inclined to agree with Sonneborn (1957) that the brave but hopeless attempts of the proponents of the biological species concept *for general use* will have to be abandoned entirely. Insistence on the use of the term "species" for a biological-genetic concept as opposed to a taxonomic-morphological concept is bound to lead in practice to logical inconsistency, terminological inconsistency and confusion.

When taxonomically defined species and experimentally defined species coincide in practice, the result is highly satisfactory and such species may be regarded as "natural" in the best sense. It would, I think, be quite wrong, however, to hold this as an ideal to be aimed at in all cases. Such an optimistic view is not supported by the facts revealed so far. For those cases where it is wished to stress genetic criteria, a special terminology should be employed.

II. THE AGGREGATE CONCEPT

In its simplest terms the aggregate is a device employed to group together for convenience a number of species (binominals). The component binomials are in taxonomic terms morphologically closely related and difficult to discriminate. Their distinguishing characters, although less pronounced and perhaps fewer in number than those which serve to distinguish between other species are, however, constant and the species appear to be effectively isolated from one another. Often they are of restricted geographical distribution (e.g. mountain species in the Mediterranean flora) and frequently show little internal variation (although the component species of aggregates *may* contain subspecies—see later).

It will be quite evident that the aggregate is no more easy to define than the species itself, yet like the latter it is a phenomenon which most taxonomists can and do recognize. It first gained currency, as *species collectivae*, at the beginning of this century in Engler's *Pflanzenreich* monographs. Often it was a confession of ignorance (and sometimes still is), in the sense that some of the binomials involved in the aggregate have been satisfactorily accounted for later as taxa of other rank; in other cases it is evident that some other disposition would be adopted if further evidence were available. Often, however, the *species collectiva* was a straightforward expression of taxonomic opinion that here was a group of small-scale, very closely related species which had more in common with one another than with other species or with other similar groups of species, yet they were felt to be on too small a scale to warrant a separate recognization.

It is important to note that no special biological connotation was attached to these groups: they were not considered to be equivalent to, or reflect, some particular level of evolution or genetic relationship. In other words, the collectiva or aggregate was a term of taxonomic convenience.

Today taxonomists employ the device in precisely this sense (Heywood, 1958b): it is, for example, quite extensively employed by Clapham, Tutin & Warburg (1952). In the interim taxonomists faced with difficult patterns of variation made evident as the result of closer and more detailed studies of groups adopted more frequently some kind of aggregation device; species groups, complexes, etc. were widely referred to in the literature. In zoological taxonomy, particularly, special terms were proposed for similar situations defined in evolutionary or biogeographical terms—the *Formenkreis* (Kleinschmidt, 1900), *Artenkreis* (Rensch, 1929), *superspecies* (Mayr, 1931). Botanical taxonomists were slow to accept such concepts although the related *Rassenkreis* idea did find more favour especially with the Wettstein school of systematists. In Austrian and

German botanical literature the *Formenkreis* is still occasionally used but is rarely seen elsewhere (Ehrendorfer, 1958, is a recent example). The relationship between these special groups and aggregates is discussed below.

As a result of cytological and experimental studies it became evident that taxonomic species could often be split into cytologically distinct units (cytospecies, cytological microspecies, etc.), and that many taxonomically defined microspecies had a similar cytological basis. (Very frequently cytologists find that their cytospecies have been anticipated by taxonomists long before, cf. the *Polypodium vulgare* group, Manton 1958). Similarly it was found that large numbers of closely related taxa in some genera were recognized as the result of some reproductive deviation such as apomixis, inbreeding, etc. The products of these cytogenetic phenomena were frequently grouped together as microspecies within an aggregate or complex. Thus there developed a tendency to associate aggregates with cytologically critical groups.

A further stage is evident in the work of some cytotaxonomists as Manton who proposes (1958) using the aggregate for cases where cytotaxonomic investigations of "Linnean" species have demonstrated the biological nature and phyletic relationships of the components. She gives as an example the *Polypodium vulgare* aggregate. This species has long been known to be polymorphic and is frequently divided into two subspecies occupying fairly distinct though partly overlapping areas: subsp. *vulgare* (4x) and subsp. *serratulum* Arc. (2x) (subsp. *serratum*). Rothmaler (1929) added a third subspecies, subsp. *prionodes* (6x) although he later regarded *P. vulgare* and *P. serratum* as separate species[1] (the latter as *P. cambricum*). Taxonomic opinion is still divided, largely because of the unreliability of the characters employed to separate the taxa. Manton and Shivas have shown that the three taxa are cytologically distinct: *P. vulgare* (4x) *P. australe* Fée (2x) and *P. interjectum* (6x). The diploid cannot pair its chromosomes with those of the tetraploid, and the hexaploid is, in origin, the amphiploid hybrid between diploid and tetraploid. The necessary minimum of taxonomic revision, according to Manton, to express these facts is to recognize the three taxa as species, together constituting the *Polypodium vulgare* aggregate. She visualises such an aggregate as the logical outcome of cytological analysis of the Linnean species *sensu lato*, regarding *sensu lato* as an intermediate state of knowledge. Details of this work were later published by Shivas (1961). Likewise Böcher (1961) favours using aggregates for cytological microspecies. A similar usage is employed by Sinskaja (1950, 1961) who defines the *conspecies* (aggregate) as a Linnaean or compound species which is divided into less extensive species, and the latter are still phylogenetically more closely related to each other than any other species.

The ultimate stage is reached by Mayr (in discussion of Manton's paper, 1958) who says that there are two aspects of the aggregate convention: the nomenclatural and the biological, the biological covering experimental situations (siblings, apomicts, etc.). This is tantamount to regarding the aggregate as an experimental group and is of course the logical consequence of the definition of the taxonomic units in genetic terms as opposed to taxonomic-morphological terms (Mayr, 1958).

A similar situation to the taxonomic versus the "biological" species concept has arisen. There seem to be three possibilities open: a) Restrict the aggregate concept to taxonomically defined situations and employ a new term for groups of experimental microspecies; b) Use the aggregate concept for both taxonomic and experimental situations; c) Restrict the aggregate concept to experimentally determined situations and employ a new term for groups of taxonomic microspecies.

Unlike the species concept problem, there is no overwhelming case for the retention

---

[1] He later regarded *prionodes* as a subspecies of *P. serratum* (Rothmaler, *in verbis*).

259

of the aggregate for taxonomy on the grounds of almost universal usage and comprehension. If the second of the alternatives listed above is followed, a difficult situation will arise through ever increasing conflict between taxonomists and biosystematists, cytotaxonomists, etc. over the definition and use of the aggregate. The solution appears to be twofold: if "biological" species as opposed to morphological species are to be recognized, irrespective of their morphological differentiation, and if it is desired to aggregate them a special grouping should be employed. Otherwise biologically defined species should be considered for formal aggregate treatment *on their taxonomic merits*, that is to say, if morphologically indistinguishable (sibling spp., cryptic polyploids, etc.) they should not be given formal names; if frequently morphologically separable and allopatric but with some degree of geographical overlap producing intermediate forms they should be treated as subspecies. Only if they are clearly separable in the vast majority of samples should they be given specific status, within an aggregate.

This last point needs considerable stressing, for one of the dangers that can be easily foreseen if the aggregate concept becomes more and more a receptacle or cover for experimental evidence is that encouragement will be given to biosystematists to give formal specific names quite irrespective of degree or nature of morphological difference and group such units within aggregates. This will bring the system of formal nomenclature into disrepute and cause endless confusion. In the case of polyploids several cytotaxonomists already hold this view. Löve (1960, 1962) e.g. maintains that with certain exceptions all polyplodemes within the floras of North Europe should be classified as distinct species, on the assumption that morphologically completely indistinguishable polyplodemes are unknown from north-west Europe. This question is also discussed in detail by Heywood (1960) and Löve (1960). A list of polyplodemes reported to be morphologically inseparable is given by Hedberg (1958) and further examples could be added, and doubtless the list will be greatly amplified as further investigations are made.

Even if cryptic polyploids are formally recognized and given specific names, they can and indeed must be recognized only by reference to the nearest taxonomic species. What then is to be gained by giving two names to what is phenotypically a single taxonomic unit? Not even the cytologist will be able to recognize his cytodeme except by reference to the taxonomic species which contains it. There is no escape from morphology in practical terms. All that is proposed here is that taxonomists continue to recognize and describe species on the basis of the minimal irreversible evolutionary and morphological divergence that yields constant and readily recognizable difference (cf. Sonneborn, 1957, p. 289).

III. TAXONOMIC AND BIOSYSTEMATIC CONSIDERATIONS

As Mayr (in Mayr, Linsley & Usinger 1953, p. 20) notes, the species is the "base-line" in the lower part of the taxonomic scheme. The aggregate, complex, superspecies, etc. are above the base-line; the components of polytypic species, i.e. subspecies, are below the base-line.

From a taxonomic consideration aggregates are to be regarded as definitely supraspecific, that is, it should be the considered opinion on the available evidence that the components are specific in status. They can in fact themselves contain subspecies, e.g.

> *Pulsatilla vulgaris* coll. Aichele & Schwegler (1957)
> *P. vulgaris* Mill.
> *P. grandis* Wend.
>   subsp. *grandis*
>   subsp. *polonica* (Blocki) Aich. & Schweg.

The aggregate is essentially similar, therefore, to a subseries or grex of some authors (cf. Rouy & Foucaud, *Flore de France*, e.g. *Ranunculus*), and is an assemblage of closely related species. The term grex was proposed instead of aggregate by Heywood (1958a) but later abandoned because of widespread usage in a different sense. Undoubtedly several series in various genera, e.g. *Rhododendron*, are each exactly equivalent to taxonomic aggregates in current interpretations and would be so termed by some authors. The main difference however is that the aggregate is a device divorced from formal nomenclature: no authority is given for aggregates and this itself raises problems which are discussed below.

There are two main points to be considered: Firstly, what term should be employed for aggregates and how should they be related to normal nomenclature. And secondly, what term should be employed for the component segregates. These two points have to be considered from a taxonomic and biosystematic viewpoint.

(a) *Aggregates or what?*

An example of the diverse terminology employed for aggregates of one sort or another can be taken from *Ranunculus auricomus* sensu latissimo which is composed mainly of apomictic biotypes and contains some sexual biotypes and probably some facultatively apomictic biotypes. It has been referred to in the following terms:

> *Ranunculus auricomus* L. coll. (Hylander, 1955)
> *Ranunculus der Auricomus*-Gruppe (Häfliger, 1943; Marklund, 1940); grupa *Auricomus* (Nyárády 1933)
> Arten aus der Verwandtschaft des *Ranunculus auricomus* L. (Koch, 1933)
> Formenkreise (Koch, 1939, Schwarz 1949)
> Conspecies (Rozanowa, 1932)
> *Ranunculus* ser. *Auricomi* (Schwarz, 1949)
> Circulus *Auricomi* (Owczinikov, 1937; Jasiewicz, 1956)
> *Ranunculus auricomus* agg., group, group of species, complex.

And no doubt several other means of designation could be sought out from the literature.

This is the sort of situation which can only lead to confusion and is similar to that prevailing today in ecology where the lack of an agreed terminology for quite simple concepts, types of vegetation units (e.g. bog, savannah: cf. E. J. Dyksterhuis, 1957), etc., has greatly contributed to the lack of understanding between ecologists in different countries which prevails today. Many of the long-standing and persisting problems of biology prove, in fact, to be the result of difficulties of language and terminology (cf. Mason and Langenheim, 1957). This is certainly true of the species problem as I have tried to indicate above.

The objection to the use of a vernacular term such as "group" is that it varies very considerably from one language to another and cannot therefore be satisfactorily abbreviated and universally understood. A Latin-derived term is preferable, such as aggregatio or collectiva (abbreviated as agg. or coll.). A number of objections have been raised to the word aggregate or the phrase "species aggregate", partly on the grounds of its similarity to a formal nomenclatural category. There is in fact a conflict between regularization of the aggregate concept and its divorce from formal nomenclature. Because of this current usage varies greatly. Aggregates are normally designated by the "parent" species, e.g.

> [The] *Pulsatilla alpina* [L.] agg.

Normally no description or summary of the characters of the aggregate is given and no authority or reference cited indicating how many species are included. This can only be ascertained from the species actually listed in a formal treatment such as a monograph or conspectus. When an aggregate is mentioned divorced from such a formal treatment, the scope of the aggregate can only be guessed at in most cases. This is one of the dangers of the method and can be seriously misleading: for example, reference to *Ranunculus auricomus* agg., could imply some or all of the constellation of apomictic microspecies surrounding *R. auricomus* sensu stricto, to some or all of those surrounding *R. cassubicus* or to some or all of the whole complex ambracing both "central" species. This lack of precision is the price that has to be paid for the informal, ad hoc, treatment of aggregates. At the same time it is one of the reasons for its attractiveness: from the identificatory point of view, for example, if determination to the level of the segregate is not possible, one is left with a specific name none the less. This is where loose-thinking enters and it can be best explained by examples.

If *Ranunculus auricomus* agg. is employed and identification is not found possible, for some season, to specific level, the material in question is referred to as *R. auricomus* agg. This is translated to mean a specimen belonging to one of a group of several species, the first described and best known of which is *R. auricomus* L. It does not mean that the specimen belongs to *R. auricomus* L. (although it could in fact be so), else if such a broad interpretation of that species is to be used, it would be referred to as *R. auricomus* with the addition of sensu lato if preferred (but see p. 66). In other words, an aggregate is not a species but a group of species, and if the precise species member of the group cannot be ascertained identification is incomplete. In a two-level classification, *both* levels cannot be species in any meaningful sense. If pressed, most of the users of the aggregate convention would no doubt agree, but in day-to-day practice the implications are passed over and often forgotten. If this is admitted then there would be no objection to employing series (or subseries) as has been done by Schwarz (1949), thus *Ranunculus* ser. *Auricomi*, except on the grounds of formality. Although there is much laxity in the nomenclature at this level of taxonomy (largely because series etc., are seldom employed outside Floras and monographs), they still have to be described and given an authority.

In the case of aggregates some degree of formality may be introduced by preceding the specific epithet with "agg.":

> *Ranunculus* agg. *auricomus* L.

An alternative would be to give the specific epithet in the plural or in the genitive, thus:

> *Ranunculus* agg. *auricomi* (genitive or plural)

This would help to avoid confusion and at the same time emphasize that it is a group and not an alternative designation of a species. Dr. P. H. Davis and Mr. B. L. Burtt have pointed out to me, however, the difficulty that many epithets are not declinable.

A second feature of such a method would be the inclusion of the original authority of the "type" species of the aggregate on the one hand and the authority for the aggregate itself. The first authory should be given for accuracy, the aggregate authority simply because if a description or differential is given (and I believe that this is important) this has to be provided by some author and reference is therefore required. The odvious linking word between the authorities is "sensu", so giving the following:

> *Ranunculus* agg. *auricomus* L. sensu Schwarz (1949)

The *sensu* author can therefore be varied. In other words the aggregate should be ascribed to any author who provides the circumscription it is intended to follow. I am fully aware that the normal use of *sensu* in nomenclatural taxonomy is to indicate misidentifications in synonymy, but the extension of meaning advocated here is, I believe, justified by the nature of the problem.

The main reason for advocating such a step (and at the same time the main difference from series, sections, etc.) is that the aggregate is a grouping of convenience intended for general usage, not only in formal works of reference but in day-to-day sources such as ecological papers, floristic lists, discussions, etc., and it is of immediate importance to know the circumscription intended. A further difference of course is that because of this direct and frequent use the aggregate bears the name of a species while the name of a section, series etc. often bears no relation to that of any of the component species.

(b)   *The Components*

The components of aggregates are customarily called segregates. They differ from the components of series, etc. in the following way. In both cases they are regarded as species, but in the former case they are "micro-species" with low-level morphological differentiation while in the latter they are "normal" species with an accustomed degree of differentiation. It is the very fact that the degree of differentiation is so low or difficult in practice that is the raison d'être of aggregates. I deplore attempts to force a cyto-genetic basis on them.

The term segregate is proposed for use as an all-purpose term of reference for aggregate components. The other available terms, such as microspecies, semi-species, etc. are mostly descriptive of different kinds of segregates. So far taxonomy has resisted any attempt to specify the biological nature of the species or infraspecific units, with the exception, perhaps, of the members of agamic complexes—and even there there are serious difficulties involved due to the partial nature of apomixis in some cases.

From a biosystematic point of view the introduction of different kinds of segregates may be considered attractive, but with the exception of a prefix for agamic segregates, and possibly some means of indication of polyploid segregates the system would be unworkable as some segregates (probably all) would be referable to more than one category. It is largely for this reason that the set of biosystematic categories proposed by Camp & Gilly (1943) has not proved workable in practice.

One of the greatest practical difficulties—that of having to use two binomials in juxtaposition when referring to a segregate while still indicating the aggregate may be overcome in the following manner:

> *Viola cenisia*   microsp.   *albanica*

(microspecies being the term proposed for segregates when their nature is not otherwise specified; alternatively segregate (abbreviated as seg.) could be used).

A similar method could be employed for referring to semispecies (cf. Valentine & Löve, 1958).

> *Silene vulgaris* semisp. *maritima*

An essential feature of this system is that from a nomenclatural aspect the segregates are not formally combined with the "parent" species but are temporarily, loosely attached. No new combinations are involved: the segregates, even in the case of semispecies, have to be described initially as binomials.

An alternative and perhaps preferable way of referring to the segregates in conjunction with the aggregates is to adopt a method similar to that employed occasionally with sections, series, etc. Thus as one may indicate the section to which a species belongs by the following formula, *Digitalis* (sect. *Tubiflorae*) *lutea*, so the aggregate to which a segregate belongs can be given, e.g. *Ranunculus* (agg. *auricomus*) *stricticaulis*.

IV.   SEGREGATES AND SUBSPECIES

One of the dangers of the regularization of the aggregate method is the temptation it puts in the way of biosystematists to describe as segregates (and thus as species) cytodemes, polyplodemes, etc. irrespective of their degree, or constancy of morphological differentiation. I can only repeat that segregates (with the one exception of semispecies) should be taxonomically specific in status but small-scale and recognizable (although with a greater amount of perseverance than is normally required). They are species in terms of constant morphological differentiation. In cases where the taxa differ in chromosome number, e.g. as members of a polyploid series and show correlated geographical distribution but are incompletely or inconstantly differentiated morphologically, they should be regarded as subspecies (Heywood 1960). Such taxa should not be considered eligible for aggregate treatment. The aggregate method should not be an alternative to subspecific treatment. Likewise it should not be used indiscriminately. I have noticed an example recently in which an aggregate comprised one species containing two subspecies. In a paper on East African *Ipomoea*, Verdcourt (1958) gives "The *I. sinensis* (Desr.) Choisy aggregate" which consists of *I. sinensis* and *I. sinensis* subsp. *blepharosepala* (A. Rich.) Meeuse. In the same paper Verdcourt discusses "The *I. involucrata* P. Beauv. group" and "The *I. obscura* (L.) Ker Gawl complex" which are aggregates in the more accepted sense. This emphasizes the need for some order out of the chaos of practice.

V. THE USE OF THE TERM SENSU LATO

In his recent List of British Vascular Plants Dandy (1958) while discussing aggregates and segregates in the Foreword, adopts what I regard as an unfortunate practice: he gives species aggregates as, e.g.

Euphrasia officinalis L. *sensu lato*

and then lists, indented, the segregates as binomials

1. E. micrantha Reichb.
2. E. scottica Wettst.
   etc.

This is open to the serious objection that if the segregates are recognized as such, i.e. as independant, then the aggregate is an artificial grouping, *not* a species. Therefore *E. officinalis sensu lato* is not a species. This is a confusing departure from normal practice. The only way in which it could be justified is if the segregates are clearly stated to be of infraspecific value but are listed in binomial form for convenience. This is not however to be encouraged (cf. Heywood, 1958c). Alternatively if *sensu lato* is retained the segregates must be reduced to infraspecific level and listed as such.

This is not just a procedural quibble—the aggregate concept is far from being appreciated and methods such as that just outlined can but aggravate an already confused situation.

References

AICHELE, D. & SCHWEGLER, H. W. 1957 – Die Taxonomie der Gattung *Pulsatilla*. *Feddes Repert.* 60: 1-230.

BELL, C. R. 1954 – The *Sanicula crassicaulis* complex (Umbelliferae). A study of variation and polyploidy. *Univ. Calif. Publ. Bot.* 27: 133-230.

BLACKWELDER, R. E. 1962 – Animal taxonomy and the New Systematics. *Survey Biol. Progr.* 4: 1-57.

BÖCHER, T. W. 1961 – Experimental and cytological studies on plant species. VI. *Dactylis glomerata* and *Anthoxanthum odoratum*. *Bot. Tidsskr.* 56: 314-335.

CAMP, W. & GILLY, C. L. 1943 – The structure and origin of species. *Brittonia* 4: 232-358.

CLAPHAM, A. R., TUTIN, T. G. & WARBURG, E. F. 1952 – *Flora of the British Isles*. Cambridge.

DANDY, J. E. 1958 – *List of British vascular plants*. London.

DAVIS, P. H. & HEYWOOD, V. H. 1963 – *Principles of angiosperm taxonomy.* Edinburgh and London.

DYKSTERHUIS, E. J. 1957 – The savannah concept and its use. *Ecology* 38: 435.

EHRENDORFER, F. 1958 – Die geographische und ökologische Entfaltung des europäisch-alpinen Ployploidkomplexes *Galium anisophyllum* Vill. seit Beginn des Quartärs. *Uppsala Univ. Arsskr.* 6: 176-181.

GILMOUR, J. S. L. & HESLOP-HARRISON, J. 1954 – The deme terminology and the units of micro-evolutionary change. *Genetica* 27: 147-161.

GRANT, V. 1957 – The plant species in theory and practice. *The Species Problem* (ed. E. Mayr): 39-80.

HÄFLIGER, E. 1943 – Zytologisch-embryologische Untersuchungen pseudogamer Ranunkeln der *Auricomus*-Gruppe. *Ber. Schweiz. Bot. Ges.* 53: 317-382.

HEDBERG, O. 1958 – Cyto-taxonomic studies in Scottish mountain plants, notably *Deschampsia caespitosa* (L.) P.B. s.lat. *Sv. Bot. Tidskr.* 52: 37-46.

HESLOP-HARRISON, J. 1962 – Purposes and procedures in the taxonomic treatment of higher organisms. *Microbiological Classification* (ed. G. C. Ainsworth & P. H. A. Sneath): 14-36.

HEYWOOD, V. H. 1958a – Flora Europaea – a progress report. *Taxon* 7: 73-79.

—— 1958b – *The presentation of taxonomic information.* Leicester.

—— 1958c – The interpretation of binary nomenclature for subdivision of species. *Taxon* 7: 89-93.

—— 1960 – The taxonomy of polyploids in Flora Europaea. *Feddes Repert.* 63: 179-192.

HYLANDER, N. 1955 – *Förtechning över Nordens växter.* E. *Kärlväxter.* Lund.

JASIEWICZ, A. 1956 – Badanie nad jaskrami z cyklu *Auricomi* Owcz. w okolicach Krakowa i w pótnocnej czesci Karpat. – De Ranunculis e circulo *Auricomi* Owcz. in regione Cracoviensi nec non in Carpatorum parte boreali crescentibus. *Fragm. Florist. et Geobot.* 2: 62-110.

KECK, D. D. 1957 – Trends in systematic botany. *Survey Biol. Progr.* 3: 47-107.

KLEINSCHMIDT, O. 1900 – Arten oder Formenkreise? *Journ. f. Ornithol.* 48: 134-139.

KOCH, W. 1933 – Schweizerische Arten aus der Verwandtschaft des *Ranunculus auricomus* L. *Ber. Schweiz. Bot. Ges.* 42: 740-753.

—— 1939 – Zweiter Beitrag zur Kenntnis des Formenkreises von *Ranunculus auricomus* L. *Ber. Schweiz. Bot. Ges.* 49: 541-554.

LEWIS, H. 1957 – Genetics and cytology in relation to taxonomy. *Taxon* 6: 42-46.

LÖVE, A. 1960 – Taxonomy and chromosomes – a reiteration. *Feddes Repert.* 63: 192-202.

—— 1962 – The biosystematic species concept. *Preslia* 34: 127-139.

MANTON, I. 1958 – The concept of aggregate species. *Upps. Univ. Arsskr.* 6: 104-112.

MARKLUND, G. 1940 – Die *Taraxacum*-Flora Nylands. *Acta Bot. Fenn.* 26: 1-187.

MASON, H. L. 1959 – Formal Instruments of the Taxonomic System. *Proc. IX Int. Bot. Congr. Abstracts* 2: 254.

MASON, H. L. & LANGENHEIM, J. H. 1957 – Language analysis and the concept environment. *Ecology* 38: 325-340.

MAYR, E. 1931 – Notes on *Halcyon chloris* and some of its subspecies. *Amer. Mus. Novitates* 469: 1-10.

—— 1958 – The evolutionary significance of the systematic categories. *Upps. Univ. Arsskr.* 6: 13-20.

MAYR, E., LINSLEY, E. G. & USINGER, R. L. 1953 – *Methods and principles of systematic zoology.* New York & London.

NYARADY, E. I. 1933 – Despre grupa *Auricomus* a genului *Ranunculus*. *Bull. Jard. Mus. Bot. Univ. Cluj* 13:

OVCZINNIKOV, P. I. 1937 – *Ranunculus. Flora SSSR* 7: 351-509.

RENSCH, B. 1929 – *Das Prinzip geographischer Rassenkreise und das Problem der Artbildung.* Berlin.

ROTHMALER, W. 1929 – Die Pteridophyten Thüringens. *Mitt. Thür. Bot. Ver.* N. F. 38: 92-

ROZANOVA, M. 1932 – Versuch einer analytischen Monographie der Conspecies *Ranunculus auricomus* Korsh. *Trav. Inst. Sci. Nat. Peterhof* 8: 139-148.

SCHWARZ, O. 1949 – Beiträge zur Kenntnis kritischer Formenkreise im Gebiete der Flora von Thüringen. IV. *Ranunculus* ser. *Auricomi. Mitt. Thür. Bot. Ges.* 1: 120-143.

SHIVAS, M. G. 1961 – Contributions to the cytology and taxonomy of species of *Polypodium* in Europe and North America. 2. Taxonomy. *Journ. Linn. Soc., Bot.* 58: 27-38.

SINSKAJA, E. N. 1950 – *Kulturnaya Flora S.S.S.R.* XIII, Vypusk I. Moscow & Ieningrad.

—— 1961 – Flora of Cultivated Plants of the U.S.S.R. (Transl. N. Landon) XIII. Perennial Leguminous Plants, Part I. Jerusalem.

SIRKS, M. J. 1952 – Variability in the concept of species. *Acta Biotheoretica* 10: 11-22.

SONNEBORN, T. M. 1957 – Breeding systems, reproductive methods, and species problems in Protozoa. *The Species Problem* (ed. E. Mayr): 39-80.

VALENTINE, D. H. & LÖVE, A. 1958 – Taxonomic and biosystematic categories. *Brittonia* 10: 153-166.

VERDCOURT, B. 1958 – Notes from the East African Herbarium. VII. Notes on African Convolvulaceae (Part 3). *Kew Bulletin* 1958: 199-217.

WALTERS, S. M. 1962 – Generic and specific concepts and the European flora. *Preslia* 34: 207-226.

266

15

Reprinted from *Biol. J. Linn. Soc.*, 1, 311–320 (Sept. 1969)

The biological meaning of species*

ERNST MAYR, F.M.L.S.

Museum of Comparative Zoology, Harvard University

Accepted for publication November 1968

The two medieval species concepts, the essentialist and the nominalist, have been replaced by the biological species concept, defined in terms of the relation (i.e. 'reproductively isolated') between populations. The species represents an important level in the hierarchy of biological entities from the molecule to the community. Six major areas are discussed, on which much of the research on species is now focused.

The spectacular successes of molecular biology in recent years have tended to distract attention from major advances of biology in other areas. To maintain balance and harmony in biology, it would seem profitable to review occasionally advances in other areas of biology. Here, I want to single out one of the most venerable concepts of biology, that of the species, and demonstrate the subtle but decisive changes which the role of the species has undergone in biology. To be sure one still encounters occasional claims that species are purely arbitrary inventions of the taxonomist, but a glance at the pages of any of our journals shows that more and more scientific papers are devoted to one or another aspect of one particular species, often in comparison to different properties in a related species.

All such research has been suffering from the uncertainty in the minds of many biologists concerning the true nature of species. There is nothing new about such uncertainty.

Darwin was fully aware of the importance of species when, in 1859, he entitled his great classic *On the Origin of Species*. Yet, even he wavered, as far as the definition of species is concerned. Sometimes he spoke of species as well defined biological units, but on other occasions he referred to them as if they were purely arbitrary aggregations of individuals, not in any way differing from varieties. It was this failure of developing a clear species concept which prevented Darwin from solving the problem of speciation. A confused concept of the species has also been a major source of controversy in paleontology. Obviously, then, we cannot profitably discuss the biological meaning of species, unless we have a definite idea what a species *is*, and how it should be *defined*.

* This paper is based on lectures given in the University of Cambridge (the Hans Gadow Lecture) and at Imperial College (a University of London Special Lecture) by the author in October 1968.

Members of the Editorial Committee, who attended the lectures as individuals agreed that their text should be made more widely available. The Linnean Society is therefore grateful to Dr Mayr, and the Universities of London and Cambridge for allowing the Society to publish this paper.

267

This, then we shall first set out to do. There is perhaps no other subject in biology for which one can document as long standing a controversy as the species concept. If one would gather together all that has ever been written about the species, it would easily fill several shelves in a library. What then is the reason for so much confusion?

There are actually many, but it would not be worth our while to pursue them all. Many of the difficulties have been removed in recent years. Let me start with a most elementary linguistic consideration. It is necessary to make a distinction between categories and taxa. The concept *tree* is a category, but actual trees such as willows, oaks, and pines are taxa which we place in the category tree. The categories employed by the taxonomist are species, genus, family, order, and so forth, but the words robin, blackbird, chiff-chaff, and blue tit signify taxa to be placed in the species category. We see here at once that there are two levels of difficulties, the delimitation of taxa and their ranking in the proper category.

Let me illustrate this with a human example. There was a widespread theory in the early 19th century that the human races had descended from the different sons of Noah and were actually different species. On the taxon level, this posed the problem whether an intermediate population, let us say the North Africans should be placed in the taxon of the Caucasians or that of the Negroes. This, then, was one species problem. The second problem was whether the proper category for each of these human types was that of the species or subspecies. This second decision depends entirely on the concept of species adopted, while on the other hand, the placing of the North Africans with either the white or the Negro race has nothing to do with the species concept as such. Much of the argument of the species concept has been due to the confusion between these two classes of problems, those having to do with the assignment of populations to taxa and those having to do with the ranking of these taxa in categories. This will all become clearer as we go more deeply into the arguments.

Let us start with a historical survey of different species concepts. Considering the reams of paper devoted to the subject, it comes as somewhat of a surprise to learn that all the countless species definitions can be assigned to no more than three basic concepts of the category of the species.

(1) *Typological or essentialist species concept*

According to this concept, the observed diversity of the universe reflects the existence of a limited number of underlying 'universals' or types. Individuals do not stand in any special relation to each other, being merely expressions of the same type. Variation is the result of imperfect manifestations of the idea implicit in each species. This species concept, going back to the philosophies of Plato (his *eidos*) and Aristotle was the species concept of Linnaeus and his followers. This school of philosophy is now usually referred to as *essentialism* following Karl Popper, and the mentioned species concept as the essentialist species concept. According to it, species can be recognized by their essential natures or essential characters, and these are expressed in their morphology. In its practical application, this species concept is usually called the morphological species concept.

In retrospect, it becomes obvious that not even Linnaeus and his followers had a strictly morphological species concept. For instance, Linnaeus described the male and the female mallard duck as two different species. When it was realized that the two so-called species were nothing but male and female, they were without hesitation combined into a single species even though there had been no change in the degree of morphological difference.

Even though morphological evidence is still used as a basis for inferences on the delimitations of biological species, a morphological species concept is no longer maintained by the modern biologist. In addition to the various conceptual reasons for its rejection are two practical ones. First, individuals are frequently found in nature that are clearly conspecific with other individuals in spite of striking morphological differences owing to sexual dimorphism, age differences, polymorphism and other forms of individual variation. An essentialist species concept is helpless in the face of caterpillar and butterfly, or sporophyte and gametophyte among plants, or whatever other drastic forms of intraspecific variation are found in nature. It is equally helpless in the face of so-called sibling species, that is perfectly good genetic species which lack conspicuous morphological differences. Its theoretical as well as its practical weaknesses are the reasons why the essentialist species concept is now universally abandoned.

(2) *The nominalistic species concept*

The nominalists (Occam and his followers) deny the existence of 'real' universals. For them only individuals exist, while species are man-made constructs. The nominalistic species concept was popular in France in the 18th century and has some adherents to the present day, particularly among botanists. Bessey (1908) expressed this viewpoint particularly well: 'Nature produces individuals and nothing more. . . . Species have no actual existence in nature. They are mental concepts and nothing more. . . . Species have been invented in order that we may refer to great numbers of individuals collectively.'

When I read statements such as this, I always remember an experience I had 40 years ago when I lived all alone with a primitive tribe of Papuans in the mountains of New Guinea. These superb woodsmen had 136 names for the 137 species of birds which I distinguished (confusing only two non-descript species of warblers). That primitive stone age man recognizes the same entities of nature as western university-trained scientists, refutes rather decisively the claim that species are nothing but a product of human imagination. The same, of course, is true for the sharp definition of animal species in our neighbourhood. When you study the birds in your woods and gardens, do you ever find intermediates between blue tits and great tits, or between thrushes and blackbirds, or between jackdaws and rooks? Of course you do not. Every species of bird, mammal or other higher animal is extraordinarily well defined at a given locality, and hybridization or intermediacy is the rare exception. Species are the product of evolution and not of the human mind. On the other hand, the nominalist species concept may well be legitimate when one deals with inanimate objects and particularly with human artifacts. It ignores, however, the fact that there is a fundamental difference between classes of *objects* that are the product of the human mind, like kinds of furniture, and classes of *organisms* that are the product of evolution rather than of human imagination. As Simpson has emphasized correctly, the basic fallacy of the nominalists is their misinterpretation of the causal relation between similarity and relationship. Members of a species taxon are similar to each other because they share a common heritage. It is not true that they belong to this taxon because they are similar, as is claimed by the nominalists. The situation is the same as with identical twins. Two brothers are identical twins not because they are so extraordinarily similar, but they are so similar because they are both derived from a single zygote, that is because they are identical twins. Incidentally, it is this same misinterpretation of the connection between similarity and relationship, that is the fatal weakness of numerical phenetics. Anyone who believes in evolution must reject the nominalistic species concept.

(3) *The biological species concept*

It began to be realized in the late 18th century that neither of these two medieval species concepts, the essentialistic and the nominalistic, was applicable to biological species. An entirely new species concept began to emerge after about 1750, but it took another 150 years before it had been thought through in all of its consequences. This third concept differs quite drastically from the concept of inanimate species. It rejects the idea of defining the species typologically as a 'class of objects'. Indeed, it breaks with all philosophical traditions by defining species purely biologically as follows: *Species are groups of interbreeding natural populations that are reproductively isolated from other such groups.*

A species, owing to the properties mentioned in this definition, has three separate functions. First, it forms *a reproductive community*. The individuals of a species of animals (the situation is somewhat different in plants) recognize each other as potential mates and seek each other for the purpose of reproduction. The species-specific genetic program of every individual ensures intraspecific reproduction. Second, the species is also *an ecological unit* which, regardless of the individuals composing it, interacts as a unit with other species with which it shares the environment. The species, finally, is *a genetic unit* consisting of a large intercommunicating gene pool, whereas the individual is merely a temporary vessel holding a small portion of the contents of the gene pool for a short period of time. In all three characteristics it is nonarbitrarily defined, and differs quite drastically from so-called species of inanimate objects.

This species concept is called 'biological' not because it deals with biological taxa, but because the definition is biological. It utilizes criteria that are meaningless as far as the inanimate world is concerned.

The species has two properties which distinguish it completely from all other taxonomic categories, let us say the genus. First of all, it permits a nonarbitrary definition, one might even go so far as calling it a self-operational definition, by stressing that it is defined by the noninterbreeding with other populations. Secondly, while all other categories are intrinsically defined, by having certain visible attributes, species are relationally defined. The word species corresponds very closely to other relational terms such as, for instance, the word brother. A given person is not a brother on the basis of certain intrinsic properties of his, but only in relation to someone else. A population is a species only with respect to other populations. To be a different species is not a matter of degree of difference but of relational distinctness.

The relational definition of the species is both the strength and the weakness of the biological species concept. It permits nonarbitrary decisions with respect to all other coexisting populations that is, with synchronic and sympatric species populations. This is where the concept is needed most frequently by the biologist and where its application faces the fewest difficulties. This is the situation sometimes referred to as the non-dimensional species. The more distant two populations are in space and time, the more difficult it becomes to test their species status in relation to each other, but the more irrelevant biologically this also becomes.

Before entering into a discussion of the biological significance of species, let me say a few words on the dimensions of this universe. Few nontaxonomists have any conception of the magnitude of biological diversity. More than one million species of animals have already been described and nearly half a million species of plants. However, our knowledge is highly uneven. Only about three new species of birds are described annually, a very small addition to the 8600 species previously recorded. But let us look at some other groups. I still remember the days when many papers were published in the genetic literature giving the name of the organism simply as *Drosophila*. This was implicitly considered as synonymous with *D. melanogaster*. Now more than 1000 species of *Drosophila* are recognized, and almost as many new species were discovered in the last 17 years as in the 170 years preceding 1950. I want to give you another statistic. One group of mites, the chiggers (Trombiculidae), are now known to be of great medical importance as vectors of scrub-typhus and other rickettsial diseases. Only three species were known in 1900, 33 in 1912, 517 in 1952, and about 2250 in 1966. It is estimated that several hundred thousand species of mites in the many different families of this order still await description. What the total of species of animals is no one knows. It may be three million, it may be five million, and it might even be ten million. Most taxonomists nowadays partition their time, devoting part of it to the more classical operations of taxonomy, the describing and classifying of species, and the other part to a study of the biological aspects of species. For nothing could be more discouraging than devoting one's life entirely to the endless collecting, describing, and naming of new species. To do only that would be nothing but stamp collecting. Describing does not make a scientist, a scientist wants to understand and explain. He wants to determine the causes of the multitude of phenomena and relations at the species level.

What are the kinds of question for which we look for a causal answer? Let me single out six major problems.

(1) *Discontinuity*. 'Why is variation in nature organized in the form of species rather than being continuous?' To be very frank, we have a descriptive answer to this question, perhaps I should say an empirical answer, but the complete causal analysis has only begun. To make clear what we are after, let us imagine a universe without species. Every individual in such a world, may, during reproduction, exchange genetic material with any other individual. What would happen under this set of rules of the game? Every once and a while mutation and recombination would produce an individual that would be particularly successful in utilizing the resources of the environment. Alas, during the next reproductive period, this unique combination of genetic factors would be broken up and its genotype lost forever.

There are two ways of preventing this and nature has adopted both. One is to abandon sexual reproduction and maintain the superior genotype through asexual reproduction as long as the environmental situation lasts for which this genotype is specially adapted. The other solution, of course, is the 'invention' of the species, if I may express myself that way, that is the acquisition of a genetic program which will permit reproduction and genetic recombination only with such other individuals as are genetically similar, that is which are conspecific.

The division of the total genetic variability of nature into discrete packages, the so-called species, which are separated from each other by reproductive barriers, prevents the production of too great a number of disharmonious incompatible gene combinations. This is the basic biological meaning of species, and this is the reason why there are discontinuities between sympatric species. We do know that genotypes are extremely complex epigenetic systems. There are severe limits to the amount of genetic variability that can be accommodated in a single gene pool without producing too many incompatible gene combinations. We still do not understand why, on the whole, hybrids are not only far more frequent but also apparently less handicapped in plants than in animals.

The mechanisms which guarantee the discreteness of species are called the *isolating mechanisms*. There is a great diversity of such mechanisms, the sterility barrier being only one, and as far as animals are concerned, one of the less essential ones. Behavioural barriers are the most important class of isolating mechanisms in animals. It is necessary to emphasize that it is coded in the genetic program of every species to what signals an individual should respond during the reproductive period. The study of isolating mechanisms has become one of the most important and fascinating areas of biology, and every textbook of evolutionary biology, cytology, genetics, or behaviour now deals with them quite extensively.

(2) The second great problem of the species is that stated in the title of Darwin's great book *The Origin of Species*. How do species multiply ? The answer to this question can now be stated in much more meaningful terms than was possible a generation ago. Species originate when populations acquire isolating mechanisms. A few special cases excepted, species multiply either by polyploidy (a process largely restricted to the plant kingdom) or by geographic speciation, that is by the genetic reconstruction of spatially isolated gene pools. The subject having been dealt with exhaustively in several recent books, I will say nothing further about it.

However, I would like to mention three sets of unsolved problems of speciation.

(a) How frequent are exceptional situations, such as the sympatric evolution of host races into full species or the essentially sympatric origin of species through disruptive selection ?

(b) What role does chromosomal reorganization play during speciation ? And how often does the acquisition of isolating mechanisms occur purely through genic mutation without any additional chromosomal reorganization ?

(c) To what extent does the acquisition of genic isolating mechanisms entail a reorganization of the entire epigenetic system ?

Some of these questions may seem peculiar to someone who has not followed the recent genetic literature. However, unless I am very much mistaken, I am discerning at the present time the emergence of a new area in genetics which constitutes a third set of problems related to the biological meaning of species:

(3) *The genetics of species.* In the 1920's when I was a student and when the battle between the mutationists and the biometricians had not yet completely died down, there was a widespread idea that Mendelian factors controlled only the variation of intraspecific characters, and that species differences were controlled by genetic factors in the cytoplasm. This idea has, of course, been dead for 40 years and even the discovery of DNA in mitochondria and other cellular organelles is not likely to lead to its revival. However, a number of phenomena have been discovered in recent years which indicate that our concept of an organism as a bag full of genes is an oversimplification. One of these phenomena is the remarkable phenotypic uniformity of most species over vast distances, a uniformity only difficult to explain as the result of gene flow. I postulated in my 1963 book that such populations are held together by sharing in a single system of epistatic interactions or, as Waddington would call it, a single system of canalizations, but the actual concrete evidence for the existence of such a system is indirect and entirely based on inference. The study of the distribution of enzyme systems by Hubby, Lewontin and others is now beginning to open the door to an entirely new realm of research. Much of this research is still unpublished. It seems, however, that the same enzyme loci are variable in many populations of *Drosophila pseudoobscura* and even have the same allele frequencies, if I understand correctly. The only exception was a peripherally isolated population. If these findings are confirmed for other species, it would bring us back to the idea that indeed a species may have a species-wide epistatic genic system on which geographic variation and other types of polymorphism are superimposed. It furthermore suggests that this basic epistatic system undergoes a genetic revolution in connection with speciation. It is, of course, far too early to base sweeping conclusions on such preliminary, unpublished results, and the only reason why I am mentioning them at all is because they fit so extremely well with some previous postulates.

Let me now cite another door that has been opened into a *terra incognita*. Until quite recently when one asked a *Drosophila* specialist how many genes *Drosophila* has, he might have said about 10,000, or if he was in a very generous mood, he might say 50,000; a mouse geneticist would have given similar answers. Yet, if one measures the amount of DNA in a single mammalian cell nucleus, one finds that it contains enough DNA for about five million cistrons, i.e. for five million genes. It is a great puzzle what the other 4,950,000 genes are doing. We still do not know, but recent studies by Britten and his group in the Carnegie Institution, and by Walker (in Edinburgh) and his group show that there is great heterogeneity in the nuclear DNA, and, in particular, that certain genomes may contain large quantities of identical DNA sequences. If such special DNA's should be species specific, as some of the evidence indicates, it would raise an entirely new set of problems. The reason I am referring to this research is to make it clear how little we still understand what I have previously referred to as the *genetics* of *species*, the very particular genetic structure of species. It is quite possible, if not probable, that the acquisition of isolating mechanisms is merely a coincidental by-product of a far more fundamental genetic event, a genetic restructuring of populations. Only the simultaneous study of several loci or several characters will give us the kind of answers we are looking for. Any day may bring further exciting new discoveries in this area.

Let me now go back to some more classical problems.

(4) *The role of species in evolution.* The biologist, when he contemplates large scale evolution, speaks of trends, adaptations, specializations, and invasions of new adaptive zones and niches. The explanation of these phenomena has, however, suffered owing to the fact that the most important part of the story, the role of the agents of these evolutionary phenomena was omitted. Actually, in each case, it is a species or a group of species that is responsible for the evolutionary events. *Species are the real units of evolution,* they are the entities which specialize, which become adapted, or which shift their adaptation. And speciation, the production of new gene complexes capable of ecological shifts, is the method by which evolution advances. The species truly is the keystone of evolution.

The role of species is to some extent comparable to the role of mutations. Most mutations are irrelevant or deleterious, but whenever there *is* any genetic improvement, it is due to the incorporation of a new mutation into an improved genotype. It is the same with species. Recent taxonomic studies have shown how frequent incipient species are. Speciation obviously is a prolific process, but the majority of new species have a short life expectancy, they become extinct again sooner or later. But one out of a 100, 1000, or 10,000 makes an evolutionary invention and is able to occupy a novel adaptive zone. Birds, bats, vertebrates, insects, they all ultimately go back to one particular, unusually successful species. Every species is a new evolutionary experiment. Most of them are failures, but an occasional one is a spectacular success. Even when we look at a group of closely related species, we find almost invariably one or the other with an unusual specialization or adaptation. In most cases this merely leads into an evolutionary dead-end street, but occasionally it opens the door to an entirely new world. To repeat, the species plays an enormously important role in evolution.

(5) *Species and ecosystems.* One of the unsolved problems relating to species is why some of them, in fact the vast majority, are so narrow in their ecological specialization while a few species seem to have an extraordinary ecological tolerance. For instance, we can say descriptively, that a certain plant host-specific moth is so specialized that its larva can live, as a leaf miner, only in the leaves of one particular species of plants, while another species of moths has such broad tolerance that it can feed on the leaves of all the species in, let us say, eight or ten families of plants. Or to give another example, one species of ants always has small colonies, and only few of these colonies per unit of area, while another species of the same or a related genus may be extremely successful and become a tramp species that is carried all over the world, establishing colonies wherever it goes. Extremely little is known so far on the reasons for such differences among species. Carson has examined this problem for the genus *Drosophila* and he found that the so-called garbage species, those that can live successfully in most countries, in most climates, and on many sources of food do, indeed, on the average differ in their caryotype from the less successful, less common, more localized species. But this is only a beginning, and the actual truth of the matter is that we have very little understanding so far of the genetic basis for the tremendous differences in eco-logical tolerance between different species. It is rather obvious that the classical method of trying to describe species differences in terms of gene frequencies and the fitness of

individual genes will not get us very far in such an analysis. The genetics of the ecological role of species is still at its very beginning.

(6) *Species and species diversity*. Up to now I have focused attention on a single species at a time, but there is another aspect to species, and that is the total diversity of species in a given region. To be sure, the total diversity of species at a given place at a given time is the product of the characteristics of all the individual species of which the total is composed. Nevertheless, as in the case of many complex systems, the analysis of the system as a whole gives us new insights in the properties of the component parts, just like the study of the water molecule reveals certain properties of the elements hydrogen and oxygen, which the study of these elements in their pure state would not or not easily reveal.

The study of species diversity is one of the most active frontiers of ecology, and the number of unanswered questions is legion. For instance, what is the ecological interaction of species? I think here, in particular, not of such rather simple-minded matters as food chains, but the far more complex problems indicated by such words as niche, competition, and exclusion. The niche concept is an old one and even Darwin referred to the 'place an animal or a plant occupies in nature' and used other similar expressions. Originally, niche was quite rightly defined as the requirements of a species. In other words, it was designed from the animal or plant outward, as something which the species requires in order to survive and prosper. Unfortunately, there has been an increasing tendency to look at nature as a huge old-fashioned roll-topped desk with an enormous number of pigeon holes, each one the niche of a species. This interpretation leads to many difficulties. There is a far better way of looking at niches, namely by defining them in terms of the genetic potential of a species to utilize certain components of the environment. The niche, then, is no longer a static property of the environment, but a reflection of the contained species. As soon as we do this, we can understand how the niche utilization can be broadened when a species invades a new area, or in another case how it can be narrowed down when the area is invaded by a new species which is more efficient in utilizing certain resources of the environment. There is nothing new in this way of looking at the niche problem, but a great deal of rather sterile controversy could have been avoided by considering niches as the outward projections of the genetic potential of species. This also helps to understand differences in species diversity between different latitudes. Where violent seasonal fluctuations make high demands on the genetic potential, comparatively few species can cope with the situation, and this is one of the reasons why there are so many fewer species in the temperate zone than in the tropics.

It has always been stated, and quite rightly so, that successful speciation depends not only on the acquisition of isolating mechanisms, but also of an ability to utilize certain resources of the environment more successfully than any competitor. The species thus is one of the important units of ecology, this importance being due to the fact that any given gene pool has only a limited ecological competence.

CONCLUSION

I am afraid this has been a rather rapid gallop through an immensely wide field. The naturalist, the student of local faunas and floras, has understood the importance of the species as a biological unit for hundreds of years. However, the ill-conceived essen-tialistic and nominalistic philosophies and their translation into arbitrarily defined morphological species taxa, has long prevented the full appreciation of the great biological importance of species. This, I feel, is now a matter of the past. Among zoologists, the students of behaviour and particularly the students of species-specific isolating mechanisms, have helped in demonstrating the nonarbitrariness of species. More recently, this is being further supported by the kind of genetic studies I men-tioned earlier and also by the studies of biochemists and immunologists. I think there can be little doubt that the species represents a level of integration—in the hierarchy of levels from the subcellular to the community—which is of the utmost importance in all branches of biology, particularly in physiology, behaviour, ecology, and evolution. It is fully as legitimate to study species as it is to study molecules, indeed for the healthy integration of all knowledge in biology, it is vitally important that this particular level of biological integration not be neglected. For it is the study of species, more than anything else, which provides a joint interest for some otherwise very different branches of biology, and thus contributes to the unity of biology as a whole.

16

Reprinted from *Am. Nat.*, **104**(936), 127–153 (1970)

THE BIOLOGICAL SPECIES CONCEPT:
A CRITICAL EVALUATION*

ROBERT R. SOKAL AND THEODORE J. CROVELLO

Department of Biological Sciences, State University of New York at Stony Brook, and
Department of Biology, University of Notre Dame

I. INTRODUCTION

A species concept has been a central tenet of biological belief since the early origins of biology as a science. The implications of this term have changed over the years: the fixed, immutable, and sharply distinct entities of the Linnaean period gave way to the more variable and intergrading units of the post-Darwinian era. For many taxonomists before and after Darwin, the species has simply implied the recognition of groups of morphologically similar individuals that differ from other such groups.

Through much of biological history there has been controversy regarding the existence of species in nature. Are species real units in nature? Can the species category be defined objectively? Given an affirmative answer to the above two questions, can real organisms be assigned to one of the nonoverlapping species so delimited? Darwin's work contributed to the recognition of species as real entities. The very title of his book, *On the Origin of Species*, stressed this category. But as Mayr (1959) has pointed out, Darwin himself was so impressed by the variability and intergradation in the material he studied that he considered the term "species" to be arbitrary, not differing in essential features from "variety." Argument regarding these questions has persisted through changing concepts of the biological universe and with increasing insights into the genetic and ecological mechanisms governing the behavior of individuals and populations. The history of these ideas and controversies is reviewed by Mayr (1957), and we shall not enlarge upon it here. Some have considered species as man-made, arbitrary units either because of their philosophical orientation or because of the difficulty of interpreting variable material from widely ranging organisms as consisting of one or more species. These arguments have been countered by evidence of the common-sense recognition of discontinuities in nature even by lay observers (see Mayr [1963, p. 17] for an account of species recognition by New Guinea natives, but see Berlin, Breedlove, and Raven [1966] for a contrary view) and also of species recognition, pre-

* Contribution no. 3 from the Program in Ecology and Evolution, State University of New York at Stony Brook. This manuscript was submitted to the previous editors and accepted by them prior to the assumption of the coeditorship of this journal by one of the coauthors.

sumably instinctive, by other organisms. Such discontinuities are most easily noted by naturalists who study local faunas and floras, and the species concept derived from such situations has been called the "non-dimensional species concept" by Mayr (1963). But in some taxa, such as in willows, groups generally assigned generic or sectional rank are more easily recognized by local naturalists than are the species.

The apparent necessity to accommodate within one species concept several aspects of organisms led to the development of the so-called *biological species concept* (hereafter abbreviated BSC). These aspects include the variation of characteristics over large geographic areas, changes in these characteristics as populations adapt to environmental challenges or interact with other populations, and the integration of individuals into populations to form gene pools through direct processes, as well as indirectly through their ecological interactions. We shall not trace the development of the concept during the 1930s. Ernst Mayr, recognized as its foremost advocate, has called the BSC a "multidimensional concept" (Mayr 1963) because it deals with populations that are distributed through time and space, interrelated through mutual interbreeding, and distinguished from others by reproductive barriers.

Since its formulation there have been objections to the BSC from a variety of sources and motives. Many taxonomists have ignored it for practical reasons. Some workers (e.g., Blackwelder 1962; Sokal 1962) have charged that the employment of the BSC is misleading in that it imbues species described by conventional morphological criteria with a false aura of evolutionary distinctness and with unwarranted biosystematic implications. In fairness we point out that some supporters of the BSC (e.g., Simpson 1961, p. 149) state clearly the difficulties of correlating phenetic and genetic species criteria even in the same taxonomic group but especially across diverse taxa. Nevertheless, such caveats do not generally affect either taxonomic practice or teaching as it filters down to the level of the introductory courses. These critics also point out that the actual procedures employed even by systematists with a modern outlook are quite different from those implied or required by the BSC. Recent trends toward quantification in the biological sciences and especially emphasis on operationalism in systematic and taxonomic procedures (Ehrlich and Holm 1962; Ehrlich and Raven 1969; Sokal 1964; Sokal and Camin 1965; Sokal and Sneath 1963) have raised fundamental questions about the BSC to discover whether it is operational, useful, and/or heuristic with relation to an understanding of organic evolution.

The general purposes of this paper are: (1) to show, by means of a detailed flow chart, that the BSC is largely a phenetic concept; (2) given the above, to show that the BSC should be at least as arbitrary as phenetic taxonomic procedure; and (3) to explore the value of the BSC to evolution by posing a set of specific questions. Specifically, we shall first review the definition of the BSC and enumerate those of its attributes that require extended discussion and analysis. Next we shall discuss three operations required for making decisions about actual populations with respect to these attributes of the BSC. Armed with an understanding of these operations, we shall then consider a flow chart of the detailed steps necessary to determine which of a set of organisms under study can be considered to form a biological species.

As a next step we shall note the difficulties of applying the BSC even in the optimal case of complete knowledge regarding the material under study, and examine how problems multiply as knowledge of the organisms diminishes.

Finally, given the difficulties of the BSC as a workable concept for the practicing taxonomist, we shall briefly examine the necessity for such a concept in evolutionary theory, its heuristic value, and the evidence for the existence of biological species in spite of the difficulty of their recognition and definition.

Although our philosophical attitude in systematics is that of empiricism and consequently we are not committed to the existence of biological species, we have approached our task with as open minds as has been possible. We recognize, as must any observer of nature, that there are discontinuities in the spectrum of phenetic variation. The question we have asked ourselves, one which we believe must be asked by every biologist concerned with problems of systematics and of evolution, is whether there is a special class of these discontinuities that delimits units (the biological species) whose definition and description should be attempted because they play an especially significant role in the process of evolution or help in understanding it.

II. THE BIOLOGICAL SPECIES CONCEPT

The number of species definitions that have been proposed since the advent of the New Systematics and that fall within the general purlieus of the BSC is very large, but an extended review and discussion of these definitions would serve little useful purpose here. Many are but minor variants of the one to be discussed below, and they share in most ways the problems that we shall encounter with it. We shall employ the classical definition of biological species as restated by Mayr (1963, p. 19) in his definitive treatise. The definition is:

Groups of	(1)
actually	(2)
or potentially	(3)
interbreeding	(4)
populations,	(5)
which are reproductively isolated	(6)
from other such groups.	(7)

We have deliberately arranged the definition in the above manner to emphasize those terms or phrases which make separate and important contributions to the overall definition. Let us briefly go through these. We are dealing with *populations* (line 5) whose members *interbreed* (line 4) *actually* (line 2) *or potentially* (line 3). The difficulties of the latter term will be taken up in the next section. There usually is more than one such population (line 1). This group of populations will not exchange genes (line 6) with other interbreeding groups (line 7). This phenomenon is referred to as *reproductive isolation.*

According to Mayr (1963, p. 20) there are three aspects of the BSC: "(1) Species are defined by distinctness rather than by difference." By this he means reproductive gaps rather than phenetic differences (Mayr, personal communication). "(2) Species consist of populations rather than of unconnected individuals; and (3) species are more unequivocally defined by their relation to nonconspecific populations ('isolation') than by the relation of conspecific individuals to each other. The decisive criterion is not the fertility of individuals but the reproductive isolation of populations."

Thus to discover whether a given set of individuals is a biological species in the sense of the above definition we must have information about three essential components of the BSC: (1) that some individuals lack distinctness (*sensu* Mayr) from other individuals and join these in comprising biological populations of interbreeding individuals (this is the meaning by implication of the term "population" in the definition of the BSC); (2) that there is a group of such populations among which interbreeding does, or could, take place (this follows from the "actually or potentially interbreeding" clause of this definition); (3) that this group lacks gene flow with other groups of populations (this covers the "reproductively isolated" portion of the definition). These three aspects of the biological species are worked into the flow chart (fig. 1) presented below.

III. FUNDAMENTAL OPERATIONS

To ascertain whether a given assemblage of organisms belongs to one or more biological species, three types of operations for grouping organisms and population samples will be found necessary (although only the third is directly implied by the definition given above). The first operation groups organisms by geographic contiguity; the second, by phenetic relationships; and the third, by reproductive relationships. In all these cases there will be some difference in the procedure when the initial grouping is of individuals into subsets (populations), and when these subsets are the basic units being grouped into more inclusive sets (species).

All grouping procedures will of necessity be based on samples of organisms and populations. Only in a minuscule number of instances will we have knowledge of all the individuals about which inferences are being made. This is not necessarily an unsatisfactory state of affairs, but it is important to specify the size of the samples required to estimate parameters of the populations with a desired level of confidence. Also, the use of samples necessitates that some assumptions be made about the spatiotemporal distribution of individuals and populations.

The grouping operations will frequently refer to the idea of *connectedness*. We shall consider two operational taxonomic units (OTUs; see Sokal and Sneath [1963, p. 121]—individuals or population samples in this context) to be connected if there exists some definable relation between them (geographic contiguity, phenetic similarity, or interfertility, for example). *Minimally* connected sets of such OTUs have at least as many such relations as permit any two OTUs to be connected via any other members of the set. *Fully* connected sets have relations between every pair of members of the set. We use these terms by analogy with their employment in graph theory (Busacker and Saaty 1965).

We shall take up the three types of operations below in the order in which they were introduced.

The first operation groups by *geographic contiguity*. In order to belong to one population, organisms must be within reach of some others, that is, have the possibility of encountering for reproductive purposes other organisms within the same spatiotemporal framework. A first prerequisite for individuals to belong to the same population is that they come from sites which would enable them to be within reach of each other, considering the normal vagility of these organisms or of their propagules. In many cases we can simply assume this when we have samples from one site containing numerous individuals such as are obtained by seining, light traps, or botanical mass collecting. In other cases (especially with large organisms) where single individuals are found at specific sites, we have to be reasonably certain that individuals from separate sites presumed to be within the same local population have intersecting home ranges. In developing a criterion of geographic connectedness among local populations we need to be concerned with the probability of members of one locality visiting members of another one to permit the necessary gene flow required by the model. Again, this will be a function of the distance between localities, the vagility of organisms, and the ecological conditions that obtain between points. Various techniques of locational analysis (see Haggett 1966) can be used for establishing these linkages. We note in passing that the essential information required for this operation is lacking for most taxa. For example, the pollen and seed ranges for most flowering plant taxa are unknown (Harper 1966).

A second operation is the establishment of *phenetic similarity* between individuals within population samples and between such samples from various areas. While the definition of the BSC does not invoke phenetic considerations, it will be shown in the next section that any attempt to apply the definition to an actual sample of organisms will need to resort to phenetics in practice. In the initial stages of a study it may be that sufficient estimates of phenetic similarity can be determined by visual inspection of the specimens. Clearly, when the material is very heterogenous such an initial sorting of the material into putatively conspecific assemblages can be profitable. When more refined analysis is indicated, a quantitative phenetic approach is necessary. Here again we need not concern ourselves with the technical details, which are by now well established through the techniques of numerical taxonomy (Sokal and Sneath 1963).

The third operation involves grouping *interbreeding individuals* into population samples and grouping *interbreeding population samples* into larger assemblages. Before discussing this in detail, a semantic digression is necessary. In most relevant texts the term "interbreeding" is not defined precisely or distinguished clearly from intercrossing, interfertility, mating, and similar terms. Recourse to a dictionary is not enlightening. The reader is aware that the very act of mating (i.e., copulation in animals with or without insemination, or pollination in plants, to name only two of the more common mechanisms of sexual reproduction) does not of itself insure the production of viable offspring and especially of fertile offspring. Clearly, the act of mating or the transfer of male gametes toward a female gamete is the single necessary precondition for successful interbreeding, but it does not in itself insure fertile offspring. We shall use the term "interbreeding" to mean crossing between individuals resulting in the production of fertile offspring, but we shall occasionally use the terms "interfertility" or simply "mating" in a similar context.

The only unequivocal, direct basis for forming interbreeding groups is to observe organisms interbreeding in nature. If we wanted to make the definition absurdly rigorous, we would wish to insist that an interbreeding population sample be one where a sufficient number of females from the local population sample is mated with a sufficient number of males in the same sample to insure reproductive connectedness to the required degree. Fertile offspring would have to result from all of these unions. Obviously such observations are unlikely. Even if we were to turn to experiments to answer the question, we could not insist on so complete a test of interfertility, both because the number of experiments would be far too great and because, in most cases such crosses would be impossible, since the biological nature of the organisms precludes more than a single mating (e.g., longevity of mating individuals, incompatibility toward further mates by an already mated female, developmental period of the young, etc.).

Thus, as noted earlier we shall have to resort to samples of field observations or of crossing experiments. The latter raise the often discussed issue of whether laboratory tests of interbreeding should be considered as evidence when contrasted with field observations. Clearly, first consideration must be given to observations of nature as it is. Success in crossing experiments might indicate "potential" interbreeding. In designing crossing experiments as criteria of interfertility, clear instructions must be given on what role these experiments will play and whether the definition to be tested will be satisfied by laboratory crossing experiments or whether field observations are required.

Added to these difficulties is the fact that most of the material systematists deal with is already dead at the time of study and cannot be brought into the laboratory or experimental garden for crossing purposes. Thus, extensive interbreeding tests are impractical, and one needs to resort to partial or circumstantial evidence on crossing for inference on interfertility. As direct evidence on interbreeding diminishes, the methods become increasingly phenetic. Phenetic information is of value in ascertaining interbreeding relationships only insofar as one may assume that phenetic similarity is directly related to ease of interbreeding. Yet we know that phenetics is an imperfect reflection of interfertility between organisms. In fact, this has been one of the main criticisms of numerical taxonomy by evolutionists.

The above arguments should not be interpreted as insistence on our part for "complete" knowledge of reproductive relationships. Just as one samples in phenetic studies to obtain estimates of phenetic structure of a larger population, so it is entirely justified to test reproductive relationships among only a sample of individuals and make inferences about a larger population. However, both sampling procedures are based on prior phenetic sorting out of specimens and populations. Thus we test reproductive relationships only among organisms likely to be interfertile, and the only way we can recognize these is on a phenetic basis. Therefore, except for the absurdly extreme reproductive test of each organism against every other one—biologically and experimentally infeasible, as well as destructive of the original taxa if it were possible to carry out such a test—reproductive tests based on samples reflect phenetic considerations in choosing the individuals to be tested. Furthermore, we must stress that even if we carried out some crossing experiments we would still need to employ phenetic inference to reason from the results of our limited number of crosses to the larger population sample, to the entire local population living today, and to the entire local population both living and dead.

Depending on the set of reproductive properties chosen by a given scientist, interbreeding will range continuously from complete interbreeding through intermediate stages to total lack of interbreeding. The two properties most often considered are connectedness and success of reproduction. If every individual in a group could interbreed with every other one of the opposite sex, *connectedness* would be complete. But the total number of possible combinations will likely be reduced; that is, some pairs may not be able to interbreed. This could be so for a variety of reasons, directly and indirectly genetic, such as sterility genes, reproductive incompatibilities, behavioral differences, seasonal isolation, etc. We are prepared to accept a sample as connected within itself if each individual is capable of interbreeding with one or more of the opposite sex in such a way that the reproductive relationships would yield a minimally connected graph (Busacker and Saaty 1965) (with $n + m - 1$ edges, where n is the number of one sex and m that of the other), with terminal members being connected to one mate only. Such a minimal interbreeding relationship is unlikely in a large biological sample because it would imply a very complex system of mating types and intersterilities; yet even such a system practiced over many generations would insure genetic connectedness among its members. A sample whose reproductive relations are less than a minimal connected set should be separated into those subsets which are connected.

But the ability to mate is clearly not enough. Fertile offspring, which have a nonzero probability of survival and of leaving new offspring, must result from such a union. This consideration leads us directly to the second property characterizing interbreeding.

Success of reproduction can be expressed as the percentage of fertile offspring resulting from a given mating measured in terms of percentage of eggs hatched, percentage of seed set, litter size, and similar criteria in the F_1 or later generations. The standards set for such criteria and acceptable levels of success will vary with the investigator.

Therefore, members of a local population sample may be considered to interbreed either if they are completely interfertile as defined above or if they are partially interfertile. In the latter case, only samples whose members show at least minimal connectedness and whose average success of reproduction is greater than an arbitrarily established value would qualify.

If organisms are apomicts or obligate selfers, then by their very nature they cannot form biological species (as has indeed been pointed out by proponents of the BSC, e.g., Simpson, [1961, p. 161] or Mayr [1963, p. 27]). If these biological facts are not known to us, they might be suggested by all individuals forming a disjoint set in this step (i.e., no individuals will reproduce with any other individual in the sample). Technically, we should no longer process such samples through the flow chart. However, a useful classification could be arrived at if we ran the individuals of each local sample through the phenetic pathways of the flow chart. We infer this because taxonomists have had no apparent difficulty in describing species by conventional methods in these forms.

Once it has been demonstrated that the individuals *within* each local population sample interbreed, we need only show that there is some gene flow among the samples studied in order to establish interbreeding among them. Once genes from population A enter population B, (and those from B enter A), interbreeding among the members of A and B provides an opportunity for the establishment of the new genes in both populations.

We can conceive of several partially interfertile population samples as a connected set. It would follow that in order to be considered actually interbreeding the several population samples would have to represent at least a minimally connected set of reproductive relationships. Therefore, not every population sample needs to be directly reproductively connected to every other population sample in the study. A *Rassenkreis* is an example of such a situation. These relationships may be somewhat difficult to represent because the paths of connection will have to pass through either the offspring or parents of mates in a zigzag fashion. However, in populations among which there is substantial gene flow, it should be possible to make a chain of connection between any two organisms by going through relatively few ancestral and descendant generations.

The term "potentially interbreeding," which is included in some definitions of the biological species, has never really been defined, let alone defined operationally. It appears to us that the only possible answer one could get to the question of whether two samples are potentially interbreeding is "don't know." At best, one would be reduced to inferences about potential interfertility from phenetic evidence (and we have already seen that this is not too reliable). It is interesting to note that in his latest work, Mayr (1969) has dropped "potentially interbreeding" from his biological species definition.

IV. FLOW CHART FOR RECOGNIZING BIOLOGICAL SPECIES

The actual flow chart is shown in figure 1. The various steps in this figure are listed in this section, each followed by an explanatory account of the reasons for the step, the manner in which it could be carried out, and inherent difficulties.

1. *Assemble phenetically similar individuals.*—This preliminary step is important because unless the individuals used for the study are "relatively" similar, it is not reasonable to suppose that they interbreed. Lacking such a procedure, one would be forced to carry out a vast amount of fruitless testing for interfertility. Cottonwoods, aphids, and field mice could all be obtained in samples from the same locality, and, while the subsequent logic of the flow chart should ensure their separation into independent biological species (if we can determine that they are not actually or potentially interbreeding populations), a large amount of unnecessary and most likely impractical work would have to be done to test for fertility between cottonwoods and field mice, for example.

Systematists have appropriately decided not to trouble about this point but to use the relatively great phenetic dissimilarity of such groups of organisms to infer that they would be intersterile if an attempt at artificial crossing were made. Substantial evidence is available, especially from plants, that individuals allocated to different orders, families, or genera are usually intersterile. However, in the vast majority of organisms we may state with certainty that decisions about the presumptive intersterility of two dissimilar individuals or populations are based on phenetics alone. But since phenetic similarity is a continuous variable (as is reproductive interrelationship), it is difficult to designate anything but arbitrary similarity levels above which individuals and populations are potentially interbreeding and hence potentially conspecific and therefore need further testing and below which they are phenetically so different that the likelihood of interbreeding (hence of conspecificity) is small enough to be neglected. In the absurdly extreme instance of cottonwoods and field mice, this phenetic comparison is made instantaneously by the taxonomist without the need for more precise and sophisticated phenetic methods. This step is stressed here mainly to make the logic of the flow chart complete. When assembling similar individuals, dimorphisms and polymorphisms may give rise to

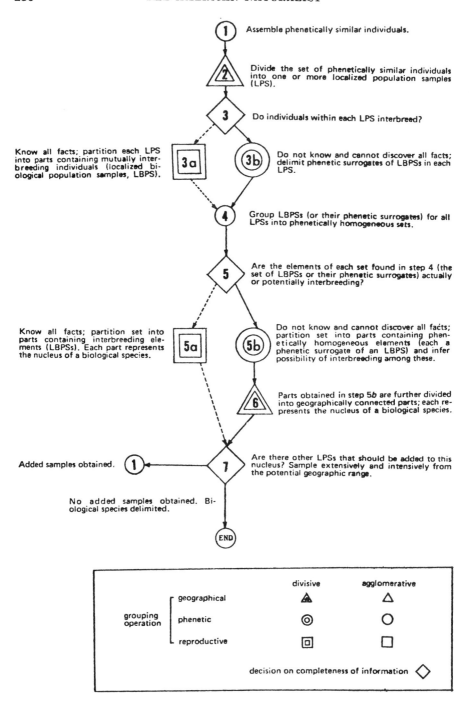

FIG. 1.—Flow chart for determining biological species. For explanation, see text.

practical difficulties, and relational criteria based on knowledge of the biology of the organisms involved may be invoked. Thus, knowing that given caterpillars give rise to given butterflies, we shall associate them, and in cases of marked sexual dimorphism we would wish to associate males and females that appear to form sexual pairs. This can sometimes be done by refined biometric techniques, but where previous knowledge or simple observations suffice these should surely be preferred.

A second point is that step 1 should not be carried out so finely that potential candidates for conspecific status are excluded. Thus the grouping should err by inclusion rather than by exclusion. Otherwise, since the flow chart will not cycle through the original sample again, some of the initial sample of organisms that also belong to the same biological species would be excluded.

2. *Divide the set of phenetically similar individuals into one or more localized population samples.*—The procedure leading to localized population samples is that of grouping by geographical contiguity as defined in Section III. Since we are at the moment concerned with the grouping of individuals to form population samples, we would be unlikely to encounter fixed geographic points from which we can create an interconnected network. Rather, we are likely to obtain a scattering of incidental collection sites from which we must draw inferences about the potential for geographic overlap of the lifetime movement ranges of the individuals concerned.

We shall define a *localized population sample* (LPS) in terms of the natural vagility of the organism. The need for such a definition stems from the biological attributes of populations as integrated gene pools which require that the members of a population be within the geographic range making such integration possible. We use the term "localized," following the conventions of the statistical geographers (Haggett 1966), rather than the more common "local" population which has certain biological, genetic and ecological connotations that, although hard to define, nevertheless are generally invoked in the minds of systematists. By localized population sample we mean to imply only connection by an external relationship, largely spatial but also temporal and ecological. Unless otherwise qualified, this does not necessarily imply genetic or phenetic similarity among its members.

Gametes or propagules will differ in the distances they travel. A distribution of such distances, if known, could serve as a measure of vagility. The ninety-ninth percentile, V, gives a near upper limit to the distances travelled. If the largest observed distance between any two members of a cluster being formed is less than kV, where k is an arbitrary constant, we may define this cluster as a localized population sample. Problems might arise with uniformly spaced individuals, but such instances invite arbitrary decisions by any procedure. Also, while the samples are likely to be phenetically similar following step 1, we have no assurance that each sample represents one and the same species. Hence the vagilities of the individuals within each sample are potentially heterogeneous as well. Percentiles other than the ninety-ninth might be employed.

Many times one will not have a distribution of exact locations at which individual specimens have been obtained because the sample will have been collected at one spot or because the collection records for the entire sample refer to one spot or to a broad area. In the former case we are clearly dealing with a sample from a localized population; in the latter we have to make a judicious definition of the area sampled. For instance, if a botanist furnishes only county records and the sample may be from anywhere within a county, the maximum straight-line distance within the county will have to stand for the greatest distance between any two members of the sample.

Of course, in most instances we will not know enough about the biology of the organisms studied to make a useful estimate of V. We therefore may have to guess at this value by analogy with known similar organisms.

The definition for localized samples given above should perhaps also include other criteria, such as time and ecological factors. The biological species definition as generally stated does not specifically refer to synchronous populations; yet, as has been repeatedly pointed out, the delimitation of species becomes much more complicated if chronistic aspects are also considered. One might very well impose an analogous criterion of chronistic connectedness on the definition and obtain samples localized in both space and time. Restriction to a given general habitat such as crowns of trees or leaf litter could also be imposed to restrict the possibility further, but we do not pursue this subject here.

Each resulting LPS is not necessarily a local population in the conventional biological sense. To be that it would have to be connected not only in the geographical sense but also by interbreeding relationships. The next step in the flow chart will impose this added constraint.

3. *Is each localized population sample, defined by geographic contiguity in step 2 above, also interbreeding within itself; that is, do its individual members interbreed among themselves?*—Localized populations that are not interfertile within themselves cannot make up the elements of a biological species population. In its rigid interpretation, we would have to ascertain whether there is either actual or potential interbreeding within each localized population sample. We have two choices in answering this question: we can either claim to know or hope to find out what the actual interbreeding relations among the organisms are—this leads us to step 3a— or we may decide that the question cannot be answered fully or at all in terms of interbreeding relationships and proceed to make inferences about these from other evidence, usually phenetics (step 3b).

3a) Knowing all the facts about interbreeding interrelationships within each LPS, we may partition it into parts containing mutually interbreeding elements. Each such part represents a *localized biological population sample* (LBPS).

The general criteria for recognizing interbreeding have been given in the previous section and will not be repeated here. The difficulties of testing even within a limited sample the interbreeding of a sufficient number of members are considerable, and in fact step 3*a* is, for all intents and purposes, impracticable. Even if all necessary crosses were feasible in theory, we have seen that sampling based on phenetics will be required sooner or later for inferences about potential interfertility of some untested members of each LPS and of the larger local population. For this reason a broken arrow leads to and from the grouping operation based strictly on reproductive criteria, 3*a*, to indicate that this is *not* the usual path.

3*b*) When we do not know and cannot discover all the facts regarding interbreeding, we have to delimit at least some phenetically homogeneous subsets in each LPS and infer interbreeding of members of each subset (we may call these subsets phenetic surrogates of an LBPS).

We may assume that markedly dissimilar organisms have already been eliminated in step 1. When eliminating grossly different organisms, one should also take care that polymorphic forms representing sexes, genetic polymorphs, or different ontogenetic or cyclomorphic stages are not excluded. If no obvious differences are present, the establishment of the homogeneity of the individuals within the sample may require sophisticated biometrical analysis. Even then, homogeneity cannot ever be proven. It can only be established that for the set of characters which has been measured the individuals appear to be homogeneous. If a heterogeneity is discovered, as, for example, in the form of a bimodality of a given character or a constriction or discontinuity in character hyperspace, we need to allocate the sampled individuals to the two or more subpopulations thus defined. Intergrades will be troublesome in this context, and final decisions on boundaries of the phenetic groups are bound to be arbitrary.

Another method for grouping the subsamples within the original LPS would be to cluster the organisms by one of the methods of numerical taxonomy. As before, such a procedure is quite arbitrary in terms of the choice of a criterion of homogeneity.

4. *Group the LBPSs (or their phenetic surrogates) for all LPSs into phenetically homogeneous sets.*—This is an agglomerative phenetic grouping procedure and is necessary as a preliminary to the rigorous test by the defined criteria for the BSC. This is so because, following the strict guidelines of the biological species definition of "actually or potentially interbreeding populations," one would have to test all samples obtained at the various localities for mutual interbreeding. As will be seen later, this is a formidable, if not impossible, task even when the samples are homogeneous within and among LBPSs, so that one may presume that they all belong to the same species. However, at this point in our procedure for determining whether a group of populations constitutes a biological species, we do not as yet know that the separate subsets in the various LBPSs defined in step 3 are similar to such a degree. All we know is that they are homogeneous *within* LBPSs. This does not necessarily mean that they are homogeneous *among* LBPSs.

Markedly different populations will already have been eliminated in step

1 of the flow chart. Thus we would no longer find one LBPS of drosophila and another LBPS of field mice. However, there might well be several species of drosophila, from the same locality, each in a single LBPSs, formed by a partition of one original LPS during step 3. We now must take all LBPSs (subsets from different LPSs) and combine them to form one or more sets whose elements are phenetically closely related LBPSs, regardless of the LBP from which they originated. It should be understood here that LBPSs in this step include not only those samples defined by step 3a, when this is possible, but must often include their phenetic surrogates established in step 3b.

When the LBPSs comprise two or more phenetically closely related but reproductively isolated groups of samples, this admixture becomes a problem. In most cases, techniques like numerical taxonomy should be able to cluster the populations correctly into those that are phenetically alike and therefore candidates for becoming a biological species, subject to further tests in this flow chart. The criterion of phenetic similarity to be employed is necessarily arbitrary, and for this step to be operational we have to establish phenetic limits. One situation where such an analysis might result in clusters undesirable for the present purpose is with marked geographic variation, possibly related to adaptation to ecological differences. Suppose there were two sibling species distributed over the area. It may well be that samples from reproductively isolated populations showing parallel ecological adaptations may cluster before joining with freely interbreeding samples from ecologically different areas. In such cases, some other form of multivariate analysis that removed the effect of ecological differences from a series of morphological variables would reveal the correct situation.

In summary, in most instances of testing for biological species the preliminary test (step 1) is carried out automatically, often already by the collector who does not bother to pick up animals other than those of the species group he is interested in. Nevertheless, it must be clearly recognized that unless the *phenetic* decisions of steps 1 and 4 are taken, one cannot in practice proceed with the determination of the specific status of these populations.

5. *Are the elements of each set found in step 4, the set of LBPSs or their phenetic surrogates, actually or potentially interbreeding among themselves?*—This question refers to the most important criterion of the BSC. In its rigid interpretation in terms of the definition, we would have to ascertain whether there is either actual or potential interbreeding among individuals of all the population samples obtained for our study. We have two choices in answering this question: we can either claim to know or hope to find out what the actual interbreeding relations among the organisms are—this leads us to step 5a— or, we may decide that the question cannot be answered fully or at all in terms of fertility relationships and proceed to make inferences about these from other evidence, usually phenetics (step 5b).

5a) Knowing all of the facts about interbreeding interrelationships among elements of this set, we may partition it into parts containing mutually interbreeding elements (LBPSs). Each such part represents the nucleus of a biological species.

As has been pointed out repeatedly by proponents as well as opponents of the biological species definition, it is impracticable to ascertain these facts in most real situations. The difficulties encountered are of many kinds. The only kind of evidence that would unequivocally answer the question posed is direct observations of marked individuals and of their dispersal (or that of their gametes or offspring), plus observations on mating and success of the progeny in the field. Laboratory experiments on interfertility could be carried out but would indicate neither whether such interbreeding would take place in the field nor whether the offspring of such unions would be viable and reproduce under field conditions.

Even if we were to admit the evidence of laboratory tests, or of crossing experiments by botanists in experimental gardens, the number of crosses required would be formidable. With only two reciprocal crosses for any pair of population samples, we would need a^2 tests for a samples (including controls within samples). Thus, for 10 local populations (a far from adequate number in most modern studies of speciation), 100 crosses would have to be made. Yet, we have no assurance that a single representative of each local sample would suffice to establish the necessary facts. After all, if an incomplete sterility barrier exists between these populations, then certain genotypes representing the population might not be able to cross while others would do so successfully. Doubtless, a more representative subsample of each population sample is needed to arrive at a decision on this matter.

On the other hand, since it was demonstrated—or inferred—in step 3 that the individuals within each sample interbreed, we have already stressed in Section III that we need only show that there is *some* gene flow among the samples being compared in order to establish interbreeding. Again, we need to distinguish between complete interbreeding, which would mean total panmixia or swamping among all population samples (an unlikely occurrence if the samples are reasonably far apart), and partial interbreeding. The latter, again, could depend on *connectedness* between some individuals in different LBPSs, which will govern the amount of gene flow, and *success of reproduction,* which refers to the percentage of fertile offspring from such crosses and the success of these offspring, evaluated by some standard. Arbitrary levels for these parameters must be designated to make the definition operational. We shall not suggest such levels here. In any event, the amount of experimental work and of field observations necessary to obtain answers for step 5a would become staggering and is clearly not practical. Sampling and inferences for the larger population are again phenetically based. For this reason there is once more (as in step 3a) a broken arrow leading to and from this operation.

5b) We do not know and cannot discover reproductive relationships among all of the elements (LBPSs) of this set. We therefore partition it into parts containing phenetically homogeneous elements (phenetic surrogates of LBPSs) and infer the possibility of interfertility among these.

This is a phenetic grouping procedure. The type of phenetic connectedness that should reflect whether samples (LBPSs) are actually interbreeding includes a high degree of overall phenetic similarity or the presence of intermediaries (introgression). Both kinds of phenetic evidence are subject to the same arbitrariness associated with the degree to which isolating mechanisms must be present before one can call two samples the same biological species. Here, we have to decide what degree of phenetic similarity must be present before considering two samples members of the same biological species. This will vary, of course, with the particular group under study and most of all with the characters chosen for analysis. As Davis and Heywood (1963), as well as critics of numerical taxonomy (e.g., Stebbins 1963), point out, morphological similarity is not a very accurate reflection of the evolutionary status of biological species. Also, overall similarity may not be the most critical phenetic relationship to be established. Phenetic evidence of introgression may be considered a more important criterion. We shall not discuss the possible procedures in detail here, since our main point is to point out the necessity of inference from phenetic evidence.

Had we been able to follow through on step 5a and define parts containing mutually interfertile elements, we could have bypassed step 6 below because we would have met the requirements of the biological species definition. Since we could not rigidly proceed by step 5a and had to resort to phenetic evidence in step 5b, we should strengthen our inferences by determining the geographical connectedness of these elements as shown in step 6.

6. *The parts of homogeneous sets of phenetic surrogates of LBPSs obtained in step 5b are further divided into one or more parts by geographic contiguity.*—This is done to increase our accuracy in the delimitation of biological species. Criteria of geographic proximity should reflect the likelihood of gene flow occurring between any two populations. Thus localities will be considered connected if some members of one LBPS at one locality have an opportunity to join a similar LBPS at the other locality. Geographical distances in such a model would be modified into ecological distances expressing the probability of propagules from one population entering the other population. We are now in a position to make joint judgments about the biological status of the resulting parts, which are phenetically homogeneous and geographically connected sets, constructed by a technique analogous to that of Gabriel and Sokal (1969) for geographic variation analysis.

It will be obvious that, since the level of phenetic homogeneity designated for assigning LBPSs to the same biological species is arbitrary, as is the accepted degree of geographic connectedness, decisions on membership in a biological species are arbitrary as well. That is, we may occasionally decide to include within the same biological species phenetically homogeneous populations that are not fully geographically connected; and, conversely, we may include populations that are phenetically distinct but seem to be fully geographically connected. Since these criteria do not, in any case, meet the formal definition of the BSC, their exact interpretation is not at issue here, unless we wish to infer "potential interbreeding" from them.

Following steps 5b and 6 we obtain the intersection of the parts resulting from these procedures. We infer that the elements in such an intersection (LBPSs or their phenetic surrogates) can represent the nucleus of a biological species. If we are prepared to accept the concept of potentially interbreeding populations, then we may simply use phenetic similarity as a criterion and bypass step 6, which implies actual gene flow in the geographic connections defined by its operations. To avoid confusion, this alternative is not shown in figure 1.

We now must ask ourselves whether the delimitation of this particular biological species can be extended to include other local populations. This is done by the final step, which follows.

7. *Are there other LPSs that should be added to the above nucleus?*— This step tests the adequacy of sampling. This question can be answered by further sampling of organisms from newly studied LPSs, starting with step 1 and repeating the entire procedure.

We define two kinds of additional sampling. *Extensive sampling* gathers further samples beyond the spatial limits of previous samples. *Intensive sampling* seeks to sample areas within the spatial limits of previous samples that have not been sampled before. This step will involve phenetic and geographic criteria, since it would be even more impractical to employ fertility criteria here as well. There is little point in going back through the flow chart, since the same information (phenetics and contiguity in distribution) will be used. In this step, as in steps 1, 3b, 4, and 5b, phenetic considerations will in the end largely delimit the biological species.

V. PHENETIC BOTTLENECKS

We now can examine the flow chart as a whole and imagine ourselves running some organisms through it to determine into how many biological species they should be divided. Let us design the optimal case for the systematic study of these organisms by the BSC criteria. Therefore we assume unlimited quantities of live material available from suitably positioned locations throughout the range of the organisms. Since tests of fertility would still require an enormous amount of experimentation, we shall imagine ourselves equipped with an all-knowing computer of unlimited capacity which will provide correct answers for meaningful questions asked of it, obviating experimental tests for interbreeding between pairs of individuals within and between locality samples. To make the situation correspond more closely to the real world about which we wish to make inferences, we shall restrict the computer's performance as follows. It cannot be queried simultaneously about the interbreeding of all individuals of interest, but it will provide correct replies to sequential questions about relationships between each and every pair of individuals.

Given the above (and assuming that we have agreed on a criterion of interbreeding as discussed in Section III), we should be able to eliminate all steps in the flow chart except those that make critical tests of interbreeding, namely, 3a and 5a. But we would find that even our phenomenal computer would soon be running overtime providing answers to the millions of questions about interbreeding results of the possible combinations of individuals which we would have to ask. Hence, even in this utopian case we would wish to avail ourselves of steps 1 and 4 for purposes of grouping individuals and populations initially by phenetic likeness so as to cut down on the number of questions about interbreeding that need to be asked. (Thus we shall avoid asking whether an individual cottonwood would cross with an individual aphid.) However, even this timesaving device would not be sufficient. We would still have so many questions to ask about interbreeding, that our patience, if not that of a computer, would soon be exhausted, and we would take certain shortcuts, that is, ask questions about interbreeding of some of the individuals while resorting to phenetic similarities of these with other untested individuals for conclusions about the entire sample. But, having made this concession (i.e., having taken the path of the solid arrows in fig. 1), we are back at steps 3b and 5b, which we call the *phenetic bottlenecks* because limitations of time will force all studies, even the imaginary optimal study just discussed, into these operations.

Hence, while the definition of the BSC does not involve phenetics, the actual determination of a biological species always will do so, even in the optimal case. As soon as we permit less favorable (and more realistic) conditions to obtain, such as more limited material and no omniscient computer but a hard-working scientist with limited resources and facilities, establishment of biological species from fertility characteristics is entirely quixotic. We are left with what is essentially a phenetic criterion of homogeneous groups that show definite aspects of geographic connectedness and in which we have any evidence at all on interbreeding in only a minuscule proportion of cases.

The above is true for all animal organisms and for most plant organisms, as well. But even in those plant groups where crossing tests (the so-called experimental taxonomy) have been applied, the basic definition of the species is of necessity phenetic because the statements that are made rest on phenetic inferences from the relatively few crosses that have actually been carried out in these groups.

Phylogenetically oriented systematists have pointed out in the past that there are practical difficulties in determining the potentiality of interbreeding in given cases. But, as we have shown here, the concept cannot be used even under optimal circumstances. Simpson (1961, p. 150) has called this a pseudoproblem. He feels that the difficulty of ascertaining whether the definition is met in a given case with a sufficient degree of probability is different from the validity of the concept as such. Yet, as will be discussed below, there is serious question that the concept is evolutionarily meaningful.

VI. DISCUSSION

The BSC is imprecise in its formulation and inapplicable in practice.— An obvious conclusion from the above flow chart and analysis is that in practice phenetics plays an essential role at several crucial points in the delimitation of a biological species. This leads to the critical question of the degree to which phenetics reflects interbreeding among individuals and populations. But many examples are known (see Davis and Heywood 1963) where phenetics can only mislead the biosystematist who is seeking the biological species. This ranges from simple polyploidy without phenotypic change and cryptic species, on the one hand, to problems of reactions to the environment, on the other. For example, small flowers are a result of dryness but can also be produced by mutation (Grant 1954). Without subjecting his material to experimental analysis the practicing systematist could not distinguish between these two causes. In other words, the inductive inference that is necessary here is often unwarranted.

Our study of the operations necessary to delimit a biological species revealed considerable arbitrariness in the application of the concept. This is in direct conflict with the claims of nonarbitrariness by proponents of the BSC. We use the terms "arbitrary" and "nonarbitrary" here in the sense of Simpson (1961, p. 115), where "a group is nonarbitrary as to inclusion if all its members are continuous by an appropriate criterion, and nonarbitrary as to exclusion if it is discontinuous from any other group by the same criterion. It is arbitrary as to inclusion if it has internal discontinuities and as to exclusion if it has an external continuity." The degree of sterility required in any given cross and the number of fertile crosses between members of populations, not to mention the necessarily arbitrary decisions proper to the hidden phenetic components of the BSC, make this concept no less arbitrary than a purely phenetic species concept, and perhaps even more so, since phenetics is but one of its components.

Relevant at this point is a contradiction in the use of the BSC regarding hybridization. This is a confusing term because at one extreme some authors call successful crosses between members of two strains a hybrid, while at the other extreme only crosses between members of two species, or between two genera, are hybrids. If a hybrid is produced in nature from two species and there is *any* backcrossing at all, then by a strict application of the BSC the two parents should belong to the same species, even if such hybrids appear in only a small part of the range of the species. But such an application is not usually made, since the investigator has some arbitrary level of frequency of crossing that he will tolerate before assigning the parents to the same species.

One of the prime complaints of the opponents of a phenetic taxonomy has been that it is typological (Inger 1958; Mayr 1965; Simpson 1961).

Whether empirical or statistical typology is an undesirable approach for a classificatory procedure is not at issue here. This question is discussed in some detail by Sokal (1962). In his most recent work on systematics Mayr (1969, p. 67) describes essentialist ideology as synonymous with typology in the following terms: "This philosophy, when applied to the classification of organic diversity, attempts to assign the variability of nature to a fixed number of basic types at various levels. It postulates that all members of a taxon reflect the same essential nature, or in other words that they conform to the same type. . . . The constancy of taxa and the sharpness of the gaps separating them tend to be exaggerated by [the typologist]. The fatal flaw of essentialism is that there is no way of determining what the essential properties of an organism are." However, it should be pointed out that, whether this is desirable or not, the BSC as advanced by its proponents is in itself a typological concept in the above sense. It is typological because it is defined by strict genetic criteria which are rarely tested, and which may not be met by its members (individuals or local populations). We shall examine below the question of whether populations in nature correspond to the biological species type erected by the new systematists. It may well be that the BSC does not reflect a widespread phenomenon in nature but rather represents a theoretical ideal to which existing situations are forced to fit as closely as possible.

It might be claimed that other variants of the biological species definition than the one employed by us could have been shown not to involve unwarranted inferences. However, a careful study of a great variety of such definitions shows this not to be the case. The definition by Emerson (1945) —"evolved (and probably evolving), genetically distinctive, reproductively isolated, natural population"—and that by Grant (1957)—"a community of cross-fertilizing individuals linked together by bonds of mating and isolated reproductively from other species by barriers to mating"—are both prone to the same difficulties. Simpson (1961, p. 153) defined "evolutionary species" as "a linkage (an ancestral-descendant sequence of populations) evolving separately from others and with its own unitary evolutionary role and tendencies." This is so vague as to make any attempt at operational definition foredoomed to failure.

Some plant biosystematists consider the BSC definition we have chosen to be genetic, and not necessarily evolutionary. Some, for example, would maintain that two populations belong to two biological species if they differ in at least one qualitative character and if there exists a certain amount of sterility between them. But this and similar definitions contain the same drawbacks of necessary phenetic inferences and arbitrariness as the concept we have discussed. It still is based in large part on phenetic inferences that may be unwarranted, and it still distorts relationships among populations by lumping them into a smaller number of biological species. The same comments apply to the definition of a biological species as a set of individuals sharing a common gene pool. This last definition may appear to have one advantage over previous ones. It does not demand that local populations be erected during the process of species delimitation. In terms of our flow chart, steps 2 and 3 would be deleted and subsequent steps reworded. Although this has the "advantage" of reducing the number of necessary steps in the process, this is more than outweighed by the increased amount of inference about gene-pool membership that now must be made from only phenetic evidence, as opposed to inferences made previously from both phenetic and geographic information.

Some essential questions about the BSC.—From the above conclusions drawn about the BSC, we see that only in rare instances, such as a species consisting entirely of one small endemic population, is the concept even partly operational in practice. But a nonoperational concept may still be of value. For example, it may be used to generate hypotheses of evolutionary importance. We shall examine several relevant questions for systematists and evolutionists concerned with the BSC. At this time we can do little more than to ask the questions and to suggest possible answers.

1. Is the BSC necessary for practical taxonomy? By practical taxonomy we mean the straightforward description of the patterns of variation in nature for the purpose of ordering knowledge. This is phenetic taxonomy, or perhaps simply taxonomy as Blackwelder (1967) sees it. The BSC is not a necessary part of the theory of practical taxonomy, although the category "species" is. The answer to question one is no.

2. Is the BSC necessary (or useful) for evolutionary taxonomy? This is a more difficult question to answer, since different workers attach different meanings to the term "evolutionary taxonomy." It may mean the relatively less complex task of putting all members believed to be derived from the same ancestral stock into the same taxon, say at the genus, or family, level. Or it may involve detailed (usually phenetically inferred) description of cladistic relationships among taxa at some categorical level. The property of interbreeding may or may not be possessed by all members of the group currently under study. Most evidence for decisions in evolutionary taxonomy (and all evidence above the level of classification where crossing is not possible, e.g., between members of two families) is based not on interbreeding but on phenetics and homologies, whether they are morphological, behavioral, physiological, serological, or DNA homologies. Most work to date, especially on DNA homologies, has involved very dissimilar taxa, such as wheat, corn, pigs, monkeys, and man. Since the biological species does not play an essential role in any of the above work, the answer to question 2 also would appear to be no.

3. Is the BSC valuable as a unique, heuristic concept from which hypotheses valuable for evolutionary theory can be generated at a high rate? It would appear that any evolutionary hypothesis generated in terms of the BSC can also be generated in terms of the less abstract localized population and perhaps generated more easily. Significantly, population genetics, both theoretical and practical, in nature and in the laboratory, concerns itself with the localized population, or a small number of adjacent localized biological populations. There are few if any insights supposedly

obtained from species that cannot be better interpreted at the population level. In fact, some would say that they can be interpreted only at the population level. Nothing is gained by additional abstraction to the species level (except perhaps in efficiency of names), but much is lost, namely, accuracy, for no two localized biological populations are alike. By forcing a large series of them into one biological species we lose the resolution of their differences. The answer to question 3 appears to be no.

4. Is the BSC necessary (or useful) for evolutionary theory? That is, does the general theory of evolution, or any particular evolutionary process, require, or use, the BSC? With respect to the general theory, the answer appears to be no. If we examine the evolutionary situation within some ecosystem, we can generate the same theory based on localized biological populations without grouping sets of interbreeding populations into more abstract biological species. Parenthetically, we may point out that what are probably the most important and progressive books on evolutionary theory that have been published within the last year or so essentially do not refer to the biological species at all. MacArthur and Wilson (1967) in their study of island biogeography, Wallace (1968) in his analysis of evolutionary mechanisms, and Levins (1968) in his theory of evolution in changing environments base their entire discussions on Mendelian populations and hardly mention the BSC. Williams (1966, p. 252) believes that the species is "a key taxonomic and evolutionary concept but [it] has no special significance for the study of adaptation. It is not an adapted unit and there are no mechanisms that function for the survival of the species."

Let us turn to evolution over geological time and consider the birth and death of a presumed biological species. Assume that a certain phenetic form appeared at time i in the fossil record, subsequently became abundant, and then became extinct at time j. What does this mean? It means only that certain populations that possessed the given phenotype were able to survive from time i to time j. Ignoring polytopic origins, this means that this favorable character combination was transmitted among several localized biological populations. Nowhere does such a process demand that this set of populations be put into one group and that it be called a biological species. This can be done, but it is not essential to evolutionary theory. Of course, it is done for convenience of reference. It orders our knowledge in a certain way, as does grouping organisms into taxonomic species, then into genera, then families, etc. Thus it would seem to us that the biological species is an arbitrary category, which may be useful in given situations but is not a fundamental unit of evolution, except possibly in a case in which there is only one local biological population, and therefore the biological species as a class has only one member.

Furthermore, if we assume a priori that all organisms can be put into some biological species, then we of necessity concentrate on finding such classes. Could it be that the occurrence of well-circumscribed biological species is *not* the rule but the exception, in biology? Although Stebbins (1963) says that 70%–80% of higher plant species conform well to the

BSC, other evolutionists, upon the accumulation of more and more evidence (e.g., Grant 1963, p. 343 ff.) recognize the frequent occurrence of borderline situations.

We do not in any of the above statements imply that reproductive barriers are either nonexistent or unimportant in evolution. Quite clearly they are of fundamental significance. But we do question whether they can be employed to define species and whether emphasis in evolutionary theory should be based on phenomena (including reproductive barriers) pertaining to the species category or to a lower category, the local population.

The answer to question 4 appears to be unclear at best.

Conclusions.—If our contention that the BSC is neither operational nor necessary for evolutionary theory is granted, what consequences result for general evolutionary theory? There would be few changes if any in terms of our understanding of speciational mechanisms. For example, the numerous important principles outlined by Mayr (1963) in his treatise on the species would still be relevant even if the term "species" as such were removed and replaced by others referring to phenetically different populations, or reproductively isolated populations, or populations with both properties. The positive aspect of such a procedure would be that evolutionary theory and research would concern themselves more with discovering and describing mechanisms bringing about population changes than with trying to bring organic diversity into an order conforming to an abstract ideal. The emphasis would be on unbiased description of the variety of evolutionary patterns that actually exist among organisms in nature, and of the types of processes bringing about the different varieties of population structure. We believe that in the long run this approach would lead to greater and newer insights into the mechanisms of evolution. Fundamentally this would be so because such an approach would free hypothesis construction in evolution from the language-bound constraint imposed by the species concept. (See Kraus [1968] for a lucid exposition of some of these issues and especially the role of the Whorfian hypothesis.) Even if the Whorfian hypothesis is only partially correct, the very fact that we need no longer put our major emphasis on species definition and description would have a liberating effect on evolutionary thinking. By not tying the variation of individuals and populations to abstract ideals or relating it to a one-dimensional nomenclatural system incapable of handling the higher dimensionality of the variation pattern, we would be led to new ways of looking at nature and evolution.

Having decided that the BSC is neither operational nor heuristic nor of practical value, we conclude that the phenetic species as normally described and whose definition may be improved by numerical taxonomy is the appropriate concept to be associated with the taxonomic category "species," while the local population may be the most useful unit for evolutionary study.

In advocating a phenetic species concept we should stress that, in concert with most numerical taxonomists, we conceive of phenetics in a very wide sense. All observable properties of organisms and populations are considered in estimating phenetic similarities between pairs of OTUs. These would include not only traditional morphological similarity but also physiological, biochemical, behavioral similarity, DNA homologies (Reich et al. 1966), similarities in amino acid sequences in proteins (Eck and Dayhoff 1966; Fitch and Margoliash 1967), ecological properties (Fujii 1969), and even intercrossability (Morishima 1969). Critics of a phenetic taxonomy have claimed that such a wide definition of phenetics makes the term meaningless, since all possible relationships among organisms are then by definition phenetic. But this is not necessarily so. Similarities over the set of all known properties are surely different from similarities based solely on the ability to produce fertile offspring.

Insistence on a phenetic species concept leads inevitably to a conceptualization of species as dense regions within a hyperdimensional environmental space in the sense of Hutchinson (1957, 1969). Current trends in evolutionary thinking do, in fact, consider this approach to species definition as a more useful and heuristic concept, and, as already mentioned, the existence of apparently "good" asexual species supports this view. However, the establishment of such an environmentally bounded species concept, an idea whose germs can be found in numerous recent papers, is beyond the scope of the present article, which limits itself to pointing out the weaknesses of the generally promulgated BSC.

SUMMARY

The term "species" has been a central tenet of biological belief since the early days of biology. But the concepts attached to the term have varied and often were not defined rigorously. The purpose of this paper is to investigate the biological species concept (BSC): to consider its theoretical aspects, how one would actually delimit a biological species in nature, whether such species exist in nature, and whether the concept is of any unique value to the study of evolution.

The classical definition of the BSC is partitioned into its essential components, and some of their aspects and problems are discussed. Three fundamental operations necessary for the delimitation of biological species in nature are described in detail. These are operations based on criteria of: (1) geographic contiguity, (2) phenetic similarity, and (3) interbreeding. Two properties of interbreeding, connectedness and success of reproduction, are defined and discussed.

A flow chart for recognizing biological species is constructed from the definition as given by Mayr. Each step involves one of the three operations mentioned above. Reasons are given for including each step, as well as the inherent difficulties of each. It can be seen that most steps are either largely or entirely phenetic, even in theory. The necessary phenetic steps are termed "phenetic bottlenecks." To test the flow chart, we assume the unrealistic but optimal situation of total knowledge about the interbreeding relations among sampled organisms. The phenetic bottlenecks remain in this optimal case, and the degree of reliance on phenetic information for the delimitation of biological species increases as we depart from the optimal situation and make it more realistic.

The BSC is found to be arbitrary (*sensu* Simpson) when attempts are made to apply it to actual data in nature, and not only because arbitrary phenetic decisions are a necessary part of the delimitation of biological species in nature.

On asking some essential questions about the value of the BSC to taxonomy and evolution, we find that the BSC is not necessary for practical taxonomy, is neither necessary nor especially useful for evolutionary taxonomy, nor is it a unique or heuristic concept necessary for generating hypotheses in evolutionary theory. Most of the important evolutionary principles commonly associated with the BSC could just as easily be applied to localized biological populations, often resulting in deeper insight into evolution.

Having decided that the BSC is neither operational nor heuristic nor of any practical value, we conclude that the phenetic species as normally described is the desirable species concept to be associated with the taxonomic category "species," and that the localized biological population may be the most useful unit for evolutionary study.

ACKNOWLEDGMENTS

We have been fortunate to have benefitted from a critical reading of an earlier draft of this paper by several esteemed colleagues, representing considerable diversity in their attitudes to the "species problem." Paul R. Ehrlich, Richard W. Holm, and John A. Hendrickson, Jr., of Stanford University, James S. Farris of the State University of New York at Stony Brook, David L. Hull of the University of Wisconsin at Milwaukee, and Arnold G. Kluge of the University of Michigan contributed much constructive criticism and helped us remove numerous ambiguities and obscurities. A similar function was performed by many members of the Biosystematics Luncheon Group at the University of Kansas. We are much in the debt of all of these individuals, even in those rare instances where we have chosen not to follow their advice.

Collaboration leading to this paper was made possible by grant no. GB-4927 from the National Science Foundation and by a Research Career Award (no. 5-KO3-GM22021) from the National Institute of General Medical Sciences, both to Robert R. Sokal.

LITERATURE CITED

Berlin, B., D. E. Breedlove, and P. H. Raven. 1966. Folk taxonomies and biological classification. Science 154:273–275.

Blackwelder, R. E. 1962. Animal taxonomy and the new systematics. Survey Biol. Progress 4:1–57.

Blackwelder, R. E. 1967. Taxonomy. Wiley, New York. 698 p.

Busacker, R. G., and T. L. Saaty. 1965. Finite graphs and networks: an introduction with applications. McGraw-Hill, New York. 294 p.

Davis, P. H., and V. H. Heywood. 1963. Principles of angiosperm taxonomy. Oliver & Boyd, London. 558 p.

Eck, R. B., and M. O. Dayhoff. 1966. Atlas of protein sequence and structure. Nat. Biomed. Res. Found., Silver Spring, Md. 215 p.

Ehrlich, P. R., and R. W. Holm. 1962. Patterns and populations. Science 137:652–657.

Ehrlich, P. R., and P. H. Raven. 1969. Differentiation of populations. Science 165:1228–1232.

Emerson, A. E. 1945. Taxonomic categories and population genetics. Entomol. News 56: 14–19.

Fitch, W. M., and E. Margoliash. 1967. Construction of phylogenetic trees. Science 155: 279–284.

Fujii, K. 1969. Numerical taxonomy of ecological characteristics and the niche concept. Syst. Zool. 18:151–153.

Gabriel, K. R., and R. R. Sokal. 1969. A new statistical approach to geographic variation analysis. Syst. Zool. 18:259–278.

Grant, V. E. 1954. Genetic and taxonomic studies in Gilia. IV. Gilia achilleaefolia. Aliso 3:1–18.

———. 1957. The plant species in theory and practice, p. 39–80. In E. Mayr [ed.], The species problem. Amer. Ass. Advance. Sci. Pub. 50.

———. 1963. The origin of adaptions. Columbia Univ. Press, New York. 606 p.

Haggett, P. 1966. Locational analysis in human geography. St. Martin's, New York. 310 p.

Harper, J. L. 1966. The reproductive biology of the British poppies, p. 26–39. In J. G. Hawkes [ed.], Reproductive biology and taxonomy of vascular plants. Pergamon, New York.

Hutchinson, G. E. 1957. Concluding remarks. Cold Spring Harbor Symp. Quant. Biol. 22:415–427.

———. 1969. When are species necessary? p. 177–186. In R. C. Lewontin [ed.], Population biology and evolution. Syracuse Univ. Press, Syracuse, N.Y.

Inger, R. F. 1958. Comments on the definition of genera. Evolution 12:370–384.

Kraus, R. M. 1968. Language as a symbolic process in communication. Amer. Sci. 56: 265–278.

Levins, R. 1968. Evolution in changing environments. Princeton Univ. Press, Princeton, N.J. 120 p.

MacArthur, R. H., and E. O. Wilson. 1967. The theory of island biogeography. Princeton Univ. Press, Princeton, N.J. 203 p.

Mayr, E. 1957. Species concepts and definitions, p. 1–22. In E. Mayr [ed.], The species problem. Amer. Ass. Advance. Sci. Publ. 50.

———. 1959. Isolation as an evolutionary factor. Amer. Phil. Soc., Proc. 103:221–230.

———. 1963. Animal species and evolution. Harvard Univ. Press, Cambridge, Mass. 797 p.

———. 1965. Numerical phenetics and taxonomic theory. Syst. Zool. 14:73–97.

———. 1969. Principles of systematic zoology. McGraw-Hill, New York. 428 p.

Morishima, H. 1969. Phenetic similarity and phylogenetic relationships among strains of Oryza perennis, estimated by methods of numerical taxonomy. Evolution 23: 429–443.

Reich, P. R., N. L. Somerson, C. J. Hybner, R. M. Chanock, and S. M. Weissman. 1966. Genetic differentiation by nucleic acid homology. I. Relationships among Mycoplasma species of man. J. Bacteriol. 92:302–310.

Simpson, G. G. 1961. Principles of animal taxonomy. Columbia Univ. Press, New York. 237 p.

Sokal, R. R. 1962. Typology and empiricism in taxonomy. J. Theoretical Biol. 3:230–267.

———. 1964. The future systematics, p. 33–48. *In* C. A. Leone [ed.], Taxonomic bio-chemistry and serology. Ronald, New York.

Sokal, R. R., and J. H. Camin. 1965. The two taxonomies: areas of agreement and con-flict. Syst. Zool. 14:176–195.

Sokal, R. R., and P. H. A. Sneath 1963. Principles of numerical taxonomy. Freeman, San Francisco. 359 p.

Stebbins, G. L. 1963. Perspectives. I. Amer. Sci. 51:362–370.

Wallace, B. 1968. Topics in population genetics. Norton, New York. 481 p.

Williams, G. C. 1966. Adaptation and natural selection. Princeton Univ. Press, Princeton, N.J. 307 p.

Reprinted from *Science*, **165**, 1228–1232 (Sept. 19, 1969)

Differentiation of Populations

Gene flow seems to be less important in speciation than the neo-Darwinians thought.

Paul R. Ehrlich and Peter H. Raven

Most contemporary biologists think of species as evolutionary units held together by gene flow. For instance Mayr (*1*) writes "The nonarbitrariness of the biological species is the result of . . . internal cohesion of the gene pool." Merrell (*2*) states "The species is a natural biological unit tied together by bonds of mating and sharing a common gene pool." This idea is founded in the pioneering work of Dobzhansky, Mayr, Stebbins, and others integrating the theory of population genetics with laboratory and field experiments and observations to produce the neo-Darwinian or synthetic theory of evolution. These workers quite logically concluded that differentiation of populations would be prevented by gene flow, and they focused their discussions of speciation on various means of interrupting that flow. In other words, they emphasized the role of mechanisms isolating populations from one another. Until quite recently there has been little reason to question this view. In the past few years, however, growing evidence from field experiments has led us to reevaluate the processes leading to organic diversity, and to conclude that a revision of this section of evolutionary theory is in order.

In this paper we suggest that many, if not most, species are not evolutionary units, except in the sense that they (like genera, families, and so forth) are products of evolution. We will argue that selection is both the primary cohesive and disruptive force in evolution, and that the selective regime itself determines what influence gene flow (or isolation) will have. Threefold evidence is presented for this. We will show that (i) gene flow in nature is much more restricted than commonly thought; (ii) populations that have been completely isolated for long periods often show little differentiation; and (iii) populations freely exchanging genes but under different selective regimes may show marked differentiation.

We finally reiterate the point (*3*) that a vast diversity of evolutionary situations is subsumed under the rubric "speciation," and that this diversity tends to be concealed by an extension of a taxonomic approach from the products of evolution to the processes leading to the differentiation of populations. *Euphydryas editha* and *Festuca rubra* are both species to the taxonomist, but knowing this does not tell us if they are evolutionary units or how they evolved. Nor does it permit us to guess how similar are their evolutionary pasts, in what way they are similar today, or to predict anything about their evolutionary futures.

Gene Flow in Nature

To what extent do populations considered to be conspecific ordinarily share a common gene pool? Mayr (*4*) estimated that "genetic exchange per generation . . . due to normal gene flow is at least as high as 10^{-3} to 10^{-2} for open populations that are normal components of species." He considered that gene flow was the principal source of genetic variation in natural populations, and we would agree that the introduction of genetic novelties into natural populations, even at a low level, may be important in supplying raw material for selection (*5*). The problem of testing Mayr's estimates and the conclusions to be drawn from them is complex. First, we must ascertain how much gene flow ordinarily occurs in nature. Second, we must determine the

amount of gene flow at which significant sharing occurs. That is, we must find the amount at which subpopulations of a species affect the evolution of other subpopulations. Both questions are difficult to answer, but at least a general picture of patterns of gene flow in nature has started to emerge recently.

Movement and Gene Flow in Animals

For many animals there is information on the movement of individuals. For instance, butterflies (except those few species which are migratory) seem to be quite sedentary as compared with what one might expect in view of their powers of movement (*6*). Birds also often seem to show less movement than they are capable of—the young of migratory species often nest near the parental nest site (*7*). There also is some evidence that birds may be stopped by "psychological barriers" (*8*). Similar restriction of movement not associated with insurmountable physical barriers has been observed in many nonaerial organisms, such as the rusty lizard (*9*). Twitty's (*10*) studies demonstrate that California newts show great perseverance and navigating ability in returning precisely to a particular stretch of stream to breed. Individuals displaced several miles in mountainous country have successfully returned to their "home pool." And, of course, the great accuracy with which salmon return to their birthplace to breed is well documented (*11*).

On the other hand, there also is abundant evidence in the literature that individuals may travel very long distances, such as in Bishopp and Laake's (*12*) release-recapture experiments with flies in which individuals were recovered as far as 17 miles (27 km) from the point of release. Small wind-dispersed terrestrial organisms may travel tremendous distances, as may some mammals (*13*). It is also clear (*14*) that extremely careful work covering the entire life history under a variety of weather conditions is necessary before reasonably definitive statements on amounts of individual movement may be made.

Of course, movement of individuals does not necessarily indicate gene flow. Anderson (*15*) has shown that the pres-

The authors are professor and associate professor of biology, respectively, at the Department of Biological Sciences, Stanford University, Stanford, California 94305.

ence of wandering individuals of *Mus musculus* as emigrants from granary populations does not indicate significant gene flow, since in general the granary demes do not admit immigrants. Ehrlich and his co-workers (*16*) have produced evidence indicating that the reproductive success of emigrant *Euphydryas editha* individuals is less than that of stay-at-homes, a situation which also probably pertains among small mammal populations (*17*).

Even reproduction by migrants or propagules may not constitute evolutionarily significant gene flow. Only if the migrants are carriers of alleles or arrangements of alleles not represented in the recipient population has gene flow occurred. In addition, if a new allele is to be passed from population to population by gene flow, one must consider the probability of its spread in each new population and its possibility of being included in the genome of migrant individuals leaving that population. Its fate in the first instance will presumably be governed by the kind of gloomy odds facing mutant genes (*18*); in no small part it will rest with its fitness in that population. One would normally expect selective barriers to the movement of genetic novelties.

Movement and Gene Flow in Plants

In plants, we have some actual estimates of gene flow between populations. Here the chances of crossing diminish rapidly with distance. In wind-pollinated species, one might expect a great deal of gene flow even between well-separated populations, but this assumption is not borne out by the available data. In *Zea mays* and *Beta vulgaris*, whose pollen is carried far and wide by wind, measurements have been made of contamination because of their agricultural importance. At distances greater than 60 feet (18.3 m), contamination by distant outcrossing in *Zea* was only 1 percent. In *Beta* plants separated by 200 meters, contamination was only 0.3 percent (*19*). Colwell (*20*) studied the dispersal of pollen of Coulter pine (*Pinus coulteri*) labeled with radioactive phosphorus. The bulk of the dispersal was within 10 to 30 feet (3 to 9 m) downwind from the source, with very little beyond 150 feet (46 m). It is obvious that, although pollen can be dispersed great distances at times, the chances of its falling on a receptive stigma at any great distance are slight.

On the other hand, a given plant normally will be completely pollinated, even in an outcrossing species, with pollen from nearby sources. A very short distance therefore will form the basis for nearly complete genetic discontinuity, even in a wind-pollinated plant.

In insect-pollinated species, Bateman (*21*) found that beyond 50 feet (15 m) there was less than 1 percent contamination between two varieties of turnips or radishes. Similarly, Roberts and Lewis (*22*) cite examples in several species of the herbs of the genera *Clarkia* and *Delphinium* where no more than 50 feet (15 m) seems to be an effective barrier. In *Linanthus parryae* the pattern of variation suggests that a very short distance effectively isolates these insect-pollinated plants (*23*). On the other hand, insects may occasionally carry pollen to somewhat greater distances. Because of their relative specificity, they actually may do so at a much higher frequency than occurs in plants whose pollen is carried by wind. An interesting demonstration of this is provided by Emerson's (*24*) studies of *Oenothera organensis*. This species is a local endemic of the Organ Mountains in New Mexico, where it occurs in isolated small colonies in the bottom of several steep-walled canyons. The colonies are separated by high ridges and are from 600 feet (183 m) to about 3 miles (5 km) apart. Emerson was able to differentiate that this species had a system of self-sterility (*S*) alleles, the majority of which occurred in more than one colony, and some of which occurred in all of the colonies. Wright's (*25*) analysis of these data led to the conclusion that intergroup crossing had to have occurred about 2 percent of the time to account for this distribution. The plants are pollinated by strong-flying hawkmoths (Sphingidae), and Gregory (*26*) believes that this figure is consistent with the known behavior and power of flight of these insects.

In tropical rain forest, trees of a given species are often separated by considerable distances. Here it would appear that either strong-flying selective pollinators must actively seek out individuals or self-pollination must be prevalent. It is of interest to distinguish between these two possibilities, but little is understood of the structure of tree populations in the tropical rain forest at present.

In plants, therefore, there is consid-

erable evidence that distances of from 50 feet (15 m) to a few miles (several kilometers) may effectively isolate populations, and there is no evidence of longer-range gene flow. Beyond these limits, there is no suggestion of gene flow at or near the amounts suggested as "normal" by Mayr (*4*).

The possibilities of gene flow between natural populations of most species are sharply limited by their wide separation. Both plants and animals are usually highly colonial, the populations being separated by relatively great distances. For example, colonies of the butterfly *Euphydryas editha* occur scattered throughout California, many of them separated by distances of several kilometers and some by gaps of nearly 200 kilometers. It has been demonstrated that there is almost no gene flow in this species over gaps of as little as 100 meters (*27*). For this reason, there seems no possibility that gene flow "holds together" its widely scattered populations. The cave-dwelling collembolan *Pseudosinella hirsuta* occurs in a series of populations in the southeastern United States. There is no gene flow between them (*28*), yet they resemble one another. *Clarkia rhomboidea* occurs in the Great Basin of the western United States as a disjunct series of similar populations in widely separated mountain ranges. These are separated by gaps of scores or hundreds of kilometers and they are genetically highly differentiated (*29*). Gene flow can have no bearing on their evolution under present conditions, and we suggest that these three examples are representative of the vast majority of plant and animal distributions.

What then is the evidence for gene flow as a cohesive force holding together plant and animal species? Basically, the evidence seems to be that they are "held together"—populations considered to belong to a given species resemble one another. But the taxonomic decision to consider them members of one species is inevitably based on the fact that they do resemble one another and does not in itself provide an explanation for the resemblance. It may be that in certain continuously distributed species—if there are such—the regular exchange of genes between populations prevents differentiation in the face of different kinds of selection pressures at different places. But such a situation has never, to our knowledge, been demonstrated convincingly in either plants or animals.

The Origin of Species

One can see that, at the very least, it is unwise to view species of sexual organisms in general as the largest group of organisms sharing a common gene pool, although it may be true in particular instances. Yet this notion is important in the history of evolutionary biology, because it has promoted the idea that a species is an evolutionary unit, and that gene flow among its populations makes it such a unit. It led also to the conclusion that sharing the gene pool gives a species "cohesion" which must be broken if further speciation is to occur.

It is appropriate now to consider what processes are critical to the multiplication of species. There is an abundance of inferential evidence indicating that, at least in many cases, gene flow is of little or no importance in maintaining many of the phenetic units we call "species." Some of the strongest evidence, of course, comes from the wide variety of organisms with asexual reproduction. When this is obligate there is, by definition, no gene flow either within or between populations. And yet these organisms tend to occur as phenetic species—presumably groups of individuals being kept similar by their continued existence under similar selective regimes. And, as Mayr (*30*) points out, the existence of groups of sibling species indicates that gene flow is not necessarily the cause of phenotypic uniformity.

It is not necessary, however, to turn to asexual organisms (with, presumably, sharply restricted genetic variability) or sibling species to find evidence of selection rather than gene flow maintaining phenetic units. This is clearly what is happening in *Euphydryas editha* in California as well as in many other butterflies with populations that are totally isolated from one another. *Erebia theano* populations in Alaska are only slightly differentiated from those isolated in Colorado, indeed from those in Europe. Yet we would be greatly surprised if the Colorado populations (occurring as scattered isolates) receive a gene originating in Alaska once per hundred millennia. *Lycaena phlaeas* remains *Lycaena phlaeas* in the Sierra Nevada of California, although almost certainly no alleles from its European or eastern American relatives have reached this area for thousands of generations. The sand crab *Emerita analoga* has a strongly disjunct Northern-Southern Hemisphere distribution with apparently no possibility of significant gene flow (*31*). In spite of this the two populations are not obviously differentiated. This is just one of many cases of a phenomenon known to marine biogeographers as "bipolarity" (*32*). Similarly, many species of plants have disjunct ranges in temperate North and South America, with varying amounts of differentiation despite a distributional gap of thousands of kilometers (*33*). Another case in point is the extreme resemblance of the marine faunas of the east and west sides of the Isthmus of Panama, which includes organisms considered to occur as pairs of relatively undifferentiated "twin species" (*32*). The close resemblance of the faunas remains, although the organisms on either side of the isthmus (that is, those which are restricted to warm seas) have presumably not exchanged genes for two million generations or more. Similarily, reef fishes often are remarkably similar throughout tropical seas, although gene flow among their populations is probably very reduced. The same can be said for plants on the numerous low atolls scattered through the Pacific. The plants which occur on them are identical everywhere, as contrasted with the plants on the high islands which present different selective regimes. Similar examples of lack of obvious differentiation in the absence of gene flow we suspect will prove to be common in all groups of organisms, just as will examples of rapid and prominent local differentiation (*34*) with or without gene flow.

In view of these considerations, we should reexamine the commonly observed situation in which island populations are more different from mainland populations than mainland populations are from one another. This difference is usually attributed to interruption of gene flow, but may more often be a function of a very different selective regime—for example, a milder climate—on the islands. Similar reasoning might be applied to other instances of differentiation on islands, for example, the case of the Galápagos finches (*35*). Isolation is always assumed to play the major role in this case, and indeed it may. But the islands, although superficially similar are ecologically very different and had depauperate faunas at the time of the original invasion (that is, there were many empty niches). Furthermore, the higher islands also show great internal diversification. If this explanation is correct, then we might expect relatively slow differentiation in the future, since much of the "ecological opportunity" is gone, and the various species have now spread over the islands.

A word is necessary here about the function of isolating mechanisms, which have received so much attention from evolutionists (*36*). There is now no reason whatever to believe that such mechanisms evolved to somehow "protect" the genetic integrity of species. Incompatibility arises because two populations are subjected to differing selective regimes, and it is often reinforced by selection operating against hybrids. It is a common but not universal result, not a cause, of the process of speciation.

The similarity of populations that are obviously isolated from one another is conventionally attributed to their existence under similar selective regimes. But similarity where isolation is thought not to have been of long duration, or where isolation is not obvious, is almost always attributed to gene flow. This assumption seems untenable in the light of our knowledge of how rapidly differentiation can occur, gene flow or no, when selection promotes it. *Biston betularia* in England in 1825 would doubtless have been considered to be uniform in appearance because its populations were exchanging genes. We now know how fallacious that conclusion would have been, since whatever level of gene flow existed was insufficient to prevent dramatic local differentiation when the selective situation changed (*37*). Similarly the butterfly *Maniola jurtina* maintains stable genetic configurations selectively over vast areas (*38*) and maintains sharp borders between the different types in spite of strong gene flow (*39*). Genetic "area effects" are also well known in *Cepaea* populations (*40*) with boundaries not coinciding with barriers to gene flow.

The formation of very local races of plants and animals is commonplace even in extreme outcrossers such as the self-incompatible wind-pollinated grasses *Festuca rubra* and *Agrostis tenuis* (*41*). Such races, which may be sharply differentiated genetically, may occupy areas in nature only a meter or so in diameter—with these races surrounded by plants of another race. The differentiation of such localized populations dependent on the interplay between natural selection, the breeding system, and gene flow, has been analyzed (*42*). The advantage of particular genotypes in reproducing under a particular, often extremely local, set of conditions may be such that recombinants and other variants are systematically eliminated. In spite of the opportunity for high levels of gene flow, the selection pressures determined experimentally in such cases seem theoretically adequate to explain the very local patterns of differentiation found, for example, in *Agrostis stolonifera (43)*.

The increasingly refined methods of genetic analysis that are being applied to natural populations are revealing more and more instances of unexpectedly local differentiation even when the organisms concerned are highly mobile and the populations appear to be continuous. In *Drosophila aldrichi*, Richardson (*44*) analyzed three populations within a 40-mile (64 km) radius of Austin, Texas, for the frequencies of six alleles concerned with a particular esterase system. The frequencies differed slightly from locality to locality but remained constant at each locality during a year. Using a similar approach, Selander (*45*) showed "microgeographic" variation between populations of the house mouse (*Mus musculus*) in a single large barn.

Thus, there is increasing evidence of extremely local patterns of differentiation in both plants and animals. We predict that such patterns may prove to be the rule, rather than the exception, for most populations of organisms.

Evidence from natural populations is supported by experimental work such as that of Thoday and his co-workers (*46*) which indicates that selection can override the effects of gene flow even when the amount of that flow is greater than would ever occur in nature. Evidence of this sort would undermine arguments about "gene flow" as a cohesive force binding together all the populations of some widespread species into a genetic entity, even if such binding were not patently impossible for most organisms on purely distributional grounds. Indeed, gene flow eventually might be discovered to play a rather insignificant role in evolution as a whole. There is substantial evidence that populations can be changed rapidly by selection. Similarly there is evidence that selection often resists such change—presumably in part because of genetic homeostasis. The most basic forces involved in the differentiation of populations may be antagonistic selective strategies, one for close "tracking" of the environment and one for maintaining "coadapted" genetic combinations—combinations which have high average fitness in environments which are inevitably variable through time.

Of course final answers about the relative evolutionary roles of selection and gene flow will not come until we have more thorough studies of natural situations. Some of the cases commonly presented as showing gene flow preventing differentiation need careful reexamination, for example, those of Hooper (*47*) and others on the development of dark-lava races in mice. If this, indeed, is a case of gene flow swamping selection, then we must learn the magnitude of both factors. In cases such as that of *Euphydryas editha*, laboratory and field experiments must be devised to determine the exact selective regimes which produce relative uniformity among populations along with temporal variability within populations, in the absence of gene flow. In this, and virtually all other situations cited in this paper, further genetic analysis is needed to determine how well phenetic uniformity or variability reflects genetic uniformity or variability. It is well known that there is no one-to-one relationship (*48*), but in general we are profoundly ignorant of the degree of overall genetic similarity, however defined (*49*), at all levels of phenetic differentiation.

Our suspicion is that, eventually, we will find that, in some species, gene flow is an important factor in keeping populations of the species relatively undifferentiated, but that in most it is not. As this becomes widely recognized we will see the disappearance of the idea that species, as groups of actually or potentially interbreeding populations, are evolutionary units "required" by theory. Modern evolutionary theory requires local interbreeding populations, far smaller groups than those normally called species, as evolutionary units in sexual organisms. It recognizes that such units will vary greatly in their genetic properties and may have a vast diversity of relationships with other such units. The evolution of larger phenetic clusters—the species, genera, orders, and so forth, of taxonomists—is easily derived from the theory, but it seems unwise to consider any of these as evolutionary units except in those cases where they can be shown to react to evolutionary pressures as units (*50*).

Summary

Evidence is presented from a variety of sources which indicates that species should not be thought of as evolutionary units held together by the cohe-sive force of gene flow. Gene flow in nature is much more restricted than commonly thought and experimental evidence is badly needed to document the extent to which it does occur. Selection itself is both the primary cohesive and disruptive force in evolution; the selective regime determines what influence gene flow has on observed patterns of differentiation. Populations will differentiate if they are subjected to different selective forces and will tend to remain similar if they are not. For sexual organisms it is the local interbreeding population and not the species that is clearly the evolutionary unit of importance.

References and Notes

1. E. Mayr, *Animal Species and Evolution* (Harvard Univ. Press, Cambridge, Mass., 1963), p. 21.
2. D. J. Merrell, *Evolution and Genetics* (Holt, Rinehart & Winston, 1962), p. 293.
3. P. H. Raven, *Univ. Calif. Publ. Bot.* **34**, 1 (1962); P. R. Ehrlich and R. W. Holm, *Science* **137**, 652 (1962); P. R. Ehrlich, *Syst. Zool.* **13**, 109 (1964).
4. E. Mayr, *Animal Species and Evolution* (Harvard Univ. Press, Cambridge, Mass., 1963), pp. 521 and 177.
5. More work like that of H. L. Carson [*Evolution* **15**, 496 (1961)] on the possible effects of single migrants or small groups of migrants is badly needed.
6. P. R. Ehrlich, *Science* **154**, 108 (1961).
7. M. N. Nice, *Trans. Linn. Soc. N.Y.* **4**, 1 (1937).
8. E. Mayr, *Systematics and the Origin of Species* (Columbia Univ. Press, New York, 1942).
9. W. F. Blair, *The Rusty Lizard, a Population Study* (Univ. of Texas Press, Austin, 1960).
10. V. C. Twitty, *Science* **130**, 1735 (1959).
11. F. Neave, J. I. Manzer, H. Godfrey, R. J. Brasseur, *Fish Res. Bd. Can. Rep. No. 563* (1962).
12. F. C. Bishopp and E. W. Laake, *J. Agr. Res.* **21**, 729 (1921).
13. See, for example, N. P. Naumov, *Proc. Symposium Thereologicum* (Prague, 1960), p. 221.
14. See, for example, W. G. Wellington, *Can. J. Zool.* **38**, 289 (1960).
15. P. K. Anderson, unpublished data.
16. P. R. Ehrlich, unpublished data; P. Labine, *Evolution* **20**, 580 (1966).
17. P. L. Errington, *Muskrat Populations* (Iowa State Univ. Press, Ames, 1963).
18. R. A. Fisher, *The Genetical Theory of Natural Selection* (Clarendon Press, Oxford, 1930).
19. A. Archimowitsch, *Bot. Rev.* **15**, 613 (1949); A. J. Bateman, *Heredity* **1**, 235 (1947).
20. R. N. Colwell, *Amer. J. Bot.* **38**, 511 (1951).
21. A. J. Bateman, *Nature* **157**, 752 (1946).
22. M. R. Roberts and H. Lewis, *Evolution* **9**, 445 (1955).
23. C. Epling, H. Lewis, F. M. Ball, *ibid.* **14**, 238 (1960).
24. S. Emerson, *Genetics* **23**, 190 (1938); *ibid.* **24**, 524 (1939).
25. S. Wright, *ibid.*, p. 538.
26. D. P. Gregory, *Aliso* **5**, 385 (1964).
27. P. R. Ehrlich. *Evolution* **19**, 327 (1965); and unpublished data.
28. K. Christiansen and D. Culver, *Evolution* **22**, 237 (1968).
29. T. Mosquin, *ibid.* **18**, 12 (1964).
30. E. Mayr, *Animal Species and Evolution* (Harvard Univ. Press, Cambridge, Mass., 1963), p. 521.
31. L. Eickstaedt, personal communications.
32. S. Ekman, *Zoogeography of the Sea* (Sedgwick and Jackson, London, 1953).
33. P. H. Raven, *Quart. Rev. Biol.* **38**, 151 (1963).
34. See, for example, R. F. Johnson and R. K. Selander, *Science* **144**, 548 (1964); E. Stodard, *CSIRO (Commonw. Sci. Ind. Res. Organ.)*

Wildlife Res. **10**, 73 (1966); G. C. Packard, *Syst. Zool.* **16**, 73 (1967); A. D. Bradshaw, *Nature* **169**, 1098 (1952); A. P. Nelson, *Brittonia* **17**, 160 (1965).

35. V. Lack, *Darwin's Finches* (Cambridge Univ. Press, Cambridge, 1947).
36. See, for example, Th. Dobzhansky, *Genetics and the Origin of Species* (Columbia Univ. Press, New York, ed. 2, 1951).
37. H. B. D. Kettlewell, *Heredity* **12**, 51 (1958).
38. W. H. Dowdeswell and K. McWhirter, *ibid.* **22**, 187 (1967).
39. E. R. Creed, W. H. Dowdeswell, E. B. Ford, J. G. McWhirter, *ibid.* **17**, 237 (1962).
40. A. J. Cain and C. Currey, *ibid.* **18**, 467 (1963); C. B. Goodhart, *ibid.*, p. 459.
41. A. Smith, *Scot. Plant Breed. Sta. Rec.* **1965**, 163 (1965).

42. S. K. Jain and A. D. Bradshaw, *Heredity* **22**, 407 (1966).
43. J. L. Aston and A. D. Bradshaw, *ibid.* **21**, 649 (1966).
44. R. H. Richardson, *Proc. Int. Congr. Genet.* **2**, 155 (1968).
45. R. Selander, "Behavior and genetic variation in wild populations," a paper presented in a symposium "Ecology and the Origin of Species" at the 1960 annual meeting of the AAAS at Dallas.
46. See, for example, J. M. Thoday, *Heredity* **13**, 187 (1959); —— and T. B. Boam, *ibid.*, p. 205; J. M. Thoday and J. B. Gibson, *Nature* **193**, 1164 (1962); J. B. Gibson and J. M. Thoday, *Heredity* **17**, 1 (1962).
47. E. T. Hooper, *Misc. Publ. Mus. Zool. Univ. Mich.* **51**, 1 (1941).

48. See, for example, J. M. Rendel, *J. Theor. Biol.* **2**, 296 (1962); see, however, J. L. Hubby and L. H. Throckmorton [*Amer. Nat.* **102**, 193 (1968)], which indicates a high correlation between phenetic and "genetic" differentiation.
49. P. R. Ehrlich, *Syst. Zool.* **13**, 109 (1964).
50. We thank the members of the Population Biology Group of the Department of Biological Sciences, Stanford University, and numerous colleagues at other institutions for discussing and criticizing the ideas presented here. Supported in part by NSF grants GB-8038 and GB-8174 (P.R.E.) and GB-7949X (P.H.R.). A version of this paper was presented in the symposium "Ecology and the Origin of Species" at the 1968 annual meeting of the AAAS at Dallas.

Part V

ALTERNATIVE CONCEPTS

Editor's Comments
on Papers 18 Through 21

The papers in this section attempt to point out alternative approaches to typological, phenetic, or biological species. Grant (Paper 18) discusses an evolutionary species concept (see Simpson, 1961) which he maintains will apply to both sexual and asexual organisms. According to this concept, the evolutionary species represents a spatio-temporal lineage of populations that evolves separately from other lineages and has its own ecological niche. This definition is not subject to the interbreeding pitfalls of the biological species concept, and it has the additional advantage of incorporating the fact that populations move and change through time. In this sense, it is a dynamic concept. However, the definition has two major drawbacks. One is that in its present form it is too vague to be applied in more than an intuitive sense to any groups of populations. The other is that much of the evidence for determining evolutionary species would have to be phenetic (or morphological) in nature, and phenetic relationships do not always reflect evolutionary relationships.

Doyen and Slobodchikoff (Paper 19) propose an operational definition of species in which species are groups of phenetically similar, interbreeding populations that share similar ecological niches. Along with this definition, they propose a methodology for delimiting species. This methodology allows species determination either with or without the use of computer techniques. Also provided is a graph model that uses numerical techniques to demonstrate species relationships. Advantages of this definition include the practical nature of the methodology and the use of phenetic data only in the initial stages of analysis. Disadvantages include the static nature of the concept and its relative inapplicability to asexual organisms.

Crowson (Paper 20) discusses five general criteria for species definition and points out the difficulties associated with each one. Crowson's conclusion is that the species is not susceptible to precise or rigorous definition, and that inexact definitions and vague basic principles are a common feature of the study of natural history. In a historical context, this alternative is not very satisfactory. Although it is certainly true that most present-day biologists rely on an inexact, almost intuitive notion of the species, this does not preclude the development of a formal, uniform species concept as more information becomes available.

Crowson does, however, bring out very well the problems involved in establishing a universal species concept that would apply to all organisms. In the last paper of this section, Stebbins (Paper 21) presents a fable that effectively summarizes our search to date for a uniform concept of species.

18

Reprinted from V. Grant, *Plant Speciation*, Columbia University Press, 1971, pp. 37–45

THE EVOLUTIONARY SPECIES

V. Grant

Introduction · The Evolutionary Species · The Species Problem in Uniparental Organisms · Degree of Integration · The Species as a Unit in Macroevolution · Species Biology

Introduction

The common animals and plants with which the early naturalists dealt were mostly biparental organisms, and they were mostly grouped into distinct species. The species concept of the naturalists was the historical and logical forerunner of the modern biological species concept, as developed by a number of students in the period from about 1929 to 1957.

The biological species concept applies to biparental organisms exclusively. Uniparental organisms are not included in this concept and, furthermore, have been explicitly excluded by some authors (i.e., Dobzhansky, 1937b, Ch. 10; Grant, 1957). The argument is that, where there are no breeding populations, there can be no biological species, for the latter is the sum total of interbreeding groups. In uniparental organisms, in short, we have arrays of clones but not true species according to the biological species concept.

It is only fair to say that this argument has not met with universal approval. Uniparental organisms do exist in the world. And the biological species concept has not dealt with them in a constructive manner. To be sure, many of the counter arguments have confused taxonomic considerations with biological ones, thus missing the real issue.

But two authors, Simpson (1951, 1961) and Meglitsch (1954), have sought and found a biological basis for species groupings common to uniparental and biparental organisms. This common denominator is the genotypic similarity between related individuals: a similarity that is brought about by community of descent and stabilizing selection in a given environment, and which leads reciprocally to a certain integration of the similar individuals into populations in their environment (Simpson, 1951; 1961, Ch. 5; Meglitsch, 1954).

These forces and their interactions are common to uniparental and biparental organisms. They provide a basis for the concept of the evolutionary species, as Simpson (1961) terms it, which is more general than the biological species concept.

The Evolutionary Species

The evolutionary species as defined by Simpson (1961, Ch. 5) is a population system which possesses the following characteristics. (1) It is a lineage, an ancestral-descendant sequence of populations existing in space and in time. (2) The lineage evolves separately from other lineages or, in other words, from other species. (3) It has its own "unitary evolutionary role," that is, it fits into its own particular ecological niche in a biotic community. (4) And it has its evolutionary tendencies, being susceptible to change in evolutionary role during the course of its history (Simpson, 1961).

These characteristics are found in both uniparental and biparental organisms. The concept of the evolutionary species therefore embraces a greater diversity of breeding systems, and is consequently more general, than the concept of biological species in biparental groups, as already noted.

The unitary evolutionary role of a species—its occupation of an ecological niche of its own in nature for which it is especially adapted— is accomplished by a combination of processes.

The processes common to both uniparental and biparental organisms are: (1) inheritance of similar genes from common ancestors; (2) spread of certain genes throughout a population system or species by natural selection and migration; and (3) inhibition of spread of these genes to other species as a result of their failure to migrate to or reproduce in a different environment. The foregoing processes all act to collect related individuals, which carry similar genes, into populations living in the same environment, whether or not these individuals reproduce sexually (Meglitsch, 1954; Simpson, 1961).

In sexual organisms the unity of the species is promoted by two additional processes not found in strictly uniparental groups. One is interbreeding, which facilitates the spread of genes within a population system. The other process is reproductive isolation, which inhibits the spread of these genes to other species (Simpson, 1961).

Sexually reproducing organisms also have the potentiality, absent in strictly uniparental forms, of engaging in natural interspecific hybridization, which detracts from the integrity of the biological species involved. Viewed from the standpoint of the evolutionary species concept, however, the important question is not whether two species hybridize, but whether two hybridizing species do or do not lose their distinct ecological and evolutionary roles. If, despite some hybridization, they do not merge, then they remain separate species in the evolutionary perspective (Simpson, 1961).

The Species Problem in Uniparental Organisms

We have seen that there are population-building forces common to both uniparental and biparental organisms. This is the basis for extending the species concept to both classes of organisms. There are also integrative forces peculiar to the biparental forms. And this suggests that the biological species is or can be a better integrated unit than the species in asexual organisms.

In fact, discrete species groupings are usually recognizable in sexually reproducing groups of organisms, as exemplified by most genera and families of mammals and birds, but are conspicuously absent in many asexual groups, as exemplified by large segments of the genera Rubus and Hieracium. This general correlation between sexuality and a species organization has been a compelling argument for the restriction of the concept of true species to sexual organisms alone (Dobzhansky, 1937b, Ch. 10).

But there are some comparisons other than that between, let us say, the cat family and the genus Rubus which can and should be made. And there are factors other than sexuality which should be taken into consideration in these comparisons. Let us return to the case of Rubus and other plant groups with a similar variation pattern.

The situation in many apomictic plant groups is complicated by the fact that asexual methods of reproduction are combined with natural hybridization. Let two sexual species hybridize. Their F_1 hybrids and various later-generation segregates, if viable, can then perpetuate themselves and multiply by asexual means. A complex array of hybrid clones develops around the original sexual species. The variations in the plant group are not circumscribed within definite limits, corresponding to species, but encompass two or more parental species and all their hybrid clones.

The variation pattern in parts of Rubus, Crepis, Hieracium, Taraxacum, and other apomictic groups is a huge network consisting of several sexual species and their various asexual hybrid derivatives. Such groups are notoriously difficult taxonomically. The biological species concept breaks down in these asexual hybrid complexes, and so, for that matter, does any alternative taxonomic concept of species. Any system of classification into subgroups which can be devised is largely arbitrary.

We note that natural interspecific hybridization is an important factor contributing to the obliteration of discrete species groups in apomictic hybrid complexes. But natural hybridization also obscures species lines in many sexual plant groups, as we shall see later.

The breakdown of the biological species organization as a result of reversion to asexual reproduction in hybrid derivatives occurs widely in plants which reproduce asexually by vegetative or agamospermous means. Autogamous plant groups, on the other hand, are often organized into good, though cryptic, biological species, even where there is some hybridization. It is probable that the low rate of outcrossing which occurs in most predominantly autogamous plants is sufficient to link the individuals into breeding populations and these into biological species (Grant, 1957; Beaudry, 1960).

The effect of uniparental reproduction per se on species organization, uncomplicated by the effects of natural interspecific hybridization, could perhaps be elucidated by an analysis of the variation pattern in parasexual or predominantly asexual groups of bacteria. Are the arrays of clones in such bacteria grouped into species-like units separated from one another by genetic discontinuities? The variation pattern is difficult to interpret in terms of the presence or absence of discontinuities, but apparently genetic discontinuities have developed between certain strains of bacteria (Stanier, 1955; Ravin, 1961). The population biology of bacteria and other nonsexual microorganisms warrants much further study.

Degree of Integration

The unity and integrity of an evolutionary species depend on the likeness and relationship of its component individuals. Likeness stems in the first place from community of inheritance. This is a factor common to both uniparental and biparental organisms (Meglitsch, 1954; Simpson, 1961, Ch. 5). Biparental organisms possess an additional factor promoting group cohesion, namely, interbreeding.

We can say that the individuals belonging to the same population and to the same species are linked by bonds of parenthood in uniparental organisms, whereas in biparental organisms the conspecific individuals are linked together by bonds of parenthood and also by mating bonds. The linkages resulting from interbreeding provide a means of integration in the populations and species of biparental organisms which does not exist in uniparental groups.

We have also seen in Chapter 1 that the distinction between biparental and uniparental reproduction does not cover the situation entirely. Existing plant species form a spectrum of breeding systems ranging from wide outcrossing at one extreme through various intermediate conditions to strict uniparental reproduction at the other extreme. It follows that the degree of integration reached in these species should vary also and, in a correlated manner, from a maximum in widely outcrossing species to a relatively loose condition in predominantly uniparental groups.

In other words, if we follow Meglitsch (1954) and Simpson (1961) in recognizing a species organization in uniparental as well as biparental organisms, then as a corollary we also have to recognize various degrees of integration in species with different reproductive biologies. Well-integrated biological species represent one condition found in nature, while the breakdown of a biological species organization in asexual hybrid complexes is another. Between these extremes we find various intermediate degrees of integration represented in the species of higher plants, as exemplified by hybridizing sexual species and predominantly autogamous species.

The Species as a Unit in Macroevolution

Various molecular biologists, in attempting to deal with organic evolution, have implicitly reduced this phenomenon to a resultant between just two forces, mutation and selection (i.e., Beadle, 1963; Jukes, 1966; and, to a lesser degree, Anfinsen, 1959). By the same token, this school of workers largely ignores the existence of species as units and speciation as a process in evolution. Since a multiplicity of species has in fact arisen in the course of evolution, any treatment of the subject which fails to take their formation into account is suspect.

The combination of mutation and selection will account for bio-chemical evolution, for the most primitive stages of biological evolution, and for some very simple evolutionary changes in higher organisms. But the mutation-selection theory does not provide an adequate explanation of the evolution of the more complex organic structures and functions. The development of plants and animals probably could not have taken place on this planet in the time available as a result of mutation and selection alone.

The characteristics by which organisms are adapted to their environmental conditions are based, in all but exceptionally simple cases, not on single genes, but on combinations of genes, usually complex combinations. The sexual process arose relatively early in evolutionary history, among unicellular forms, as a mechanism for producing combinations and recombinations of different genes. At the same time, divergent specializations, based on different gene combinations, arose in response to different sets of environmental conditions within a common area. The advantageous effects of sex could be combined with the preservation of divergent specializations only by the erection of barriers to hybridization, as we have seen in the preceding chapter.

In short, we have to go well beyond mutation and selection in our search for an adequate explanation of organic evolution. The development of complex adaptations required sexual reproduction, and this in turn called for the formation of reproductively isolated species.

There has been no doubt in the minds of professional evolutionists concerning the central place of species in evolution, ever since Darwin entitled his book *On The Origin of Species*. It is widely agreed among modern evolutionary biologists that the diversity of species in the world is a system which permits the continued maintenance of different specialized ways of life. On the relation of species to phyletic evolution, however, there has been less unanimity, three main viewpoints having been put forward.

Huxley (1942, 387–89) regarded speciation as a process generating diversity but having no bearing on progressive evolutionary trends. Mayr (1963, p. 621) later pointed out that, while most species are indeed evolutionary dead ends, a small but significant minority of them hit upon a combination of favorable characteristics and ecological opportunities which enable them to become the progenitors of new dominant groups. There is no denying the validity of this view. In addition, I have suggested (Grant, 1963, pp. 566–68) that speciation may be inextricably involved in some cases of phyletic evolution, where a progression takes place as a series of successive speciational steps.

Species Biology

The natural or evolutionary species is one of the basic units of organization of living material. As such, and in company with other biological units, the species possesses certain general properties of its own, which can be discovered and elucidated by scientific study. By scientific study

318

we mean that species should be regarded not only as an inexhaustible number of particular entities with particular features, as in purely descriptive taxonomy, but also and more importantly from the generalizing standpoint of theoretical biology.

Whether the evolutionary species has received its fair share of analytical scientific study is open to serious debate. As compared with molecular biology, cytology, morphology, general physiology, population genetics, and such-like fields dealing with other levels of biological organization, the investigation of species is still in its infancy. As a result the species is one of the most poorly understood of all basic units of biological organization. Species biology is not even recognized officially in most quarters as an accredited field of study (Mayr, 1963, p. 11).

The reasons for this situation are partly historical. It is suggested here that the underlying reasons for the lag in development of species biology may also be partly psychological or psycho-genetical.

The diverse major branches of biology call for very different methods of research and for very different modes of thinking. The mathematical population geneticist, the experimental biochemist, the descriptive morphologist, the museum taxonomist—to name a few—all have distinctive and divergent approaches. A descriptive cytologist and an experimental cytogeneticist will look at the same set of chromosomes from quite different points of view. Likewise, descriptive systematic biologists and analytical population biologists can look at the same species and see them in entirely different lights.

Undoubtedly the various characteristic thought patterns in biology are products of training. Probably they have a hereditary basis too. Men and women with inherent aptitudes for analytical work would not be expected to go into or remain in purely descriptive fields, and vice versa. In any case, the population of biologists is observably polymorphic for mental traits, whether these are products of nurture or nature or both.

It is very interesting that the best analytical minds in biology have been drawn in disproportionate numbers to the investigation of the microscopic units of organization. Conversely, the species has traditionally been the province chiefly of descriptive-minded taxonomists whose writings, from Linnaeus to the present day, show little use of analytical methods and little grasp of abstract concepts, such as are needed in order to put species biology on a scientific basis.

319

The situation is aggravated by the much greater complexity of the biological phenomena to be analyzed at the species level than at the various microscopic and submicroscopic levels of organization. As a result of this disparity between levels, a degree of analytical ability which is good for dealing with the smaller biological units may be quite inadequate to handle populations and species. More than one reductionist biologist who has won distinction, if not a Nobel prize, for his work on microscopic or molecular processes has later turned his attentions unsuccessfully to the processes of organic evolution, as the recent literature shows only too clearly.

Yet species biology has not been without its spokesmen since Darwin and Wallace in the last century. Among important modern works dealing with the biology of plant and animal species we can mention: *Apomixis in Higher Plants* (Gustafsson, 1946–1947); *Variation and Evolution in Plants* (Stebbins, 1950); *Stages in the Evolution of Plant Species* (J. Clausen, 1951); *Animal Species and Their Evolution* (Cain, 1954); *Principles of Animal Taxonomy* (Simpson, 1961); and *Animal Species and Evolution* (Mayr, 1963).

The ability to recognize and deal analytically with species phenomena thus seems to be rare in the polymorphic population of biologists. This may be why our understanding of speciation processes has lagged behind other fields of biology. But equally important is the fact that the rare combination of analytical and compositionist abilities is present at all. This relatively rare type of worker has been responsible for the development of population genetics and population ecology in recent decades and will be responsible for the future development of species biology.

REFERENCES

Anfinsen, C. B. 1959. The Molecular Basis of Evolution. John Wiley, New York.

Beadle, G. W. 1963. Genetics and Modern Biology. American Philosophical Society. Philadelphia, Pa.

Beaudry, J. R. 1960. The species concept: its evolution and present status. *Revue Canadienne de Biologie*, 19:219-40.

Cain, A. J. 1954. Animal Species and Their Evolution. Hutchinson and Co., Ltd., London; and Harper and Row, New York.

Clausen, J. 1951. Stages in the Evolution of Plant Species. Cornell University Press, Ithaca, N.Y.

Darwin, C. 1859. On the Origin of Species. Reprinted by Harvard University Press, Cambridge, Mass., 1964.

Dobzhansky, Th. 1951. Genetics and the Origin of Species, 3rd ed. Columbia University Press, New York.

Grant, V. 1957. The plant species in theory and practice. In: The Species Problem. Ed. by E. Mayr. Amer. Assoc. Adv. Sci. Publ. 50, pp. 39–80.

Grant, V. 1963. The Origin of Adaptations. Columbia University Press, New York.

Gustafsson, A. 1946–1947. Apomixis in higher plants. *Lunds Universitets Årsskrift* 42–43:1–370.

Huxley, J. S. 1942. Evolution: the Modern Synthesis. George Allen and Unwin, London.

Jukes, T. H. 1966. Molecules and Evolution. Columbia University Press, New York.

Mayr, E. 1963. Animal Species and Evolution. Harvard University Press, Cambridge, Mass.

Meglitsch, P. A. 1954. On the nature of species. *Systematic Zool.* 3:49–65.

Ravin, A. W. 1961. The genetics of transformation. *Advances in Genetics* 10:61–163.

Simpson, G. G. 1951. The species concept. *Evolution* 5:285–298.

Simpson, G. G. 1961. Principles of Animal Taxonomy. Columbia University Press, New York.

Stanier, R. Y. 1955. Specific and intraspecific categories in microorganisms. In: *Biology Colloquium.* Oregon State College, Corvallis, Oregon.

Stebbins, G. L. 1950. Variation and Evolution in Plants. Columbia University Press, New York.

Wallace, A. R. 1889. Darwinism: An Exposition of the Theory of Natural Selection. Macmillan, London.

321

19

Reprinted from *Syst. Zool.*, **23**(2), 239–247 (1974)

AN OPERATIONAL APPROACH TO SPECIES CLASSIFICATION

JOHN T. DOYEN AND C. N. SLOBODCHIKOFF

Abstract

Doyen, J. T., and C. N. Slobodchikoff (Division of Entomology and Parasitology, University of California, Berkeley, Cal. 94720 and Department of Biology, Northern Arizona University, Flagstaff, Ariz. 86001) 1974. An operational approach to species classification. Syst. Zool. 23:239–247.—Operational biological classification at the species level is analyzed as a series of sequential steps employing phenetic, reproductive, and ecological parameters. The first step involves segregation of individuals or populations into phenetically similar groups. Numerical techniques for objectively assessing phenetic similarities are well established, and are the method of choice. The next major step involves reproductive grouping, whenever possible. Reproductive isolation may be a sufficient criterion for species status in the case of sympatric populations. In other cases species decisions are usually deferred until the following step, or ecological grouping, which is based on ecological similarities and differences, quantified and analyzed with numerical methods. Species limits may be visualized graphically by considering phenetic, ecological, and reproductive similarities as axes of a three dimensional space. Populations may be plotted within this space and may be tested for conspecific status by existing computer techniques. [Numerical taxonomy; species determination.]

Species are groups of populations placed in the same taxonomic category. The commonest criteria used in defining species groupings are reproductive (or biological) and phenetic. While both criteria are vigorously defended by their proponents, neither has been entirely satisfactory in defining taxonomic species. We believe that the species is an idealized concept, and that different groups of biological populations only approximate the ideal. Just as the behavior of gases is idealized in theory, with no actual gas having exactly the requisite properties, so also are groups of populations of organisms idealized as species units, with few such groups, if any, having all the properties of idealized species. The primary value of grouping populations into species is utility. It is convenient to deal with units larger than local populations, even though these units may not accurately reflect the evolutionary changes occurring within populations. Organizing biologically similar populations into larger groups allows generalized statements to be made without the cumbersome necessity of defining each population. At the same time, the human need for a simple answer to the question, "What is that organism?" is satisfied.

The intent of this paper is to critically evaluate the roles of the reproductive and phenetic species concepts, and to propose a generalized procedure for delimiting species units. This procedure incorporates ecological as well as reproductive and phenetic information. A simple graphic model is used to illustrate one way in which the method might be applied.

A simple statement of the biological species definition is that of Mayr (1969a): "Species are groups of interbreeding natural populations that are reproductively isolated from other such groups." The sole criterion delimiting species in this definition is reproductive isolation (Mayr, 1969b). If two populations interbreed they are the same species; if they cannot interbreed they are different species. Although the idea of defining all species on the basis of a single characteristic is very attractive, the biological species definition suffers several difficulties which have been pointed out frequently in the recent literature.

Pheneticists object to the biological species definition because reproductive isolation can seldom be demonstrated. They object to the evolutionary approach to systematics on the grounds that it is subjective and allows too much latitude for interpretation by individual taxonomists (Sokal and Sneath, 1963; Ehrlich, 1961). They proposed instead to define species as groups of phenetically similar individuals that are separated from other such groups by phenetic gaps (Michener, 1970). In practice, this definition seems to be used by most evolutionary taxonomists as well as by pheneticists, the two groups differing mainly in their methods of analysis and interpretation of results.

The phenetic definition is not without practical and theoretical difficulties of its own. As Sokal and Crovello (1970) point out in a defense of the phenetic definition and as Hull (1970) points out in a critique of Sokal and Crovello's interpretations, some form of biological interpretation is necessary to describe what is actually happening in nature. Sokal and Crovello discuss the difficulties of grouping polymorphic populations into one species, or associating diverse larval stages of insects with the appropriate adult stages. In such cases the pheneticists rely on a broader definition of a species, a definition that includes the concepts of reproductive continuity, discontinuous variation within populations, and discontinuous variation between stages of an individual's life cycle.

OPERATIONAL DEFINITION OF SPECIES

Although reproductive isolation plays a very significant role in the evolution of populations, the reproductive criterion alone is not sufficiently rigorous to delineate groups of similar populations, particularly when hybridization between groups of dissimilar populations occurs. Similarly, the phenetic criterion alone is insufficient for the purpose of describing the complex interrelationships that exist among groups of similar populations. Therefore, we propose to delineate species by applying the following three major parameters: phenetic, re-

productive, and ecological. Species may then be defined as groups of phenetically similar populations that have the capability to interbreed, and share similar ecological characteristics.

On a practical level, this definition may be applied by using the following sequence: 1) phenetic association into groups based on easily obtained morphological or physiological characteristics; 2) categorization into secondary groups by geographic distribution; 3) application of the reproductive criterion, if possible; 4) further categorization according to ecological characteristics. The sequence and interrelationships of these steps are shown in Fig. 1 and are analyzed immediately below.

1. Phenetic grouping

This is the most elementary level of classification. If done intuitively, it involves combining individuals into phenetically homogeneous groups according to the judgment of the taxonomist. If done numerically, it is formalized so that exactly the same characters are objectively measured and compared over all individuals, the groups being constructed by precisely defined algorithms. In either case, the resulting groups might be called provisional phenetic groups. Sokal and Crovello (1970) have described in detail the various steps involved in constructing phenetic groupings, and no further elaboration is needed here. It should be pointed out, however, that phenetic grouping is an arbitrary procedure. It is the responsibility of the individual taxonomist to decide what levels of similarity or dissimilarity are significant. These levels vary among different taxonomic groups and among different methods of analysis. In the absence of information to the contrary, very dissimilar groups can be considered distinct species without further testing, as indicated in Fig. 1. Phenetically similar groups, however, require further testing. The procedure described here differs from typical phenetic methods in that phenetic data are restricted to morphological and physiological characteristics.

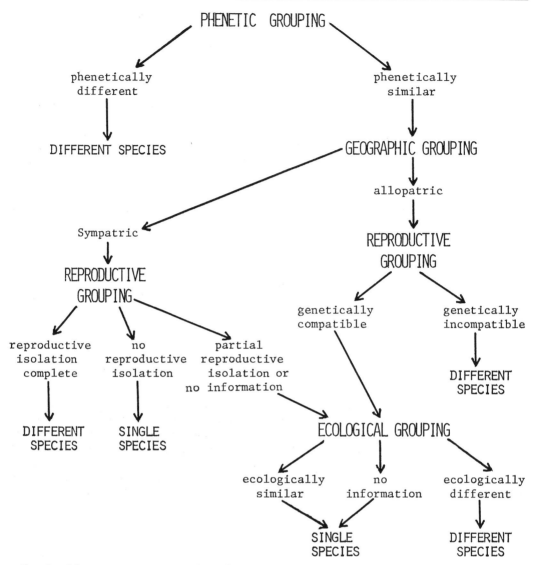

Fɪɢ. 1.—Schematic representation of the decision-making process suggested for determining whether groups of OTUs represent distinct species. Major categories used in making decisions appear in large capitals. Various possibilities for each category are in lower case, and outcomes are in small capitals. More detailed discussion of each step appears in the text.

Reproductive isolation and ecological features are considered in separate steps, detailed below.

2. Geographical grouping

Once provisional phenetic groupings of individuals have been assembled, the groupings are categorized according to geographic distribution. If the phenetic groups are allopatric, reproductive incompatibility is considered significant only if it has a genetic basis, and ecological factors usually assume a primary role in subsequent analysis. If they are sympatric, the hypotheses that may be formed at this stage are that the groups are probably either a) distinct separate species or b) polymorphs of a single species. In either case both reproductive and ecological factors play a significant role in the subsequent decision-making process.

Geographical grouping is useful in detecting gradual variation in the form of clines, zones of intergradation or introgression, or in inferring the presence of physical barriers separating phenetically similar populations. Numerical phenetic techniques have been extremely productive at this stage of analysis. Univariate techniques (Gabriel and Sokal, 1969) provide a superior means of analyzing geographic variation in single characters, while various multivariate methods can be used to detect parallel patterns of variation in more than one feature. In general, we feel that the greatest contribution of numerical phenetic methods has been in describing and analyzing geographic variation.

3. Reproductive grouping

After phenetic and geographic groupings have been determined, reproductive grouping is attempted. If the provisional phenetic groups are allopatric, the reproductive criterion is usually inapplicable, unless it can be shown that the groups are genetically incompatible, since apparent behavioral or ecological reproductive isolation under artificial conditions may be artifactual. If the phenetic groups are sympatric, reproductive isolation of any sort is considered sufficient for species status, if the isolation can be demonstrated under natural conditions. In this context, ecological and especially behavioral reproductive isolation among populations has been documented among a diverse array of organisms (for example, Mayr, 1963:89–110). Except for occasional individual hybrids, reproductive isolation can be considered an all-or-none phenomenon at this level. If population hybridization occurs, whether extensive or limited to a narrow overlap zone or occasional hybrid swarms, species status should be judged on the basis of ecological similarities and differences. For example, two morphologi-

cally similar species of European crows, *Corvus cornix* and *C. corone*, are largely allopatric, but hybridize in a narrow zone of overlap. They are rather different ecologically, and on this basis have been considered separate species (Sibley, 1961).

Asexual organisms present no special problem at this level of grouping, since reproductive information may be considered as being unavailable. As in the case of allopatry, species decisions are deferred until the ecological grouping of asexual populations. Reproductive information for asexual organisms is not always totally unavailable. The occasional appearance of sexual forms in parthenogenetic animal populations (Wilson & Woodcock, 1960) suggests that bisexuality may simply be suppressed under certain ecological conditions. In some organisms the bisexual condition regularly alternates with the asexual one, as in cyclically parthenogenetic species of aphids (Aphididae, Homoptera, Insecta) and cynipids (Cynipidae, Hymenoptera, Insecta). A particularly interesting example involves the wasp *Aphytis mytilaspidis* (Le Baron) (Aphelinidae, Hymenoptera, Insecta), where different populations reproduce sexually or parthenogenetically. Rössler and DeBach (1973a) hybridized the parthenogenetic and bisexual races, without reduction of fecundity or survival of the offspring. In this case the sexual and asexual forms differ in developmental periods at various temperatures, in host preference, and in host suitability (Rössler and DeBach, 1973b). For this reason, the sexual and asexual forms might be considered distinct species despite their genetic compatibility. This example clearly demonstrates that reproductive isolation and species status cannot be assumed solely on the basis of asexuality.

4. Ecological grouping

Many provisional phenetic groups will cycle to this level of decision making, since geographic information alone is insufficient for clarifying species status, and reproductive information is often insufficient or unavailable. Closely related (e.g., phenetically similar) groups of populations, though often very similar morphologically and physiologically, frequently differ markedly in many ecological characteristics, especially if sympatric. For this reason, ecological criteria should have broad applicability in distinguishing species from infraspecific entities. As indicated in Fig. 1, ecological grouping is based on differences and similarities among the ecological coordinates of the provisional phenetic groups. The ecological coordinates of each phenetic group are represented as a point in a hyperspace whose axes represent environmental or biotic factors. Dissimilarities between provisional phenetic groups can then be analyzed by various multivariate techniques. This method of comparison closely corresponds to the definition of niche proposed by Hutchinson (1965). We prefer not to use the term niche in the systematic context because of continuing changes in definition and methods of quantification (see Vandermeer, 1973, for a historical treatment of niche theory). For the purposes of taxonomic analysis, a simple measure of ecological distance, analogous to the taxonomic distance of Sokal and Sneath (1963) is probably most appropriate:

$$d_{ij} = \frac{\sqrt{\sum_{k=1}^{n} (P_{ik} - P_{jk})^2}}{n}$$

d_{ij} = ecological distance between populations i, j.

P_{ik}, P_{jk} = scores for populations i, j on ecological factor k.

The phenetic approach to ecological differentiation was used by Martinez et al. (1965) in measuring food preference distances among *Drosophila* species. However, they used the proportions of each species on each food source as ecological dimensions, which converts each distance to a measure of resource overlap, with the range from 0 in the case of complete overlap to 1 in the case of no overlap. More realistic measures of ecological overlap,

based on information theory, are discussed by Colwell and Futuyma (1971) and Pielou (1972). These methods of quantifying niche overlap and Vandermeer's (1973) sophisticated methods for comparing species by ecological coordinates are based on competition for resources, and require estimates of the frequencies of each species on each resource or in each habitat. Because this information is unavailable for most species, and because many ecological factors cannot logically be treated as resources (e.g., temperature requirements), we prefer the simple distance for assessing ecological similarities.

The data used in specifying ecological distances may be extremely variable, depending upon the populations being examined as well as the availability of information. Some general categories which are probably important in nearly all instances include habitat or community preference, spatial distribution, resource utilization, reproductive strategy and phenology. Habitat or community preference encompasses both biotic and abiotic factors. For example, bird species might occur in certain climatic situations but also require trees for nesting sites. Insects might require plants for adult food or shelter and specific soil types for development of immature stages. Differences in spatial distribution may indicate the presence of extrinsic factors conditioning abundance, but may also be of adaptive significance in themselves. For example, some species of tenebrionid beetles annually aggregate in sheltered overwintering sites, while others in the same habitat remain dispersed throughout the year. Migratory flocks of birds are other aggregations not exclusively mediated by extrinsic factors. For most organisms, data regarding resource utilization is often relatively easy to gather, compared to the other categories of ecological information. Pertinent information may include different host preferences, differential growth rates, varying foraging strategies, and differential effects on given resources. Rudimentary phenological information is sometimes available from museum specimens, particularly if certain life history stages are restricted to short time periods. In contrast, uncovering the details of seasonal abundance, onset and termination of reproduction, or the abiotic or biotic factors which may condition these events usually requires sustained and concentrated effort.

Ecological characteristics have occasionally been used as primary characteristics for differentiating species. A notable example involves the *Anopheles maculipennis* (Insecta: Diptera: Culicidae) complex, which consists of morphologically very similar populations which differ markedly in ecological attributes (Hackett and Missiroli, 1935; Bates, 1940). Fujii (1969) analyzed ecological characters of different geographical strains of two species of bean weevils (Insecta: Coleoptera: Bruchidae), using numerical phenetic methods. The resulting phenograms separated the species and meaningfully ordered the strains according to their geographical origin. In most other cases, ecological data have been combined with morphological characteristics to determine a single similarity value. For example, Moss (1969) included four ecological characters among a total of 62. Reasons for considering ecological characteristics separately are discussed below.

As with the other criteria of species status, there are some problems with the ecological grouping when applied independently of phenetic and reproductive considerations. For example, males and females of some species of birds (Selander, 1966), lizards (Schoener, 1967, 1968), and fish (Keast, 1966) have slightly different foraging and feeding strategies, and thus have slightly different ecological coordinates. An extreme example is found in the Huia, an extinct New Zealand bird. Males had stout, straight beaks and were reported to have dug into rotting wood for grubs and other insects, while females had slender, curved beaks and probed for insects in wood crevices (Selander, 1966). In such cases ecological differences tend to be restricted to a few factors, and males and females can

usually be associated by averaging many ecological characteristics. Extreme ecological polymorphism is found when different life stages of an organism do not utilize the same resources or occur in different habitats, as in the case of many holometabolous insects. Strict application of the ecological criterion (or the phenetic one) would require recognition of separate species for each life stage. In practice, such polymorphism is a problem only for groups of organisms whose life histories are unknown. After the life stages have been associated, they are logically members of a single species because of genetic continuity.

Inaccurate estimates of species status could also result from ecological convergence among OTUs occupying similar niches, just as morphological convergence may obscure phenetic relationships. Various procedure for differential weighting have been proposed to minimize the effects of convergent characters, but no single method is acceptable to all or even most taxonomists. The merits of various strategies of weighting are clearly documented by Hull (1970) and Moss and Hendrickson (1973). At this point it is desirable only to emphasize that weighting or not weighting are equally arbitrary procedures. Merely including some characters in a study while excluding others constitutes weighting, whether or not some characters are numerically weighted more strongly than others. In general, any one of the three parameters, phenetic, reproductive or ecological, is inapplicable in some situations if used as the sole arbiter of species status. When all three criteria are applied, the difficulties inherent in each are minimized.

Pheneticists may voice the objection that reproductive and ecological characters ought to be included in the initial level of phenetic grouping. While it is true that ecological data, particularly, are best analyzed by numerical methods, we believe separate levels of grouping are necessary for the following reasons. First, phenetic application of the reproductive criterion would sometimes necessitate weighting re-

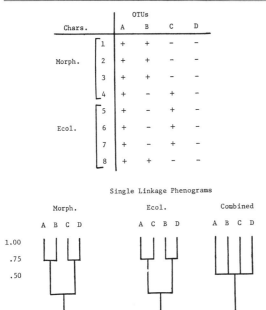

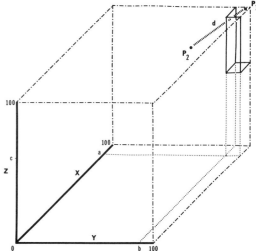

FIG. 2.—Hypothetical OTU x character matrix and phenograms derived from character sets based on: (a) only morphological characters; (b) only ecological characters; (c) all characters combined. All phenograms are based on single linkage clustering. Similarities are calculated using the simple matching coefficient.

FIG. 3.—Three dimensional space containing the axes X, Y, and Z. P₁ and P₂ are populations plotted in this three dimensional space, and are separated by distance d. Taxonomic limits a, b, and c are assigned for the axes as criteria for conspecific status. Populations falling within the solid rectangle (at the upper right of figure) formed by these criteria are conspecific with P₁, while populations falling outside the solid rectangle are not conspecific with P₁. In this figure, P₁ and P₂ are not conspecific. See text for further explanation.

productive compatibility more heavily than all the other characters combined. Second, if two closely related sympatric populations maintain separate gene pools, the populations may be expected to show distinct ecological differences, even if the two populations are phenetically similar. This ecological displacement is analogous to morphological character displacement. Therefore, averaging morphological and ecological similarities might obscure relationships at either level. A simple example may clarify this point. A character matrix for four imaginary species or OTUs is shown in Fig. 2. Morphological characters appear above, ecological characters below. The similarities of each OTU pair are calculated by the simple matching coefficient and clustered by single linkage (Sokal and Sneath, 1963), using a) only morphological characters, b) only ecological characters and c) all characters combined. While dis-

tinct clusters result from using either character set separately, combining all characters produces a phenogram with only one intermediate level of clustering. Although the taxonomist might conclude that all four OTUs in the last phenogram represent species level taxa, it would be much more valuable to know that the four OTUs consisted of two morphologically similar pairs (a-b and c-d) and that within each pair the two OTUs were very different ecologically. Biologically, this situation might exist between two species pairs of morphologically similar phytophagous insects. If each morphological pair occurred sympatrically, the respective members would be expected to differ ecologically in order to reduce competition or hybridization. The differences might include separate hosts, different portions of the hosts being used as food, different activity periods, and a wide variety of other factors.

GRAPHIC MODEL

The relationships among the criteria used for defining species can be visualized with a simple graphic model (Fig. 3). Consider a three-dimensional space which contains three axes, x, y, and z, representing ecological, reproductive, and phenetic relationships, respectively. The units along each axis may be denoted as the percent similarity between populations, ranging from 0–100. The three-dimensional space will then contain the set of points (x, y, x) which satisfy the inequalities,

$$0 \leq x \leq 100$$
$$0 \leq y \leq 100$$
$$0 \leq z \leq 100$$

Points representing populations may be plotted in this three-dimensional space by the following procedure.

Percent similarity between populations is calculated for each parameter and is stored in a square matrix of order n, where n equals the number of OTUs (Operational Taxonomic Units, Sokal and Sneath, 1963; in this case, the OTUs are populations). Methods of calculating percent similarity will vary for each parameter. For example, in calculating percent similarity for populations along the phenetic axis (z), the raw phenetic data may be used to compute coefficients of association for the OTUs, such as product-moment correlation or taxonomic distance. The coefficients may then be recomputed so that each OTU in the OTU × OTU matrix would have a similarity value of 100 along the principal diagonal of the matrix, and correspondingly lower similarities as each OTU is matched with other OTUs, with a minimum similarity of 0. Reproductive percent similarity values (axis y) may be obtained directly from a square matrix containing percent viability of offspring resulting from crosses between all the OTUs. Ecological percent similarity values (axis x) may be obtained from a recalculation of ecological distance between OTUs (see above).

If there are n number of populations, n number of plots are made, to show the rela-

tive positions of all the OTUs to each OTU. Coordinates are provided by the rows of the matrices. In plot 1, OTU 1 has the coordinates (100, 100, 100) and is represented by a point at the upper right limit of the three-dimensional space. All the other OTUs for plot 1 either coincide with this point (if their percent similarities with OTU 1 have the coordinates: 100, 100, 100), or are distributed between this point and a point represented by the coordinates (0, 0, 0). Plot 2 repeats this procedure for OTU 2, so that OTU 2 has coordinates of (100, 100, 100), and Row 2 of each matrix supplies the coordinates for each OTU. The plotting procedure is repeated until the spatial positions of all the OTUs have been plotted with reference to OTU n, and the nth row of each matrix has been used for the OTU coordinates.

This procedure allows the spatial relationships of all the OTUs to be analyzed relative to each OTU, within the context of ecological, reproductive, and phenetic parameters. The spatial relationships between the OTUs may be expressed in distances between the points. The distance between two OTUs may be calculated by the formula

$$d(P_1 P_2) = \sqrt{(x_1 - x_2)^2 + (y_1 - y_2)^2 + (z_1 - z_2)^2}$$

where P_1 and P_2 are populations, (x_1, y_1, z_1) are the coordinates of P_1, (x_2, y_2, z_2) are the coordinates of P_2, and P_2 is closer to the origin of the three axes than P_1. The distances may in turn be stored in a distance matrix. Although the model allows visualization of the relative positions of populations, it is still up to individual taxonomists to decide how close two populations have to be in the three-dimensional space in order to be conspecific. The decision may be facilitated by assigning lowest limits of species acceptability along each axis. For example, if a taxonomist decides that a is the lowest percent similarity acceptable for conspecific status along the ecological (x) axis, b is the lowest percent similarity acceptable for the reproductive (y) axis, and c is the lowest acceptable percent similarity for the phenetic (z) axis, then populations falling within a space satisfying the inequalities

$$a \leq x \leq 100$$
$$b \leq y \leq 100$$
$$c \leq z \leq 100$$

would be conspecific, while populations falling outside of this space would not be conspecific. We suggest the following limits be applied for conspecific status: a minimum of 90 percent similarity along the x (ecological) and y (reproductive) axes, and a minimum of 60 percent similarity along the z (phenetic) axis. We have chosen the 60 percent similarity value along the phenetic axis because many species tend to be phenotypically plastic, to at least some extent.

This graphic model presupposes that information concerning all three parameters is available. Once the minimum limits are established by the taxonomist, a digital computer can easily analyze the phenetic, reproductive, and ecological data, make the necessary population comparisons, and provide decisions on which populations are similar enough to be grouped together as species.

REFERENCES

BATES, M. 1940. The nomenclature and taxonomic status of the mosquitoes of the *Anopheles maculipennis* complex. Ann. Entomol. Soc. Amer. 33:343–356.

COLWELL, R. K., AND D. J. FUTUYMA. 1971. On the measurement of niche breadth and overlap. Ecology 52:567–576.

FUJII, K. 1969. Numerical taxonomy of ecological characteristics and the niche concept. Syst. Zool. 18:151–153.

HACKETT, L. W., AND A. MISSIROLI. 1935. The varieties of *Anopheles maculipennis* and their relation to the distribution of malaria in Europe. Riv. Malariol. 14:45–109.

HULL, D. L. 1970. Contemporary systematic philosophies. Ann. Rev. Ecol. Syst. 1:19–54.

HUTCHINSON, G. E. 1965. The Ecological Theatre and the Evolutionary Play. Yale University Press, New Haven.

KEAST, A. 1966. Trophic interrelationships in the fish fauna of a small stream. Univ. Michigan, Great Lakes Res. Div. Publ. 15:51–79.

MARTINEZ, P., M. C. MALDONADO, AND R. LEVINS. 1965. Ecology and genetics of Puerto Rican

Drosophila: I. Food preferences of sympatric species. Carib. Jour. Sci. 5:29–37.

MAYR, E. 1963. Animal Species and Evolution. Harvard University Press, Cambridge.

MAYR, E. 1969a. Principles of Systematic Zoology. McGraw-Hill, New York.

MAYR, E. 1969b. The biological meaning of species. Biol. J. Linn. Soc. 1:311–320.

MICHENER, C. D. 1970. Diverse approaches to systematics. *In*: Dobzhansky, Hecht and Steere (eds.), Evolutionary Biology, Vol. 4. Appleton-Century-Crofts, New York.

MOSS, W. W., AND W. A. WEBSTER. 1969. A numerical taxonomic study of a group of selected strongylates (Nematoda). Syst. Zool. 18:423–

MOSS, W. W., AND J. A. HENDRICKSON. 1973. Numerical taxonomy. Ann. Rev. Ent. 18:227–258.

PIELOU, E. C. 1972. Niche width and niche overlap: a method for measuring them. Ecology 53:687–692.

RÖSSLER, Y., AND P. DEBACH. 1973a. The biosystematic relations between a thelytokous and an arrhenotokous form of *Aphytis mytilaspidis* (Le Baron) Hymenoptera: Aphelinidae I. The reproductive relations. Entomophaga 17:391–423.

RÖSSLER, Y., AND P. DEBACH. 1973b. The biosystematic relations between a thelytokous and an arrhenotokous form of *Aphytis mytilaspidis* (Le Baron) Hymenoptera: Aphelinidae. 2. Comparative biological and morphological studies. Entomophaga 17:425–435.

SCHOENER, T. W. 1967. The ecological significance of sexual dimorphism in size in the lizard *Anolis conspersus*. Science 155:474–477.

SCHOENER, T. W. 1968. The *Anolis* lizards of Bimini: resource partitioning in a complex fauna. Ecology 49:704–726.

SELANDER, R. K. 1966. Sexual dimorphism and differential niche utilization in birds. Condor 68:113–151.

SIBLEY, C. G. 1961. Hybridization and isolating mechanisms. *In*: W. F. Blair (ed.), Vertebrate speciation. Univ. Texas Press, Austin.

SOKAL, R. R., AND T. J. CROVELLO. 1970. The biological species concept: a critical evaluation. Amer. Nat. 104:127–153.

SOKAL, R. R., AND P. H. A. SNEATH. 1963. Principles of Numerical Taxonomy. W. H. Freeman and Company, San Francisco.

VANDERMEER, J. H. 1973. Niche theory. Ann. Rev. Ecol. Syst. 3:107–132.

WILSON, F., AND L. T. WOODCOCK. 1960. Temperature determination of sex in a parthenogenetic parasite, *Ooencyrtus submetallicus* (Howard), (Hymenoptera: Encyrtidae). Austral. J. Zool. 8:153–169.

Manuscript received April, 1973
Revised October, 1973

20

THE SPECIES IN BIOLOGICAL SYSTEMATICS

R. A. Crowson

> The Oak dies as well as the Lettuce, but its Eternal Image and
> Individuality never dies, but renews by its seed.
>
> WILLIAM BLAKE
> (annotations to his picture
> of the Last Judgement)

Human beings have long been impressed by the permanence and
distinctness of the individual kinds of living things; the saying 'God
made the species, all else is the work of man' expresses an attitude which
is still widely held. Even Darwin [44], by calling his famous book *The
Origin of Species*, showed the influence of this mode of thought. Modern
critics (e.g. Mayr [140a]) have pointed out that nowhere in his work
does Darwin offer a satisfactory definition of the species, nor does he
account adequately for that feature of species-formation which is now
regarded as all-important—the origin of discontinuity. Various recent
systematists have tried to repair the omission of Darwin, and to formulate a set of criteria by reference to which it may be decided whether
a given assemblage of organisms belongs to one or several species. The
fact that this can at least be attempted, whereas none has even pretended
to formulate comparable definitions for higher taxonomic categories
like genera, families and orders, is taken as evidence of the superior
objectivity of the species. These definitions, it must be emphasised, are
concerned only to establish minimal requirements for species-difference,
they offer no assistance in deciding at what point the difference between
two species becomes great enough to entitle them to different genera,
etc. The implications of this state of affairs are considered further in
Chapter 5.

The criteria which have been used in attempts to define the species
may be summarised under five headings:

1. *Museum criteria*

(*a*) Among members of one species, there is normally a limited and continuous variation in characters of structure and pigmentation, whereas a discontinuity in one or both these respects will normally show itself when members of two different species are compared.

(*b*) A species has normally a limited and continuous area of natural distribution, rarely coinciding exactly with that of any other species.

2. *Ecological criteria*

(*c*) Between members of different species, there are normally differences of habits and behaviour, not bridged by transitional forms.

(*d*) It is very rare to find, in nature, matings between members of different species.

3. *Physiological criterion*

(*e*) Within a species, there is normally the same kind of limited and continuous variation in physiological and biochemical characters as there is in structural ones, and the same type of unbridged gap when members of two different species are compared.

4. *Genetical criteria*

(*f*) Sexual crossings between members of one species are normally fully fertile, giving offspring with characters of the same species and themselves fully fertile, whereas interspecific crosses usually yield infertile offspring or none at all.

(*g*) Between members of two different species there are normally differences in large numbers of hereditary factors (genes), usually accompanied by complex chromosomal differences (inversions, translocations, reduplications, etc.); intraspecific variation generally involves far fewer factors, and only simple chromosomal changes (if any) are found in it.

5. *Palaeontological criterion*

(*h*) A species has a limited and continuous range in time.

These eight criteria make quite an impressive list, but rarely (if ever) could they all be applied to one particular case, and each of them is subject to difficulties of application and to exceptions. Each of them will need further critical consideration.

The museum criteria are given pride of place because of the widespread current belief that the proper place for a systematic botanist or zoologist is in a museum, and from the fact that the large majority of described species in both kingdoms are accepted as such purely on the museum criteria. The first thing that needs to be noted about them is that they are reliable only when adequately representative (of the full ecological and geographical range of the species) material is available. Many of the 'species' which have been described as such from the study of scanty museum material have been found subsequently, when more material became available, to grade completely into other species. The museum criteria offer no general means of deciding whether or not two specimens belong to the same species by comparing one with the other; a satisfactory comparison needs to be made with a representative series. The current convention that a single specimen, the Holotype, is the only satisfactory basic criterion for a species would be difficult to justify logically on any theory but that of Special Creation.

This difficulty is particularly manifest in the 'clines' of Huxley [103]. A cline may be defined as a gradual and progressive change in the characters of a species when it is traced along an extensive tract of natural distribution—a number of cases have been described in which the end forms of such a cline look like distinct species and even behave as such when artificially brought together, though they are linked in nature by an unbroken breeding chain. Few museums have adequate representative material from the whole length of such clines; the museum systematist has usually to work with collections in which most of the specimens are taken from only a few, often widely separated, points on a cline. He may well describe them as a series of subspecies, or even full species. Clines will be considered further in the next chapter.

Other difficulties for the museum systematist are presented by species showing what is called 'polymorphism' and by those with 'alternation of generations'. A polymorphic species is one in which two or more distinct phenotypes coexist frequently or constantly in natural populations; the differences between the forms are often sharp and unbridged, and appear to be determined by only one or two genetic factors. Botanical examples are the common Primrose (*Primula vulgaris* L.) with its 'pin-eyed' and 'thrum-eyed' forms, and various 'heterostylic' species of *Limonium*; entomologists will be familiar with the two colour forms of the female in the Clouded Yellow butterfly (*Colias croceus*) and in the Silver-washed Fritillary (*Argynnis paphia*). Other animals manifesting colour polymorphism, such as the snail, *Cepea nemoralis*, and species of *Adalia* among the ladybirds (Coccinellidae), show more or less continuous variation (probably because several pairs of alleles are concerned and some or all of them do not show complete dominance) and present less difficulty to the museum systematist.

Alternation of generations is a term which may be applied to rather diverse phenomena. The succession of haploid and diploid (or gametophyte and sporophyte) generations is familiar to botanists, but it is probably not very common for systematists to describe the haploid and diploid forms of the same plant as different species, though this may have happened on occasion in the Algae. The 'perfect' and 'imperfect' forms of the same fungus have no doubt at times been ascribed to different genera, but the difference between them is probably not a simple haploid–diploid one.

In animals, alternation of generations is rarely if ever a matter of haploid and diploid individuals; except for such special cases as the males of the Hymenoptera, the haploid stage in animals is represented only by the gametes. Alternation of bisexually-reproducing and unisexual (parthenogenetic) forms is not uncommon in some groups of animal, e.g. Insecta, Crustacea, Protozoa; in many groups of 'colonial' animals such as the Coelenterata, Polyzoa, Tunicata, we find 'vegetative' budding alternating with sexual reproduction. There are also cases, at least among the Insecta, in which the alternating generations are both bisexual; a good example is furnished by the central European butterfly *Araschni alevana*. This species has two broods in a year, one with the adults emerging in the spring, the other flying in the later summer; the two forms differ strikingly in colour-pattern, and without breeding investigations a museum systematist could hardly discover that they are not two distinct species.

A further difficulty in the application of the first museum criterion is that differences of this sort are at times exceedingly slight between what are by all other criteria perfectly 'good' species. A well-known example in the animal kingdom is in the genus *Drosophila* (the fruit-flies beloved of geneticists), where *D. pseudoobscura* and *D. persimilis* were recognised as distinct solely as a result of breeding experiments—only after the geneticists had discovered that these forms behaved like distinct species were some exceedingly slight 'museum' differences between them found; it is safe to say that on museum criteria alone none would ever have suspected that two species were present. Two rather similar cases in the animal kingdom were known long before the *Drosophila* one— the Grey Dagger and Dark Dagger moths (*Acronycta psi* L. and *A. tridens* Schiff.), and the Chiffchaff and Willow Warbler (*Phylloscopus collybita* Vieill. and *P. trochilus* L.) among birds. The moth-collectors of the last century were in the habit of breeding their species, and it was thus that the distinctness of the two *Acronycta* was discovered (there is a well-marked colour difference in their larvae); the *Phylloscopus* species were first suspected to be distinct from differences in their behaviour and song, e.g. by Gilbert White [199]. In each of these cases very slight 'museum' differences have subsequently been discovered to separate the species.

In plants, apart from the special case of polyploids which we shall consider later, few instances of what the Americans call 'sibling species' have been recorded. There have indeed often been reports of breeding barriers between plants which do not show evident differences in the herbarium, but such forms have rarely been named as independent species. Botanists commonly refer to such cases as manifesting the phenomena of 'incompatibility' rather than as sibling species. Plant systematists in general seem to rely more exclusively on the museum criteria than do their zoological colleagues; this and other differences are discussed by Turrill *et al.* [193c].

A recent review by Maheshwari (in [215]) entitled 'The Plant Species in an Age of Experiment' distinguishes between 'phenospecies' and 'biospecies', the former being defined on museum criteria, the latter on genetical, ecological and physiological ones. In discussing biospecies he states 'according to this concept, the real species or biological species, as contrasted to the more or less artificial species of the typologists and morphologists, is a natural and non-arbitrary unit of a genetically closed population system that has lost its ability to inbreed with other species'. His final conclusion is 'The species problem is still fluid', and he considers that the phenospecies will retain its practical utility for a long time to come.

The first museum criterion has two great advantages, the ease with which such comparisons can be made, and its applicability to fossils as well as to existing organisms. To compare all the species of a moderate-sized genus in respect of several characters of structure or pigmentation might take a systematist a week, whereas a similar comparison in respect of ecological, physiological or genetical characters might take years of research.

The second criterion expresses the fact that good systematists look at the labels of their specimens. As a principle, it is open to two major objections—first, that there are some species with discontinuous natural distributions, and second, that there are now very numerous species with discontinuous distributions attributable to human influence. Discontinuous natural distributions are found in 'relict' species, whose former continuous areas have become fragmented through extinction by natural (non-human) causes in parts of them. Typical European examples are the more or less sub-arctic forms, which probably had a wide range as far south as the Alps during the last glaciation, but now have widely separated occurrences in the Alps, the Scottish mountains, and in those of Scandinavia. There are also cases where particular species, by some rare non-human means of long-range transport, have established isolated colonies (e.g. on oceanic islands) far outside their normal range. But the impact of human action on the natural plant and animal worlds, which must have been considerable for a long time past in much of the world, is now so enormous and rapidly increasing that, at least in many terrestrial groups, the conception of natural distribution has become an unreal and perhaps unrealisable ideal.

For modern animals, the ecological criteria are probably almost as good in principle as the museum ones, but too few species have been studied from this point of view to make them generally applicable. Habits in plants are largely habits of growth, with resulting differences in general shape etc., and thus become absorbed into the museum criteria. The second ecological criterion may be applied to those lower plants (fungi, algae, etc.) which show conjugation, and could perhaps be extended to cover the development or non-development of pollen-tubes on particular kinds of stigma by the pollen-grains of Angiospermae or Coniferae. A general limitation of the ecological criteria is that they are only properly applicable to species living in the same area—a given species may show habit-differences in different parts of its range, in relation for instance to differing climatic conditions, and organisms living in different areas do not have the opportunity of sexual crossing.

The physiological criterion is in principle of equivalent value to the first museum one, and like it is not limited in its application to forms inhabiting the same area. Even more, however, than the first ecological criterion, it suffers from the lack of the necessary knowledge to make it applicable in most cases. All that can be said is that, where closely related species have been adequately investigated by laboratory physiologists, physiological differences between them have been found. There have been cases among animals in which physiological differences have provided the first indication of the existence of a previously unrecognised species; the mosquito, *Anopheles maculipennis*, provides a well-known example. Investigation of this species as a 'vector' of the malaria parasite, *Plasmodium*, revealed that two forms of the mosquito existed, one breeding mainly in brackish water and capable of spreading the *Plasmodium*, the other restricted to fresh water and not a carrier of malaria. The brackish-water form was first separated as a 'race' *atroparvus*, and then, when it proved to be reproductively isolated from typical *maculipennis*, and distinguishing characters between the two were found in the egg stage, *atroparvus* came to be accepted as a 'good' species.

It is now widely believed that the genetical criteria for species are the most truly fundamental, and many attempts have been made to formulate a new, genetical definition of the species which will make clear its true nature from an evolutionary point of view. In all these attempts, attention is concentrated on the species as a potentially interbreeding unit. Any two non-allelomorphic hereditary factors which occur in different members of the same species may be brought into combination as a result of crossing between the individuals in question or between their progeny; the species may thus be considered to possess a potential 'common gene-pool', a reservoir of hereditary variability on which selection can work. The gene-pools of two different species on the other hand are considered to be irrevocably cut off from one another. On this view the essential feature of species formation is the irrevocable splitting of a previous common gene-pool. This may well be the true explanation of such superior objectivity as the species possesses in comparison with other categories (cf. Dobzhansky [49]), but it will also explain why this objectivity is by no means absolute. A definition of the species on this basis may be satisfactory when applied to forms living at the same time and in the same area, but difficulties may be expected if the attempt is made to apply it to forms living in different islands or continents, or in different geological eras. A gene-pool may be as effectively split by impassable geographical barriers as by behavioural or genetic bars to crossing. On this criterion, specimens of a given species which, by some rare accident, have become established on a remote oceanic island, should immediately acquire the status of an independent species. If the genetical criterion for species is the really fundamental one, then we should expect the objective basis for species-differentiation to disappear when the forms compared are from widely separated areas.

In fact, numerous cases have been recorded, particularly among flowering plants and birds, in which species from Europe and species from the Far East, or species from the Far East and species from North

America, differ strikingly and constantly in phenotypic characters, yet will produce fertile hybrids when artificially brought together. In some groups of birds, notably the ducks, such hybridisable forms may differ so much in appearance that systematists have placed them in different genera. Many well-known horticultural varieties, e.g. *Magnolia soulangeana*, have originated as hybrids of American and Asiatic species.

A further difficulty confronting the genetical definition of the species is mainly botanical, and concerns the treatment of polyploid forms. Most animals have separate sexes and an 'x–y' system of sex-determination (one sex, usually the male, having an odd pair of sex-chromosomes), and for various reasons connected with this system polyploid animals are usually sterile. In the evolution of most groups of animals, polyploidy seems to have occurred rarely or not at all—the exceptions being mainly in those groups which do not have the x–y sex-determining system. In plants, however, this system of sex-determination is comparatively rare, and doubling of the chromosome number is frequently possible without necessarily involving loss of reproductive capacity; the polyploid individuals can either reproduce vegetatively or (being usually hermaphrodite) fertilise themselves. The commonest type of polyploid individual in nature is the tetraploid; these, when crossed with an ordinary diploid produce triploid offspring which are invariably sterile. By doubling the number of chromosomes, we seem to have produced at one bound a breeding barrier like that between two distinct species. This breeding barrier is not, however, really irrevocable; it can be bridged in one direction by producing further tetraploids from the original diploid stock, and cases have been recorded of diploid individuals arising spontaneously from a tetraploid stock.

The genetical criterion for species also breaks down in dealing with those organisms which do not manifest sexual reproduction, e.g. the apomictic *Hieracium* (Compositae), and in such animals as the familiar stick-insect (*Carausius morosus*) and the celebrated Protozoan *Amoeba proteus* (*Chaos chaos* aucct.). In such forms, the genetical criterion would logically require the recognition of every individual as a separate species.

The second genetical criterion (*g* of the original set) is free from the special objections to the first, but is only applicable where (1) the forms being compared can be crossed to yield fertile offspring, thus violating criterion (*f*), or (2) detailed chromosome maps have been prepared from linkage studies—these require an enormous amount of work for their preparation, and are only available for a very few species of organisms, or (3) the so-called 'giant chromosomes' occur, as in the salivary gland chromosomes of the insect order Diptera; these have been found in very few groups of organisms.

Support for the belief that the breeding criteria are the really fundamantal ones for the species can be adduced from the fact, well known to zoological systematists, that in those animals in which mating is an active process, species differences are usually most striking in the secondary sexual characters, while in animals with sedentary adults this is not usually the case. In Angiospermae, closely related species often differ most obviously in their flowers, and such differences may be analogous to secondary sexual characters in animals. Some pollinating insects, notably bees, have been shown to have a tendency to go from one flower to another of the same species rather than to one of a different kind—obvious floral differences between species will facilitate this sort of discrimination and thereby increase the chances of successful pollination (cf. [63]).

It is undoubtedly true that, in animals with separate sexes, species differences are apt to be most striking and obvious in the secondary sexual characters, particularly of the males. This observation does not, however, justify the dogma, widely accepted among entomologists in recent times, that the examination of the male genitalia provides a sufficient and infallible guide to the correct discrimination of species. The observations of E. B. Ford [67] concerning the butterfly species *Papilio dardanus* are relevant here:

> Within the region just delimited, the species is subdivided into five races. Two of these, Dardanus and Meseres, comprise a western type. They are larger than the others and the males are less heavily marked with black; moreover, their genital armature differs slightly from that of the eastern and southern forms but not in such a way as to prevent interbreeding with them. This difference is indeed controlled on a single factor basis, subject slightly to the effects of modifiers: the presence of a long spine on the inner surface of the valve in the eastern type is dominant to its absence, which characterizes the western one in which genitalia of the eastern type occur rarely. The point is worth noting, since the anatomy of the genitalia is so often treated uncritically by taxonomists as a criterion of specific differences in Lepidoptera and some other insects. Statements on the structure of these organs are generally made in an unscientific manner: the number of individuals in each species that have been examined in order to establish their characteristics is not recorded nor is any indication given of their variance.

A striking example of the emphasis placed on male sexual characters by some entomological systematists is provided by Coiffait [32a], who not merely erected a new species but even placed it in a separate genus *Sectophilonthus* Coiffait, for a single specimen of a beetle which, while showing all the outward characters of the well-known *Philonthus decorus* Grav., had a strikingly aberrant form of aedeagus (male intro-mittent organ). It seems far more probable that *rossicus* Coiff. represents merely an unusual mutant or teratological form of *P. decorus*.

To these reflections, it may be relevant to add another. The male genitalia of insects are frequently rather complex and very 'three-dimensional' structures, of which two-dimensional pictures are apt to give misleading impressions. The precise appearance of such a picture may depend considerably on the angle from which the specimen is viewed, and on the manner in which the specimen was prepared for observation. The combination of these effects offers a good deal of freedom to the well-known selective powers of the human mind—those powers by which significant shapes are seen in Rohrschach inkblots. It is often only too easy, for an honest observer with a preconceived idea in his head, to persuade himself that he can perceive significant similarities and differences in such comparisons—similarities and differences which are not 'objective' in the sense that they would not be noticed by an observer with different preconceived ideas. It is probable that a good deal of published work, in which insect species are claimed to be distinguishable with dogmatic certitude by reference solely to the male genitalia, is more or less unsound.

The palaeontological criterion (*h*) underlies the use of 'zone fossils' for dating and correlating sedimentary rocks by geologists, and must be taken as a statement of faith rather than as one with really adequate empirical verification. If it is difficult at times to apply many of the criteria for species to forms widely separated in space, the difficulties are even greater when the forms are separated in time. In those cases where we have a full and continuous record of a 'lineage' in fossil animals (few such cases are known in plants), we find a history of gradual and continuous change, rather like that along a cline. Fossils from the bottom of such a lineage may differ from those from the top in a sharp and unbridged way which would satisfy any museum systematist's idea of good species, yet be connected by a perfect series of intermediate forms in intervening layers. Extended lineages of this sort are, fortunately for the palaeontological systematist, not very common in the fossil record.

It is only the gappiness of the record which makes the task of classifying fossils in the accepted fashion practicable.

From direct geological evidence, and perhaps more often from indirect deductions based on geographical distribution (see Chapter 11) it is sometimes possible to estimate the time taken for one species to split into two 'good' ones or for a species to change sufficiently for systematists to regard it as having become a different one. An average figure of a million years would not be an unreasonable guess; however, there are many existing forms treated as species which are undoubtedly much younger than this. It must not be supposed that a law of nature exists according to which after a period of a million years the descendants of a given species must become specifically distinct from their ancestor; it may be quite common for a period of this order to be accompanied by little or no phenotypic change in a particular lineage. This problem will be further discussed in Chapter 9, where classification is considered in relation to phylogeny.

To sum up our conclusions in this chapter, we may assert that the species, though not quite as God-given and objective a category as some have imagined it to be, does have some objective basis, at least when comparisons are being made between sexually reproducing organisms living in the same area and at the same time. It does not, however, seem likely that any really objective basis could be found for species-difference between animals or plants inhabiting different continents or different geological periods. Non-sexually reproducing plants and animals likewise present difficulties for those who work by 'objective' definitions of the species as a category. The species is no exception to the rule that the concepts and categories employed in natural history are never susceptible to precise, rigorous or final definition; any scientist who is not content to operate with more or less vague and inexact basic principles and ideas is temperamentally unsuited to the study of natural history.

REFERENCES

32*a*. Coiffait, H. 1965. Sectophilonthus—remarquable genre de Philonthini nouveau pour la région Paléarctique. *Zool. Zhurn.* 44: 615–617.

44. Darwin, C. 1859. *The Origin of Species.* London.

49. Dobzhansky, T. 1958. Species after Darwin. In S. A. Barnett (ed.), *A Century of Darwin.* Heinemann.

63. Faegri, K. & Van Der Pijl L. 1966. *Pollination Ecology.* Pergamon Press.

67. Ford. E. B. 1964. *Ecological Genetics.* London.

103. Huxley, J. 1939. Clines: an auxiliary method in Taxonomy. *Bijdr. Dierk.* **27**: 491–520.

140*a*. Mayr, E. 1963. *Animal Species and Evolution.* Cambridge, Mass.

193*c*. Turrill, W. B., *et al.* 1942. Differences in the systematics of plants and animals and their dependence on differences in structure, function and behaviour in the two groups. *Proc. Linn. Soc. Lond.,* **153**: 272–287.

199. White, G. 1784. *The Natural History of Selborne.*

215. Maheshwari, P. 1967. The plant species in an age of experiment. In B. R. Sheschachar (ed.), Symposium on Newer Trends in Taxonomy. *Bull. Nat. Inst. Sci. India* 34.

21

Reprinted from *Taxon*, **18**(4), 357–359 (1969)

COMMENTS ON THE SEARCH FOR A 'PERFECT SYSTEM'

G. Ledyard Stebbins *

Summary

A fairy story on biosystematics making the point that there do not exist in nature groups of individuals which must be grouped in only one way as objective, uncontestable species. On the other hand, species are not purely subjective groupings, carved out of an amorphous welter of varying populations. The organized systems of populations, forming an irregular variation pattern, is characterized by modes of similar variants separated by larger or smaller gaps of discontinuity. The best system for any group is one synthesized from data of all kinds.

The proper classification of the genus *Citrus* and its relatives raises again a question which has plagued systematists ever since the time when Darwin questioned the Linnean dictum that species are discrete entities, created by God in a particular form, and that the task of systematists is to discover, define, and classify these God-given species. This question has often been posed in the form of two absolute alternatives. Are species completely objective entities, which exist in nature in only one form, which we must discover, recognize and describe? Or are they purely man made artefacts, having no real existence except in the mind of the taxonomist? In my opinion, neither of these extreme points of view is acceptable. Species have a basis in nature, but this basis is not so rigid that we can recognize them in only one way.

I should like to illustrate my point of view on this question by a fairy tale. As might be expected, it concerns a wise monarch, whom we can call King Linnius XIV, who announced to his people that he was seeking the ideal mate for his fair daughter, and the prince who would inherit his kingdom. The princess, he said was residing in an apartment concealed among the acres of dense shrubbery which surrounded the palace. Any knight who could find his way through the shrubbery and discover the fair daughter, whom he called the Perfect System, would wed her and inherit the kingdom. Those who fail would be banished forever from the royal presence.

Among the many suitors who accepted the challenge, the first was Sir Tradition. He came equipped with ruler, hand lens, and Latin Dictionary. He measured, he recorded trichomes and glands, he constructed keys and Latin descriptions. The result was a meticulous analysis of the shrubbery, artistic in its neatness. But he did not discover the fair daughter, the Perfect System, and was banished from the royal presence.

Next came Sir Biosist, fully equipped with experimental garden, flowerpots, forceps and bags for emasculation and isolation, and envelopes for seed collections. He transplanted, he grew, he measured, and hybridized. He obtained F^1's, F^2 segregates, hybrids viable and inviable. He recognized ecodemes, gamodemes, and superdemes; and constructed intricate circles of hybrid affinity. Nevertheless, he too failed to discover the fair daughter, the Perfect System.

Third in line was Sir Cytotax, reeking of ill-smelling acids, and with crimson-

* Department of Genetics, University of California, Davis, California, U.S.A. — Part of a paper on 'The effect of assexual reproduction on higher plant genera', presented at the International Citrus Symposium, University of California, Riverside, and reproduced from the symposium's Proceedings with the permission of the organizers.

stained fingers. He snipped and fixed, spread and squashed. He found chromosomes large and small, acrocentric, telocentric, and metacentric, heterochromatic and nucelolus organizing. He recognized inversion heterozygotes, translocation heterozygotes, autopolyploids, allopolyploids, segmental allopolyploids, and segmental-genomic-auto-allo-polyploids of the 3rd to the 7th degree. However, the fair daughter, the Perfect System, eluded him as well, and banishment was his fate.

The fourth suitor, young and brash, was Sir Biokem. His paraphernalia of equipment included an ultracentrifuge, spectrophotometer, densitometer, elution columns of various lengths, electrophoretic field, Ouchterlony Plates, hypodermic, and pet rabbit. He stabbed and extracted, incubated and ultracentrifuged, obtained banding patterns, sedimentation gradients, concentric crescents, and pages of graphs. But he was no more successful in finding the fair daughter than those who went before him.

Fifth came Sir Kompute, accompanied by his intelligent robot with flashing lights, whirring disks, and clicking dials. He gathered up all of the data which had been obtained and abandoned by his predecessors, gave them to his robot, and set him to work. Lights flashed, disks clicked, and wheels whirred. The robot ground out OTU's, BTU's, branching diagrams, and yards of perforated tape, enough to line the walls of the halls throughout the castle. But still, he failed to find the fair daughter, the Perfect System, and another banishment was ordered.

Then, after a few days' interval, there arrived at the palace a young man, slightly built and of serious mien, but with a twinkle in his eye. Dressed in a simple costume, he was alone and carried nothing in his hands.

"Who are you?" asked King Linnius, "And why do you come into our royal presence? Do you think that you can find our fair daughter, with nothing at all to aid you, when five doughty and learned knights, equipped with the latest scientific tools, have failed?"

"Your Royal Highness, I am Sir Skeptik. I have not come to find your fair daughter, but to call your bluff. The reason why my predecessors have failed is that there is no fair daughter to be found. First give me proof that she exists, and then I will do my utmost to find her."

At this all the courtiers grew wroth, stamped, and cursed. "Your majesty," they said, "simple banishment is too good for this impudent youth who questions your royal veracity. Let him be condemned to a lifetime appointment at Tularemia Subnormal Institute for Lower Education, where applications for research grants automatically fall into the circular file before leaving the campus."

But the wise King Linnius answered in this fashion. "Sir Skeptik," he said, "you have devined the truth. I do not have a fair daughter, full grown and ripe, ready for your hand. All I have is this little girl, seven years old. She is intelligent, responsive, and eager to learn. I beg you to teach her as much as you see fit of the learning which your predecessors vainly applied to their efforts to find their way through my shrubbery. In this way, you may fashion her into the kind of bride whom you would like to have, and who would aid you the most in truly understanding the knowledge which you and your peers have acquired. Then when she is full grown and ready, you may have her hand, and you two shall inherit our kingdom. I feel confident that you will rule it wisely and well."

Sir Skeptik did as he was told and eventually inherited the kingdom. He and his queen, the Synthetic System, ruled long and wisely, enjoying the approbation and acclaim of all of their peers and subjects. Or so goes the fairy story.

The point which I would like to make is that there do not exist in nature groups of individuals which must be grouped in only one way as objective, uncontestable species. On the other hand, species are not purely subjective groupings, carved out of an amorphous welter of varying populations.

What we have is an organized system of populations and groups of populations, which form an irregular variation pattern. This pattern is characterized by modes or clusters of similar variants, separated from each other by larger or smaller gaps of discontinuity. These gaps exist because various potential intermediate variants either have never been formed or have been unable to survive under existing conditions.

In sexually reproducing, cross fertilizing groups of higher organisms the coherence of the modal clusters of variants is maintained by crossing and gene exchange between them. Their individuals share a common gene pool. Gaps are maintained by diverse and variously developed barriers to gene exchange collectively designated as reproductive isolation. Consequently, we cannot understand the variation pattern within a group without a full knowledge of the reproductive biology of the populations which make it up. Moreover, the difficulties which taxonomists encounter in classifying a group are in direct proportion to the extent of deviation which this group displays from the norm of reproductive biology in higher organisms. This norm is sexual reproduction with exclusive or predominant cross fertilization and free gene recombination between interfertile individuals or populations. The best system for each group must be synthesized from the available data of all kinds, with due regard for the extent of agreement or divergence which this group displays from the norm.

BIBLIOGRAPHY

Amadon, D. 1950 The species—then and now. Auk, 67:492-497.

Amadon, D. 1966. The superspecies concept. Syst. Zool., 15:245-249.

Anderson, E. 1936. The species problem in Iris. Ann. Mo. Bot. Gard., 23:457-509.

Anderson, E. 1940. The concept of the genus: II. A survey of modern opinion. Bull. Torrey Bot. Club, 67: 363-369.

Arkell, W. J. 1956. The species concept in paleontology. Syst. Assoc. Publ. 2, pp. 97-99.

Bachmann, H. 1905. Der Speziesbegriff. Verh. Schweiz. Naturforsch. Ges., 87:161-208.

Bacon, Francis. 1626. Silva silvarum. London.

Baker, H. G. 1952. The ecospecies—prelude to discussion. Evolution, 6:61-68.

Beaudry, J. R. 1960. The species concept: its evolution and present status. Rev. Can. Biol., 19:219-240.

Berg, L. C. 1950. On botanical nomenclature and botanists' concepts of species (in Russian). Priroda, 9:30-33.

Berlin, B. 1973. Folk systematics in relation to biological classification and nomenclature. Ann. Rev. Ecol. Syst., 4:259-271.

Berlin, B., D. E. Breedlove, and P. H. Raven. 1966. Folk taxonomies and biological classification. Science, 154:273-275.

Bessey, C. E. 1908. The taxonomic aspect of the species question. Am. Nat., 42:218-224.

Bianci, V. L. 1916. The species and its subordinate taxonomic forms (in Russian). Zool. Zh., 1:287-297.

Blackwelder, R. E. 1962. Animal taxonomy and the new systematics. Surv. Biol. Prog., 4:1-57.

Blair, W. F. 1943. Criteria for species and their subdivisions from the point of view of genetics. Ann. N.Y. Acad. Sci., 44:179-188.

Bochantsev, V. P., and C. U. Lipshits. 1955. On the question of the scope of the species in higher plants (in Russian). Bot. Zh., 40:542-547.

Boucot, A. J. 1953. Life and death assemblages among fossils. Am. J. Sci., 251:25-40.

Bremekamp, C. E. B. 1959. Specific and infraspecific delimitation: 1. The practical aspect of the problem. Proc. K. Ned. Akad. Wet., Ser. C, 62:91-99.

Brien, P. 1962. Réflexions sur la classification, la spéciation, et l'évolution en biologie. Bull. Soc. R. Sci. Liège, 31:233–246.

Britton, N. L. 1908. The taxonomic aspect of the species question. Am. Nat., 42:225–242.

Brooks, J. L. 1957. The species problem in freshwater animals. In: E. Mayr (ed.), The species problem. Am. Assoc. Adv. Sci. Publ. 50, pp. 81–123.

Burma, B. H. 1949a. The species concept: a semantic review. Evolution, 3:369–370.

Burma, B. H. 1949b. The species concept: postscriptum. Evolution, 3:372–373.

Cain, A. J. 1953. Geography, ecology, and coexistence in relation to the biological definition of the species. Evolution, 7:76–83.

Cain, A. J. 1954. Animal species and their evolution. Harper & Row, New York.

Cain, A. J. 1959a. Taxonomic concepts. Ibis, 101:302–318.

Cain, A. J. 1959b. The post-Linnaean development of taxonomy. Proc. Linn. Soc. Lond., 170:234–244.

Camp, W. H. 1951. Biosystematy. Brittonia, 7:113–127.

Camp, W. H., and C. L. Gilly. 1943. The structure and origin of species. Brittonia, 4:323–385.

Carson, H. L. 1957. The species as a field for gene recombination. In: E. Mayr (ed.), The species problem. Am. Assoc. Adv. Sci. Publ. 50, pp. 23–38.

Chernov, S. A. 1941. The species problem (in Russian). Tr. Zool. Inst. Akad. Nauk SSSR, 6:5–15.

Chodat, R. 1914. La notion scientifique de l'espèce. Bull. Soc. Bot. Genève, 2:83–226.

Ciferri, R. 1932. The criteria for definition of species in mycology. Ann. Mycologici, 30:122–136.

Clausen, J. 1951. Stages in the evolution of plant species. Cornell Univ. Press, Ithaca, N.Y.

Clausen, J., and W. M. Hiesey. 1958. Experimental studies on the nature of species: IV. Genetic structure of ecological races. Carnegie Inst. Wash. Publ. 615.

Clausen, J., D. D. Keck, and W. M. Hiesey. 1939. The concept of species based on experiment. Am. J. Bot., 26:103–106.

Clausen, J., D. D. Keck, and W. M. Hiesey. 1940. Experimental studies on the nature of species: I. Effect of varied environments on western North American plants. Carnegie Inst. Wash. Publ. 520.

Clausen, J., D. D. Keck, and W. M. Hiesey. 1945. Experimental studies on the nature of species: II. Plant evolution through amphiploidy and autoploidy, with examples from the Madiinae. Carnegie Inst. Wash. Publ. 564.

Clausen, J., D. D. Keck, and W. M. Hiesey. 1948. Experimental studies on the nature of species: III. Environmental responses of climatic races of *Achillea*. Carnegie Inst. Wash. Publ. 581.

Cowan, S. T. 1959. Bacterial classification—problems and developments. In: V. Bryson (ed.), Microbiology yesterday and today. Institute of Microbiology, N.J.

Crombie, A. C. 1950. The notion of species in medieval philosophy and science. Actes du VIème Congrès International d'Histoire des Sciences, Amsterdam, 1:261–269.

Cuénot, L. 1936. L'espèce. G. Doin et Cie, Paris.

Cuénot, L. 1951. L'évolution biologique. Masson et Cie, Paris.

Darlington, C. D. 1940. Taxonomic species and genetic systems. In: J. Huxley (ed.), The new systematics. Clarendon Press, Oxford, pp. 137–160.

Darwin, C. 1859. The origin of species. London.

Davidson, J. F. 1954. A dephlogisticated species problem. Madroño, 12:246–254.

Davis, P. H., and V. H. Heywood. 1963. Principles of angiosperm taxonomy. D. Van Nostrand Co., Princeton, N.J.

De Candolle, A. P. 1813. Théorie élémentaire de la botanique. Paris.

Dementiev, G. P. 1954. Remarks on the species and some aspects of speciation in zoology (in Russian). Zool Zh., 33:525–537.

Desikachary, T. V. 1973. Status of classical taxonomy. In: N. G. Carr and B. A. Whitton (eds.), The biology of blue-green algae. Bot. Monogr., 9:473–481. Univ. California Press, Berkeley.

Diamond, J. M. 1966. Zoological classification system of a primitive people. Science, 151:1102–1104.

Dillon, L. S. 1966. The life cycle of the species: an extension of current concepts. Syst. Zool., 15:112–126.

Dobzhansky, Th. 1935. A critique of the species concept in biology. Philos. Sci., 2:344–355.

Dobzhansky, Th. 1937a. Genetic nature of species differences. Am. Nat., 71:404–420.

Dobzhansky, Th. 1937b. Genetics and the origin of species. Columbia Univ. Press, New York.

Dobzhansky, Th. 1958. Species after Darwin. In: S. A. Barnett (ed.), A century of Darwin. William Heinemann, London.

Dobzhansky, Th. 1972. Species of *Drosophila*. New excitement in an old field. Science, 177:664–669.

Dubinin, V. B. 1953. Concepts of species in zoology (in Russian). Zool. Zh., 32:1095–1109.

Dubinin, V. B. 1954. Concepts of species in parasitic animals (in Russian). Tr. Probl. Tematich. Sovesch. Zool. Inst. Akad. Nauk SSSR, 4:163–185.

Du Rietz, E. 1930. The fundamental units of biological taxonomy. Sven. Bot. Tidskr., 24:333–428.

Ehrlich, P. R. 1961. Systematics in 1970: some unpopular predictions. Syst. Zool., 10:157–158.

Fedotov, D. M. 1940. On the problem of species in paleontology (in Russian). Paleontol. Obzor, 2:2–9.

Ford, E. B. 1964. Ecological genetics. London.

Gates, R. R. 1938. The species concept in the light of cytology and genetics. Am. Nat., 72:340–349.

George, T. N. 1956. Biospecies, chronospecies, and morphospecies. Syst. Assoc. Publ. 2, pp. 123–137.

Gerbilski, N. L. 1957. Intraspecific biological differentiation and its significance for the species in the domain of fish (in Russian). Vestn. Leningr. Univ. Ser. Biol., 21:82–92.

Ghiliarov, M. C. 1954. Species, population, and biocenose. (in Russian). Zool. Zh., 33:769–778.

Ghiselin, M. T. 1974. A radical solution to the species problem. Syst. Zool., 23:536–544.

Gilmour, J. S. L. 1940. Taxonomy and philosophy. In: J. Huxley (ed.), The new systematics. Clarendon Press, Oxford, pp. 461–474.

Gilmour, J. S. L. 1958. The species: yesterday and tomorrow. Nature, 181:379–380.

Gilmour, J. S. L., and J. Heslop-Harrison. 1954. The deme terminology and the units of micro-evolutionary change. Genetica, 27:147-161.

Ginsburg, I. 1938. Arithmetical definition of the species, subspecies, and race concept, with a proposal for a modified nomenclature. Zoologica, 23:253-286.

Gloger, C. L. 1856. Über den Begriff von "Art" ("Species") und was in dieselbe hinein gehört. J. Ornithol., 4:260-270.

Godron, D. A. 1853. De l'espèce et des races chez les êtres organisés, Vol. 1. J. B. Baillière et fils, Paris.

Gozis, M. des. 1886. Recherche de l'espèce typique de quelques anciens genres. Montluçon.

Grant, V. 1957. The plant species in theory and practice. In: E. Mayr (ed.), The species problem. Am. Assoc. Adv. Sci. Publ. 50, pp. 39-80.

Grant, V. 1964. The biological composition of a taxonomic species in Gilia. Adv. Genet., 12:281-328.

Grant, W. F. 1960. The categories of classical and experimental taxonomy and the species concept. Rev. Can. Biol., 19:241-262.

Hairston, N. G. 1958. Observations on the ecology of *Paramecium*, with comments on the species problem. Evolution, 12:440-450.

Haldane, J. B. S. 1956. Can a species concept be justified? Syst. Assoc. Publ. 2, pp. 95-96.

Harlan, J., and J. Wet. 1963. The compilospecies concept. Evolution, 17:497-501.

Harland, S. 1936. The genetic conception of species. Biol. Rev., 9:83-112.

Harper, R. A. 1923. The species concept from the point of view of a morphologist. Am. J. Bot., 10:229-233.

Hedberg, O. 1958. The taxonomic treatment of vicarious taxa. Uppsala Univ. Arsskr., 6:186-195.

Heywood, V. H. 1958. The interpretation of binary nomenclature for subdivision of species. Taxon, 7:89-93.

Hohriakov, M. K. 1955. On species in fungi (in Russian). Bot. Zh., 40:34-45.

Hohriakov, M. K. 1964. Problems of species and speciation in fungi (in Russian). Tr. Vses. Inst. Zasch. Rast., 23:159-166.

Holodkovski, N. A. 1910. On biological species (in Russian). Izv. Akad. Nauk, 4:751-771.

Hull, D. L. 1973. Darwin and his critics. Harvard Univ. Press, Cambridge, Mass.

Hull, D. L. 1974. Philosophy of biological science. Prentice-Hall, Englewood Cliffs, N.J.

Hutchinson, G. E. 1969. When are species necessary? In: R. C. Lewontin (ed.), Population biology and evolution. Syracuse Univ. Press, Syracuse, N.Y., pp. 177-186.

Huxley, J. 1939. Clines: an auxiliary method in taxonomy. Bijdr. Dierkd., 27:491-520.

Huxley, J. 1942. Evolution: the modern synthesis. Harper & Row, New York.

Iuzepchuk, S. V. 1939. The species problem in light of Darwin's teachings (in Russian). Sov. Bot., 6:12-34.

Iuzepchuk, S. V. 1958. Komarov's concept of species (in Russian). In: Problema vida v botaniki (The species problem in botany), Vol. 1. Moscow and Leningrad.

Jones, K. 1961. The status and development of abrupt ecospecies. Recent Adv. Bot:862-866. Toronto Univ. Press.

Karpov. S. P. 1962. The species problem in microbiology (in Russian). In: Problemi vnutrividovih otnosheni (Problems of intraspecific relationships). Tomsk.

Klein, B. I. 1945. Concepts of species in general and medicinal microbiology (in Russian). Mikrobiologia, 14:35-44.

Klein, R. M., and A. Cronquist. 1967. A consideration of the evolutionary and taxonomic significance of some biochemical, micromorphological, and physiological characters of the Thallophyta. Q. Rev. Biol., 42:108–296.

Komarek, J. 1973. Prospects for taxonomic developments. In: N. G. Carr, and B. A. Whitton (eds.), The biology of blue-green algae. Bot. Monogr., 9:482–486. Univ. California Press, Berkeley.

Komarov, V. L. 1940. Studies of species in plants (in Russian). Moscow and Leningrad.

Krasilnikov, N. A. 1947. Concepts of species in bacteria (in Russian). Mikrobiologia, 16:381–393.

Krilov, G. V. 1967. The species and intraspecific categories in woody plants (in Russian), In: Soveschanie po obiemu vida i vnutrividovoi systematiki (Symposium on the scope of species and intraspecific systematics). Leningrad.

Kudriavtsev, V. I. 1951. On the problem of species in microorganisms (in Russian). Tr. Inst. Mikrobiol. Akad. Nauk SSSR, 1:86–107.

Kuhn, E. 1948. Der Artbegriffen der Paläontologie. Eclogae Geol. Helv., 41:389–421.

Kuprevich, V. F. 1949. The species problem in heterotrophic and autotrophic plants (in Russian). Moscow.

Kursanov, L. I. 1945. Concepts of species in lower plants (in Russian). Mikrobiologia, 14:210–214.

Lamarck, J.-B. 1802. Recherches sur l'organisation des corps vivants. Paris.

Lamarck. J.-B. 1907. Discours d'ouverture (an VII, X, XI, et 1806). Bulletin Scientifique de la France et de la Belgique, Vol. 40. Paris.

Legendre, P. 1972. The definition of systematic categories in biology. Taxon, 21:381–406.

Legendre, P., and P. Vaillancourt. 1969. A mathematical model for the entities species and genus. Taxon, 18: 245–252.

Lehman, H. 1967. Are biological species real? Philos. Sci., 34:157–167.

Lewis, H. 1967. The taxonomic significance of autopolyploidy. Taxon, 16:267–271.

Lindroth, C. H. 1957. The Linnean species of carabid beetles. J. Linn. Soc. Lond. Zool., 43:325–341.

Linnaeus, C. 1735. Carolus Linnaei, sveci, methodus.

Linnaeus, C. 1737. Critica botanica.

Linnaeus, C. 1740. Systema naturae, ed. 1.

Linnaeus, C. 1751. Philosophia botanica.

Linnaeus, C. 1753. Species plantarum.

Linnaeus, C. 1758. Systema naturae, ed. 10.

Linnaeus, C. 1764. Ordines naturales.

Lotsy, J. P. 1918. Qu'est-ce qu'une espèce? Arch. Neerl. Sci. Exact. Nat., Ser. 3b:57–110.

Lotsy, J. P. 1925. Species or linneon. Genetica, 7:487–506.

Lotsy, J. P. 1931. On the species of the taxonomist in its relation to evolution. Genetica, 13:1–16.

Löve, A. 1951. Taxonomical evaluation of polyploids. Caryologia, 3:263–284.

Löve, A. 1960. Taxonomy and chromosomes—a reiteration. Feddes Repert., 62:192–202.

Löve, A. 1962. The biosystematic species concept. Preslia, 34:127–139.

Löve, A. 1964. The evolutionary framework of the biological species concept. Genetics Today, Proc. XI Internat. Congr. Gen., pp. 409–415.

Lwoff, A. 1958. La notion d'espèce bactérienne à la lumière des découvertes récentes: l'espèce bactérienne. Ann. Inst. Pasteur, 94:137–141.

Maheshwari, P. 1967. The plant species in an age of experiment. In: B. R. Sheschachar (ed.), Symposium on newer trends in taxonomy. Bull. Natl. Inst. Sci. India, Vol. 34.

Manton, I. 1958. The concept of the aggregate species. Uppsala Univ. Arsskr., 6:104–112.

Maslin, T. P. 1968. Taxonomic problems in parthenogenetic vertebrates. Syst. Zool., 17:219–231.

Mayr, E. 1942. Systematics and the origin of species. Columbia Univ. Press, Ithaca, N.Y.

Mayr, E. 1949. The species concept: semantics versus semantics. Evolution, 3:371–372.

Mayr, E. 1957. Difficulties and importance of the biological species concept. In: E. Mayr (ed.), The species problem. Am. Assoc. Adv. Sci. Publ. 50, pp. 371–388.

Mayr, E. 1963. Animal species and evolution. Harvard Univ. Press, Cambridge, Mass.

Mayr, E. 1970. Populations, species, and evolution. Harvard Univ. Press, Cambridge, Mass.

Mayr, E., E. G. Linsley, and R. L. Usinger. 1953. Methods and principles of systematic zoology. McGraw-Hill, New York.

Meglitsch, P. A. 1954. On the nature of the species. Syst. Zool., 3:49–65.

Metchnikov, I. I. 1950. Essay on the question of the origin of species (in Russian). In: Izbranie proizvidenie (Selected works). Moscow.

Michener, C. D. 1963. Some future developments in taxonomy. Syst. Zool., 12: 151–172.

Michener, C. D. 1970. Diverse approaches to systematics. In: Th. Dobzhansky, M. K. Hecht, and W. C. Steere (eds.), Evolutionary biology, Vol. 4. Appleton-Century-Crofts, New York, pp. 1–38.

Moore, J. A. 1957. An embryologist's view of the species concept. In: E. Mayr (ed.), The species problem. Am. Assoc. Adv. Sci. Publ. 50, pp. 325–338.

Nalivkin, D. V. 1964. Species determination in paleontology (in Russian). In: Voprosi zakonomernosti i form razvitia organicheskovo mira (Questions of regularities and forms of development of the organic world). Moscow.

Ognev, A. I. 1944. Problems of systematics. The species question (in Russian). Zool. Zh., 23:1–16.

Palilov, A. I. 1957. On the question of the philosophical basis of the species problem (in Russian). Uch. Zap. Beloruss. Gos. Univ., Ser. Biol., 37:3–40.

Paramonov, S. Ia. 1943. What is a species in biology? (in Russian). Sov. Bot., 2:3–18.

Parker, H. W. 1956. Species transgressions in one horizon. Syst. Assoc. Publ. 2, pp. 9–15.

Pirie, N. W. 1955. The principles of microbial classification; summing up. J. Gen. Microbiol., 12:382–386.

Polianski, V. I. 1956. Species in lower algae (in Russian). Akad. Nauk SSSR, Moscow.

Polianski, V. I. 1958. Concepts of species in algology (in Russian). In: Problema vida v botaniki (The species problem in botany), Vol. 1. Moscow and Leningrad.

Poulton, E. B. 1903. What is a species? Proc. Entomol. Soc. Lond., 1903, pp. lxxvii–cxvi.

Prosser, C. L. 1957. The species problem from the viewpoint of a physiologist. In: E. Mayr (ed.), The species problem. Am. Assoc. Adv. Sci. Publ. 50, pp. 339–369.

Quatrefages, A. de. 1892. Darwin et les précurseurs français. Paris.

Ramsbottom, J. 1938. Linnaeus and the species concept. Proc. Linn. Soc. Lond., 1938:192–219.

Ray, J. 1686. Historia plantarum. London.

Reed, G. 1923. The species concept from the point of view of a physiologist and bacteriologist. Am. J. Bot., 10:234-238.

Regan, C. T. 1926. Organic evolution. Rep. Br. Assoc., 1925.

Robson, G. C. 1928. The species problem. Oliver & Boyd, London.

Rotai, A. P. 1962. Paleontological methods and the problem of species in stratigraphy (in Russian). Kiev Univ., Kiev.

Runemark, H. 1961. The species and subspecies concepts in sexual flowering plants. Bot. Not., 114:22-32.

Ruse, M. 1969. Definitions of species in biology. Br. J. Philos. Sci., 20:97-119.

Ruse, M. 1971. The species problem: a reply to Hull. Br. J. Philos. Sci., 22:369-371.

Sanson, A. 1900. L'espèce et la race en biologie générale. Schleicher Frères, Paris.

Savich-Liubitskaia, L. I., and Z. N. Smirnova. 1958. Concepts of species in bryophytes (in Russian). In: Problema vida v botaniki (The species problem in botany), Vol. 1. Moscow and Leningrad.

Schaeffer, P. 1958. La notion d'espèce bactérienne à la lumière des découvertes récentes: la notion d'espèces après les recherches récentes de génétique bactérienne. Ann. Inst. Pasteur, 94:167-178.

Schultz, R. J. 1973. Unisexual fish: laboratory synthesis of a "species." Science, 179:180-181.

Scudder, G. G. E. 1974. Species concepts and speciation. Can. J. Zool., 52:1121-1134.

Semenov-Tian-Shanski, A. S. 1910. Taxonomic boundaries of the species and its subunits (in Russian). Zan. Akad. Nauk, 25:1-29.

Sherman, V. B. D. 1962. Species concept in bacteria. In: G. W. Leeper (ed.), The evolution of living organisms, Vol. 1. Univ. Press, Melbourne, pp. 213-221.

Shimwell, J. L., and J. G. Carr. 1960. Are species of bacteria unclassifiable? Leeuwenhoek Ned. Tijdschr., 26:383.

Shull, G. H. 1923. The species concept from the point of view of a geneticist. Am. J. Bot., 10:221-228.

Simpson, G. G. 1943. Criteria for genera, species, and subspecies in zoology and paleozoology. Ann. N.Y. Acad. Sci., 44:145-178.

Simpson, G. G. 1951. The species concept. Evolution, 5:285-298.

Simpson, G. G. 1953. The major features of evolution. Columbia Biol. Ser. 17.

Simpson, G. G. 1961. Principles of animal taxonomy. Columbia Univ. Press, New York.

Sinskaja, E. N. 1948. Dynamics of species (in Russian). Moscow.

Sirks, M. J. 1952. Variability in the concept of species. Acta Biotheor., Ser. A, 10:11-22.

Slobodchikoff, C. N., and H. V. Daly. 1971. Systematic and evolutionary implications of parthenogenesis in Hymenoptera. Am. Zool., 11:273-282.

Smirnov, E. S. 1938. Species construction from a taxonomic point of view (in Russian). Zool. Zh., 17:387-418.

Smith, J. M. 1965. Modern approaches to the species concept. The geneticist's approach. Proc. R. Entomol. Soc. London, Ser. C, 30:22-23.

Sneath, P. H. A. 1957. Some thoughts on bacterial classification. J. Gen. Microbiol., 17:184-200.

Sneath, P. H. A. 1958. Some aspects of Adansonian classification and of the taxonomic theory of correlated features. Ann. Microbiol. Enzymol., 8:261-268.

Sneath, P. H. A., and R. R. Sokal. 1962. Numerical taxonomy. Nature, 193:855-860.

Sneath, P. H. A., and R. R. Sokal. 1973. Numerical taxonomy. W. H. Freeman and Company, San Francisco.

Sokal, R. R. 1974. The species problem reconsidered. Syst. Zool., 22:360–374.

Sokal, R. R., and P. H. A. Sneath. 1963. The principles of numerical taxonomy. W. H. Freeman and Company, San Francisco.

Sonneborn, T. M. 1957. Breeding systems, reproductive methods, and species problems in Protozoa. In: E. Mayr (ed.), The species problem. Am. Assoc. Adv. Sci. Publ. 50, pp. 39–80.

Spurway, H. 1954. Review of Patterson and Stone, 1952. Ann. Hum. Genet., 19:154–156.

Spurway, H. 1955. The subhuman capacities for species recognition and their correlation with reproductive isolation. Proc. XI Internat. Ornithol. Congr.

Stakman, E. C. 1923. The species concept from the point of view of a plant pathologist. Am. J. Bot., 10:239–244.

States, J. S. 1969. Some aspects of basidiocarp morphogenesis in *Gloephyllum* (*Lenzites*) *saepiarium* (Fries) Karsten, a xerophytic polypore. Ph.D. thesis, Univ. Alberta, Edmonton.

Stebbins, G. L. 1950. Variation and Evolution in plants. Columbia Univ. Press, New York.

Stent, G. S. 1975. Limits to the scientific understanding of man. Science, 187:1052–1057.

Stepanov, D. L. 1959. Polytypic conception of species in paleontology (in Russian). Paleontol. Zh., 3:3–14.

Sylvester-Bradley, P. C. (ed.). 1956. The species concept in paleontology. Syst. Assoc. Publ. 2.

Tahtadzhian, A. L. 1955. Some questions of the theory of species in systematics (in Russian). Bot Zh., 6:789–796.

Thibault, P. 1958. La notion d'espèce bactérienne à la lumière des découvertes récentes: la notion d'espèce dans le groupe *Shigella*. Ann. Inst. Pasteur, 94:213–218.

Thoday, J. M., and J. B. Gibson. 1970. Probability of isolation by disruptive selection. Am. Nat., 104:219–230.

Thomas, G. 1956. The species conflict—abstractions and their applicability. Syst. Assoc. Publ. 2, pp. 17–31.

Trojan, P. 1962. Analysis of the species concept in the genus *Tabanus* L. (Diptera) as shown by taxonomic practice. Ecol. Polska, Ser. A.T., 10:123–229.

Turesson, G. 1922. The species and variety as ecological units. Hereditas, 3:100–113.

Turesson, G. 1925. The plant species in relation to habitat and climate. Hereditas, 6:147–236.

Valentine, D. H. 1949. The units of experimental taxonomy. Acta Biotheor., 9:75–88.

Valentine, D. H., and A. Löve. 1958. Taxonomic and biosystematic categories. Brittonia, 10:153–166.

Van Baalen, C. 1973. Mutagenesis and genetic recombination. In: N. G. Carr and B. A. Whitton (eds.), The biology of blue-green algae. Bot. Monogr., 9. Univ. California Press, Berkeley.

Van Niel, C. B. 1955. Classification and taxonomy of the bacteria and blue-green algae. In: A century of progress in the natural sciences, 1853–1953. California Academy of Sciences, San Francisco.

Vasiliev, V. N. 1965. On the continuing survival of the species (in Russian). In: Problemi sovremenoy botaniki (Problems of contemporary botany), Vol. 1. Moscow and Leningrad.

Vasilkov, B. P. 1965. On the species problem (in Russian). In: P. A. Baranov (ed.),

Sporovie rastenie Srednei Azii i Kazahstana (Cryptogamic plants of Central Asia and Kazakhstan).

Vavilov, N. I. 1931. The Linnean species as a system (in Russian). Tr. Prikl. Bot. Genet. Sel., 26:109-134.

Vendrely, R. 1958. La notion d'espèce bactérienne à la lumière des découvertes récentes: la notion d'espèce à travers quelques données biochimiques récentes et le cycle L. Ann. Inst. Pasteur, 94:142-166.

Volkova, E. V., and A. I. Filukov. 1966. Philosophical questions of species theory (in Russian). Moscow.

Voronihin, N. N. 1951. On some algae of the Vorovsk reserve in connection with the species question (in Russian). Tr. Vses. Gidrobiol. Obsch., 3:217-220.

Wallace, A. R. 1859. On the tendency of varieties to depart indefinitely from the original type. J. Linn. Soc. Zool., 3:53-62.

Wallace, A. R. 1889. Darwinism: an exposition of the theory of natural selection, with some of its applications. London.

Walters, S. M. 1962. Generic and specific concepts and the European flora. Preslia, 34:207-226.

White, M. J. D. 1959. Speciation in animals. Aust. J. Sci., 22:32-39.

White, M. J. D. 1968. Models of speciation. Science, 159: 1065-1070.

Winogradsky, S. 1952. Sur la classification des bactéries. Ann. Inst. Pasteur, 82:125-131.

Zavadski, K. M. 1954. On some questions of the theory of species and speciation (in Russian). Vestn. Leningr. Univ., 10:3-15.

Zavadski, K. M. 1957. On the question of differentiation of species in higher plants. Vestn. Leningr. Univ., 21:18-44.

Zavadski, K. M. 1961. Studies of species (in Russian). Leningrad.

Zavadski, K. M. 1968. Species and speciation (in Russian). Leningrad.

AUTHOR CITATION INDEX

SUBJECT INDEX

Acetobacter, 135
Acetosa, 228
Achillea, 231
Acronycta psi, 334
Acronycta tridens, 334
Adalia sp., 333
Adanson, M., 54, 236
Adaptation, 17, 132, 135, 274, 298
Aesculus carnea, 245
Aesculus hippocastanum, 245–246
Aesculus pavia, 245–246
Agrostis stolonifera, 307
Agrostis tenuis, 306
Aldrovandus, 13
Allele, 211, 305–307
  self-sterility, 305
  substitution, 248
Allopatry, 325
Amoeba proteus, 338
Anadara, 183
Anaximander, 103
Angiospermae, 336, 339
Annonaceae, 229
Anopheles maculipennis, 327, 336
Anthraconaia, 172
Aphelinus, 157
Aphidae, 156, 325
Aphytis, 152, 154–156, 159, 161–162, 164
Aphytis chilensis, 159
Aphytis chrysomphali, 159, 162
Aphytis coheni, 165–166
Aphytis fisheri, 161, 163
Aphytis holoxanthus, 152
Aphytis lingnanensis, 162–163, 165–166
Aphytis maculicornis, 155, 161, 163

Aphytis melinus, 161–163
Aphytis mytilaspidis, 157, 325
Araschni alevana, 334
Argynnis paphia, 333
Aristotle, 1, 11, 16–19, 46, 97, 268
Asexual organisms, 315
Asexual reproduction, 4, 126–128, 172, 272–306, 315, 325
  agamospermy, 239, 245, 316
  apogamety, 127
  apomixis, 127, 156–157, 163, 224, 228, 244, 259, 284, 315
  autogamy, 215, 228, 316–317
  automixis, 156–157
  parthenogenesis, 127, 325, 334
  parthenogenesis, cyclical, 156
  thelytoky, 155–157
  vegetative, 239, 244
Aspidiotus hederae, 163

Bacon, F., 20
Bacteria, 126, 139–140, 145, 147, 316
Beta vulgaris, 305
Beyrichia jonesi, 186
Binom, 73, 133, 141, 220, 256
Biston betularia, 306
Blue-green algae, 126
Brassica longifolia aperta, 21
Brucella abortus, 135
Bruchidae, 327
Bryoxiphium norvegicum, 225
Buffon, G., 21, 31, 205

Capsicum chinense, 246
Capsicum pendulum, 246

About the Editor

C. N. SLOBODCHIKOFF is currently an Assistant Professor of Biology at Northern Arizona University, Flagstaff. He was born in Shanghai, China, and came to the United States in 1949. He received a Ph.D. from the University of California, Berkeley, in 1971. His Ph.D. work involved a study of variation patterns, speciation, and behavior of a group of parasitic wasps. Since that time, he has been working on various problems in population biology, including studies of selection in parthenogenetic wasps, behavior of beetle populations, and predator–prey interactions.